CALCULUS
without
analytic
geometry

Under the General Editorship of
Professor Dan E. Christie
Bowdoin College

CALCULUS

without analytic geometry

Barry Mitchell

Bowdoin College

D. C. HEATH AND COMPANY

A Division of Raytheon Education Company

Lexington, Massachusetts

Jacket and cover design by Edward Karr.

Copyright © 1969 by Raytheon Education Company

Printed in the United States of America

Library of Congress Catalog Card Number: 73–76531

PREFACE

This book is written for the student who has the potential for pursuing a course of study in advanced mathematics, but who is nevertheless not one of those rare individuals who come to college working on unsolved problems in group theory. In a word, the book contains the course which I would like to have had as a freshman. The content of the book has been kept down to what can be taught in a year's course, with classes meeting three or four times per week. In these days of eight and nine hundred page textbooks, brevity may not be considered an attribute. Nevertheless, I believe that students should learn early that in mathematics conciseness is a goal, and that the calculus, when stripped of superfluous detail, is short, if not always sweet.

The first chapter is, for the most part, an attempt to give an axiomatic treatment of the numbers in a style which is as informal and free from symbolism as possible. One should not spend too much time on this chapter. It is there for the student who is precocious enough to wonder what a number is. Also it provides an introduction to the idea of a proof. However, one can waste a lot of time trying to prove that two plus two equals four to someone who has never for a moment doubted it, and one is best advised to get on with the more serious business of the second chapter as quickly as possible.

This second chapter deals with as much of the theory of limits and derivatives as can be done without using least upper bounds. In particular this means that square roots do not appear in any form until the third chapter. This delay is attributable to a concern for the student who tends to worry about circular reasoning. Already from the first chapter he has the sine function on his conscience, and has been told that he must await the final chapter before he will be made an honest man.

Chapter III centers around the least upper bound axiom and, in particular, the intermediate and mean value theorems. The real life counterparts of the theory of maxima and minima are given their due, as are the rules of graph sketching.

Chapter IV is devoted to the theory of the Riemann integral. The equivalence of the Riemann and Darboux definitions of the integral is treated in full generality. The necessary ingredient, Darboux's theorem (theorem 6.2), may prove to be rather thorny for some. In any case the last section on Duhamel's principle can be skipped without too much harm.

The log function is introduced as an integral at the beginning of Chapter V, and general exponents are dealt with here for the first time.

There follows enough of the technique of antidifferentiation to give the student a good idea of where tables of integrals come from. The applications of the integral are confined to volumes and surfaces of revolution and lengths of paths. The use of Duhamel's principle to justify some of the integral formulas may seem a little pretentious. A more relaxed approach would consist in simply treating these formulas as definitions.

The last chapter on series is fairly conventional, although at the end there is a section on rearrangement of terms and multiplication of series. These last matters are usually omitted from freshman courses, but in the form they are given here I don't think that they are too difficult to be included.

If a word is needed to justify the bare minimum of analytic geometry, let me say only that my own early impressions of the calculus saw it as being mysteriously tied up with properties of conic sections and changes of coordinate systems, and it came as a somewhat pleasant surprise when I discovered that this was not the case. I have also refrained from making a big issue of elementary set theory, for fear of giving the reader the impression that there is something difficult about taking the union or intersection of two sets, or worse still, something interesting.

I am indebted to Dan Christie for the interest he has taken in the book, and for the helpful criticism which he has offered. Miss Miriam Bernard, Mrs. Nancy MacDonald, and Mrs. Jean Hughes have all done an excellent job in typing the manuscript. I wish also to express my appreciation to Mr. Ronald Moore and Miss Martha Allen of D. C. Heath and Company for their cooperation during the production of the book.

B. Mitchell

Bowdoin College

TABLE OF CONTENTS

VI Series   243

PROLOGUE

The apple fell down instead of up,
And Newton invented the calculus
And the laws of motion.
And this led to relativity,
Which in turn led to the atomic bomb
And the hydrogen bomb.
And then they invented a bomb
Which would split the earth.
But the dropping of the bomb
Was a political holocaust:
The bomb fell up instead of down,
Soon after which the moon went out,
Leaving the nation
Without a national direction.
Whereupon calculus was banned
    from the schools,
All calculus books were burned,
And Newton was removed from
    Westminster Abbey.
But man has an infinite capacity
    for forgiving,
And for forgetting,
And the calculus has been reinstated,
With the proviso that no
    mention be made
Of physics.

THE NUMBERS   I

1. NAMES

In mathematics we give names to things so that we can talk about them. This is, of course, the main reason for naming people. However, in order to save time and space, the names we give objects in mathematics are usually much shorter than the names we give people. Thus, instead of giving a number an elegant name such as Lionel Lionheart, we are more apt to call it something like 7, or x, or perhaps ϵ (which is the Greek letter for e and is called epsilon).

Another time- and space-saving practice in mathematics is that of replacing certain words and phrases which occur over and over again by appropriate abbreviations. For example, the expression "is greater than" is one which appears so often that it is usually replaced by the shorter symbol ">." The method of naming things and finding short forms for certain expressions is generally referred to as *notation*. A proper choice of notation is useful not only in saving space and time, but also in helping us to imagine and classify the notions which we are talking about. Thus "$x > y$" is more suggestive than a notation such as "$x \square y$" in denoting the fact that x is greater than y.

In any event, there are two common misconceptions with regard to mathematical symbolism. The first is that in finding symbols to represent things, the mathematician is doing mathematics. The truth is that in such cases the mathematician is more concerned with saving himself ink than he is with mathematics. The second misconception consists in looking through a mathematical work and concluding that it is terribly difficult because one does not know the symbols. The situation is entirely analogous to someone looking through a children's book written in Latin and concluding that, because he does not know Latin, the story is too difficult for him to understand.

Owing to the fact that there are not enough acceptable names to go around, it frequently arises that a number of people have the same name. This usually creates no problem. If two people are known as Lionel Lionheart, it is usually clear in any given context which one of them is in question. When there is danger of confusion we may refer to one of them as Lionel Lionheart I and the other as Lionel Lionheart II. The same situation prevails in mathematics. Here a very common name is x, but it is seldom the case that the same x is in question in two different discussions. When we run the risk of confusing

x's, we may call one of them x_1, and the other x_2 (read "x sub one" and "x sub two").

It happens also that one person may have more than one name. Thus the same man who is known as Lionel to some may be known as Lord Lionheart to others. In mathematical language we would say that Lionel equals Lord Lionheart. The statement "x equals y," which is usually abbreviated to read "$x = y$," means nothing more and nothing less than the fact that x and y are both names for the same thing. With this in mind, it is not very astounding that $x = x$ always, that if $x = y$, then $y = x$, and that if $x = y$ and $y = z$ (or, as we sometimes write, $x = y = z$) then $x = z$. If x and y are not names for the same thing, then we write "$x \neq y$" (read "x is not equal to y").

In any case it is essential to distinguish between the names we give things and the things themselves. An object may exist whether or not we give it a name, and the facts which are true for that object and its relationship to other objects do not depend in the least on what we call it. Thus, if x and y are both names for a number (that is, if $x = y$) and if z denotes another number, then the sum of the two numbers in question can be written either as $x + z$ or as $y + z$ (that is, $x + z = y + z$). In other words, the fact that we can add the same thing to both sides of an equation results from the simple observation that the sum of two numbers is something which depends on the numbers themselves and not on what we call them.

Perhaps the situation here is somewhat different from that which we encounter in naming people. It is conceivable that a man named Lionheart might undergo a slight change in behavior if his name were changed, for example, to Chickenheart. On the other hand, it is perfectly safe to assume that mathematical objects are not affected in the least by what we call them.

2. SETS

A *set* is simply a collection of things. The things which make up a set are called its *members*, or sometimes its *elements*. Sets are usually denoted by capital letters. If x is a member of a set S, then we write $x \in S$. In other words "$\in$" is an abbreviation for the expression "is a member of." If x is not a member of S, then we write $x \notin S$.

If a set has few enough members, then we can write down a membership list for it. We sometimes denote such a set by simply placing braces around its membership list. Thus, if the members of a set S are a, b, c, and d, then we write

$$S = \{a, b, c, d\}.$$

Obviously a set does not depend in any way on the order in which the secretary lists its members. Thus $\{c, b, d, a\}$ is the same as the set S above. Also, if the name of a member appears more than once in the membership list, this does not mean that one member has somehow multiplied itself to become several members. It simply means that the secretary has made a redundancy. Thus, if a, b, and c are distinct, but $d = b$, then the set $\{a, b, c, d\}$ has three members, not four. It is the same as the set $\{a, b, c\}$. In listing the members of a set in the examples and exercises which will follow, we shall always assume that there are no redundancies.

If every member of a set T is also a member of a set S, then we say that T is a *subset* of S, and we write $T \subset S$. Thus we have

$$\{a, d\} \subset \{a, b, c, d\}.$$

Notice that according to our definition, every set is a subset of itself. A subset of a set which is different from the set itself (that is, which is missing one or more members of the set) is called a *proper* subset. Thus, $\{a, c\}$ is a proper subset of $\{a, b, c\}$.

The *union* of two sets S and T is the set consisting of all those elements which are either in S or in T (or possibly both). The union is denoted by $S \cup T$. On the other hand, the *intersection* of the two sets, denoted by $S \cap T$, consists of all those elements which are members of both S and T. For example, if S is $\{a, b, x, t\}$ and T is $\{b, c, d, x, y\}$, then $S \cup T$ is the set $\{a, b, c, d, x, y, t\}$, whereas $S \cap T$ is the set $\{b, x\}$.

One set which frequently arises is the set $\{\ \}$, that is, the set which has no members in it. It is called the *empty* set, and is sometimes denoted by $\emptyset$. The fact that is has no members means that we can state any fact we wish about each of its members without fear of contradiction. For example, if S is any set, then each member of $\emptyset$ is also a member of S. Thus, $\emptyset$ is a subset of any set S.

Most of the sets which we shall be concerned with in this book will be subsets of the real numbers (which we have not yet encountered). However, the ideas and language of sets appear continually throughout mathematics, and in fact all of mathematics can be completely formulated in terms of sets.

EXERCISES

1. For each pair of the following sets, give the union and the intersection:

   $\{a, b, c\}, \quad \{a, c, x, y\}, \quad \{a, x\}, \quad \{y\}.$

   Which of them are subsets of one of the others?

2. What is the set of all female past presidents of the United States? Is it true that they were all young and pretty?

3. ORDERED PAIRS

A *pair* is a set consisting of two members. Thus, if a and b are distinct, then $\{a, b\}$ is a pair, and is the same as the pair $\{b, a\}$. The set $\{a, a\}$ is not a pair since it has only one member.

On the other hand consider the symbol (,). Regard the blank space to the left and right of the comma as pigeonholes numbered one and two respectively. If we place an element in the first pigeonhole, and then place an element (possibly the same one) in the second pigeonhole, we get what we call an *ordered pair*. Thus, (a, b) and (b, a) are ordered pairs, and furthermore if $a \neq b$, then these ordered pairs are not the same since the pigeonholes are filled differently in the two cases. Since it is legitimate to enter the same name in both pigeonholes, (a, a) is a perfectly good ordered pair.

If A and B are any two sets, then we can form a new set, called the *cartesian product* of A and B and denoted by $A \times B$, whose members are all those ordered pairs having a member of A in the first pigeonhole and a member of B in the second pigeonhole. Thus, if $A = \{a, x, z\}$ and $B = \{b, t\}$, then $A \times B$ is the set consisting of the six members (a, b), (a, t), (x, b), (x, t), (z, b) and (z, t).

The word "cartesian" is in honor of the French mathematician René Descartes (1596–1650), who was the first one to think of the points on a plane as ordered pairs of real numbers. The reason for the word "product" is found in exercise 2.

EXERCISES

1. Let A be the set $\{a, b\}$ and let B be the set $\{b, x, y\}$. List the members of each of the sets $A \times B$, $B \times A$, $A \times A$, $B \times B$.
2. If A has m members and B has n members, how many members has $A \times B$?
3. If A is a set with five members, how many pairs of members of A are there? How many ordered pairs?

4. FUNCTIONS

Let A and B be sets, and suppose that each member of A has a member of B assigned to it. We call such an assignment a *function* from A to B. It may be the case that some member of B is assigned to two or more members of A, and on the other hand it may be that there are members of B which are not assigned to any member of A. What is important is that every member of A have just one member of B assigned to it.

We shall usually denote functions by small letters f and g, or the corresponding capital letters F and G, and occasionally by the Greek letter ϕ (phi). If f is a function from A to B, then A is called the *domain* of f, and the subset of B consisting of all those elements which are assigned to members of A is called the *image* of f. If x is a member of A, then the member of B which is assigned to x is denoted by $f(x)$. It is important to distinguish between $f(x)$, which denotes a single member of B, and f, which denotes all the assignments considered collectively.

Example 1: Let A be the set $\{a, b, c, d\}$ and let B be the set $\{p, q, r, s, t\}$. Then a function f from A to B can be defined by

$$f(a) = q, \quad f(b) = t, \quad f(c) = p, \quad f(d) = t.$$

The image of f in this case is the set $\{p, q, t\}$. This is just one of $5^4 = 625$ possible functions from A to B.

Another example of a function is suggested by the telephone dial. Here we can assign to each letter of the alphabet which appears on the dial the digit which is found in the same hole with it. In this case the domain is a certain proper subset of the letters of the alphabet and the image is a certain (proper) subset of the set of digits $\{0, 1, \ldots, 9\}$ (see the telephone dial).

Let f be a function from A to B, and let g be a function from B to C. If a is a member of A, then $f(a)$ is a member of B, and so $g(f(a))$ is a member of C. The function which assigns to each member a in A the member $g(f(a))$ in C is called the *composition of f by g*, and is denoted by $g \circ f$.

Example 2: Let

$$A = \{a, b, c\}, \quad B = \{p, q, r, s\}, \quad C = \{x, y, z\},$$

and define functions f from A to B and g from B to C by the rules

$$
\begin{array}{ll}
f(a) = r & g(p) = x \\
f(b) = p & g(q) = z \\
f(c) = q & g(r) = z \\
 & g(s) = y
\end{array}
$$

Then $g \circ f$ is given by

$$
\begin{array}{l}
(g \circ f)(a) = g(f(a)) = g(r) = z, \\
(g \circ f)(b) = g(f(b)) = g(p) = x, \\
(g \circ f)(c) = g(f(c)) = g(q) = z.
\end{array}
$$

Let f be a function from A to B, and let $\overline{A}$ be a proper subset of A. Then the *restriction* of f to $\overline{A}$ is that function $\overline{f}$ from $\overline{A}$ to B such that $\overline{f}(a) = f(a)$ for every a in $\overline{A}$. The functions f and $\overline{f}$ are *not* the same, since they do not have the same domain. Two functions are the same only when they have the same domain and make the same assignments to each member of the domain.

EXERCISES

1. Let A, B, and C be sets with five members, four members and six members respectively. Assign names to the members, and write down a function from A to B and one from B to C. Then give the composition of these two functions. How many functions are there from A to B? From B to C? From A to C? Is it true that every function from A to C is the composition of a function from A to B by one from B to C?

2. How many functions are there from A to B when A has only one member? How many are there when B has only one member?

5. ONE TO ONE CORRESPONDENCES

If a function f from A to B has the property that every member of B is assigned to precisely one member of A, then f is called a *one to one correspondence* from A to B.

Example: If A is $\{a, b, c\}$ and B is $\{x, y, z\}$, then the function f defined by

$$f(a) = y, \quad f(b) = x, \quad f(c) = z$$

is a one to one correspondence from A to B. This is just one of six one to one correspondences from A to B. (What are the others?)

If A is any set, then there is an obvious one to one correspondence from A to A. This is the function f such that $f(a) = a$ for all a in A. In other words f assigns each member of A to itself, and for this reason f is called the *identity* function for A.

If f is a one to one correspondence from A to B, then there is an obvious function g from B to A. This is the function which assigns to the member b of B that unique member a of A such that $f(a) = b$. Thus $g(f(a)) = a$ for all a in A, and $f(g(b)) = b$ for all b in B, so that $g \circ f$ and $f \circ g$ are the identity functions for A and B respectively. The function g, which is also a one to one correspondence, is called the *inverse* of f. In the above example, the inverse g is given by

$$g(x) = b, \quad g(y) = a, \quad g(z) = c.$$

Notice that we cannot talk about the inverse of a function which is not a one to one correspondence. The reason is that either there is a member b in B which f does not assign to any member of A (so that there is nothing in A to assign to b) or there is a member b in B which f assigns to more than one member of A (so that there are too many things in A to assign to b).

EXERCISES

1. Let $A = \{a, b, c, d, e\}$ and $B = \{p, q, r, a, d\}$. Write down a one to one correspondence from A to B and give its inverse. How many one to one corespondences are there from A to B?

2. How many one to one correspondences are there from $\{a, b, c\}$ to $\{x, y, z, t\}$?

3. Let f be a function from A to B and let g be a function from B to A such that $g \circ f$ and $f \circ g$ are identity functions on A and B respectively. Show that f is a one to one correspondence.

4. Let f be a one to one correspondence from A to B, and let g be a one to one correspondence from B to C. Show that $g \circ f$ is a one to one correspondence from A to C.

6. OPERATIONS

Consider any set A, and suppose that to every ordered pair of elements both of which come from A, there has been assigned some element which is again in A. We call such an assignment an *operation* on A. Thus, an operation on A is just a function from $A \times A$ to A. Given an operation on A, let us denote the member of A which is assigned to the ordered pair (a, b) by $a * b$. If $a \neq b$, then since (a, b) and (b, a) are different ordered pairs, there is no reason to suppose that they have been assigned the same member of A. In other words, there is no reason to suppose that $a * b$ is the same as $b * a$. If it is the case that $a * b = b * a$ for all a and b in A, then we say that the operation is *commutative*.

If a, b, and c are any members of A (possibly two or all of them the same) then we can take $a * b$ (which is a member of A) together with the member c to give us $(a * b) * c$. On the other hand, we could take the two members a and $b * c$ to give us $a * (b * c)$. Again there is no reason to suppose that $(a * b) * c$ and $a * (b * c)$ are the same. If it is true that $(a * b) * c = a * (b * c)$ for all members a, b, and c of A, then we say that $*$ is an *associative* operation.

As an example, let A be the set $\{x, y, z\}$. Let us take

$x * x = y$	$y * x = x$	$z * x = z$
$x * y = x$	$y * y = x$	$z * y = y$
$x * z = z$	$y * z = x$	$z * z = z$

Then $y * z = x$, whereas $z * y = y$, and so our operation is not commutative. It is not associative either, since $(x * y) * y = x * y = x$ whereas $x * (y * y) = x * x = y$. This is just one of the $3^{3^2} = 19{,}683$ possible operations on the set A.

EXERCISES

1. Consider the following operation on the set $\{x, y\}$:

$x * x = x$	$y * x = y$
$x * y = y$	$y * y = x$

   Show that this operation is both commutative and associative.

2. Consider the following operation on the set $\{x, y\}$:

$x * x = x$	$y * x = x$
$x * y = x$	$y * y = y$

   Show that this operation is both commutative and associative.

3. If A is a set with 10 members, how many possible operations are there for A? Do you suppose that most of them will be either commutative or associative?

7. THE REAL NUMBERS

There is one set which everybody is familiar with, more or less. This is the set R of all *real numbers*, which consists of the natural numbers 1, 2, 3, . . . , their negatives $-1, -2, -3, \ldots$, the rational numbers or fractions, such as $\frac{3}{4}, -\frac{5}{8}, \frac{71}{56}, \ldots$, the irrational numbers (i.e., those which can't be expressed as fractions) such as $\sqrt{2}$ and π, and the number 0. (The reader who has been told that 0 is not a number will have to regard this bit of information as a deliberate attempt to undermine his understanding of mathematics.) Since the real numbers are the only numbers which we shall encounter in this book, we shall do away with the word "real" and simply call them numbers.

Among the countless possible operations on this set, there is one which is quite well known, namely the operation known as *addition*, which assigns to the ordered pair of numbers (a, b) their sum $a + b$. The fact that this operation is commutative, or in other words that $a + b = b + a$ is so familiar that most people never even think about it. The same thing can be said of the associative rule $(a + b) + c = a + (b + c)$, which says in words that the result of adding c to the sum of a and b is the same as adding the sum of b and c to a. The number 0 has the special property that if we add it to any number, we get that number back; in symbols, $0 + a = a$. Also if we start with a number a, then its negative $-a$ can be regarded as that number which when added to a gives 0; in symbols, $(-a) + a = 0$.

Another well known operation for the numbers is that called *multiplication*, which assigns the product ab to the ordered pair (a, b). The commutativity and associativity rules $ab = ba$ and $(ab)c = a(bc)$ are as familiar as the corresponding rules about sums. The number 1 has the special property that if we multiply it by any number we get that number back. Also if we start with a number a which is not 0, then its inverse a^{-1} is such that $a^{-1}a = 1$.

There is also a rule involving both sums and products. This is the *distributive rule*, which says that if a, b, and c are any numbers, then $a(b + c) = (ab) + (ac)$. Let us collect into a list the rules we have so far stated for the operations of addition and multiplication.

I. $a + b = b + a$ for all numbers a and b.

II. $(a + b) + c = a + (b + c)$ for all numbers a, b, and c.

III. There is a special number 0 with the property that $0 + a = a$ for all numbers a.

IV. For each number a there is a number $-a$ with the property that $(-a) + a = 0$.

V. $ab = ba$ for all numbers a and b.

VI. $(ab)c = a(bc)$ for all numbers a, b, and c.

VII. There is a special number 1, not equal to 0, which has the property that $1a = a$ for all numbers a.

VIII. For each number a not 0 there is a number a^{-1} with the property that $a^{-1}a = 1$.

IX. $a(b + c) = (ab) + (ac)$ for all numbers a, b, and c.

EXERCISES

1. The real numbers are not the only mathematical system possessing two operations satisfying rules I–IX. For example, consider the set consisting of only two members x, y, and define the following two operations on this set:

$$
\begin{aligned}
x + x &= x & y + x &= y \\
x + y &= y & y + y &= x \\
xx &= x & yx &= x \\
xy &= x & yy &= y
\end{aligned}
$$

Show that with x playing the role of 0 and y playing the role of 1, these two operations satisfy all of the laws. (You have already shown that these operations are commutative and associative in the first two exercises of § 6. Hence the only thing to verify which will take a little work is rule IX.)

2. Consider the operation on the numbers which assigns to the ordered pair of numbers (a, b) the number $a - b$. Is this operation commutative? Is it associative?

3. Consider the operation on the numbers which assigns to the ordered pair of numbers (a, b) the number $(a + b)—(ab)$. Is this operation commutative? Is it associative?

4. In rule IX, place a plus sign in place of each multiplication sign, and a multiplication sign in place of each plus sign. Is the resulting equation always true? If not, find three numbers a, b, and c for which it is not true. On the other hand, find three numbers for which it is true.

8. THE RULES OF THE GAME

The nine rules which we have already listed are only a few of the familiar facts about the numbers. We have not mentioned the rule $0a = 0$, nor have we mentioned the cancellation rule for sums: if $a + x = a + y$, then $x = y$. The list could be added to indefinitely. However, the facts would eventually become less obvious than the ones we have stated and would require proofs. Some readers may even be skeptical about the nine rules we have already stated, and not without reason. Perhaps the rules are more or less obvious for the whole numbers, but there is certainly room to question their validity for all numbers. There may even be some who have asked themselves the question, "What is a number?" Is it a collection of apples, or is it a mark on a ruler? Sometimes we are told that a number is a decimal. If this is the case, then anybody who has ever tried to multiply together two infinite decimals may justifiably wonder if the situation regarding the numbers is well in hand.

At this point we propose an interesting game. It is the game which we shall be playing throughout the rest of this book. It is to suppose that we know nothing about the numbers except that they form a set with two operations satisfying the 9 rules we have listed (and later on a few more rules) and to see how many of the familiar facts (and possibly even some unfamiliar ones) we can prove about the numbers on the basis only of these rules. Henceforth the rules I–IX will be referred to as *axioms*.

Let us begin by proving the cancellation law mentioned above.

Theorem 8.1: *If a, x, and y are any numbers such that $a + x = a + y$, then $x = y$.*

Proof: The reader who says that this is obvious and doesn't need to be proved has missed the point. We reason as follows. By axiom IV there is a number $-a$ such that $(-a) + a = 0$. Adding this number to both sides of the given equality $a + x = a + y$, we obtain

$$(-a) + (a + x) = (-a) + (a + y).$$

Then applying the associativity axiom II to both sides, we have

$$((-a) + a) + x = ((-a) + a) + y.$$

By axiom IV this gives us

$$0 + x = 0 + y,$$

and so applying axiom III gives us $x = y$ as required. ∎

(The mark ∎ will be placed to indicate the end of a proof. When the proof is too easy to be included, or when it is to be left as an exercise, we shall place ∎ after the statement of the theorem.)

Axiom III says that $0 + a = a$, but it does not say anything about $a + 0$. However, bringing axiom I into play, we have $a + 0 = 0 + a$, and so $a + 0 = a$. Similarly, it follows from axiom IV that $a + (-a) = 0$. In general, axiom I permits us to take any theorem about the sum of two numbers and obtain a new theorem by interchanging the numbers. Thus, for example, we have the following corollary of theorem 8.1. (A *corollary* is just a theorem which follows easily as a side result of another theorem.)

Corollary 8.2: If $x + a = y + a$, *then* $x = y$. ∎

Axiom III tells us that there is a special number 0 which has the property that when we add it to any number, we get that number back. However, the axiom does not rule out the possibility of there being another such special number. Nevertheless, using corollary 8.2 we can prove that there is only one such special number. In fact, we shall prove that if x is a number such that the result of adding it to just one number gives that number back, then x is 0.

Theorem 8.3: *If x and a are any numbers such that $x + a = a$, then $x = 0$.*

Proof: By axiom III, we have $0 + a = a$. But we are given that $x + a = a$ also. Hence, $x + a = 0 + a$, and so applying corollary 8.2 (with 0 playing the role of y) we obtain $x = 0$. ∎

Likewise axiom IV does not say there is only one number which when added to a gives 0. Nevertheless, using corollary 8.2 again, we shall prove:

Theorem 8.4: *If $x + a = 0$, then $x = -a$.*

Proof: By axiom IV, we have $(-a) + a = 0$. But we are given that $x + a = 0$ also. Hence, we have $x + a = (-a) + a$, and so applying corollary 8.2 (with $(-a)$ playing the role of y) we obtain $x = -a$. ∎

Corollary 8.5: *If x is any number, then $-(-x) = x$.*

Proof: By axiom IV, $(-x) + x = 0$. In view of axiom I, this can also be written $x + (-x) = 0$. Hence, by theorem 8.4 (with $-x$ playing the role of a) we see that $-(-x) = x$. ∎

Consider the expression $a\,b + c$. As the expression stands, there is nothing to indicate whether it is to mean $(a\,b) + c$ or $a(b + c)$. However, in order to avoid writing too many parentheses, we agree that this expression should mean $(a\,b) + c$. The convention is that in any expression where there are no parentheses to indicate whether we should add first or multiply first, priority goes to multiplication. The reader is probably familiar with this rule in any case, but without realizing that there is a choice in the matter. Under this convention the distributive axiom IX reads

$$a(b + c) = ab + ac.$$

Theorem 8.6: *For any number b we have $0b = 0$ and $b0 = 0$.*

Proof: Since $0b = b0$, it suffices to show that $b0 = 0$. In the expression bb, write the first b as it is and the second b as $0 + b$. This gives us

$$bb = b(0 + b)$$
$$= b0 + bb. \quad \text{(axiom IX)}$$

The result then follows from theorem 8.3 with $b0$ playing the role of x and bb playing the role of a. ∎

We can see now why we had to exclude 0 in the statement of axiom VIII. For if there were a number 0^{-1} such that $0^{-1}0 = 1$, then since by theorem 8.6 we have also $0^{-1}0 = 0$, this would give us $0 = 1$. This is the unhappy state of affairs we have guarded against in axiom VII.

Notice also that if $x \neq 0$, then since $x^{-1}x = 1$, it follows again from theorem 8.6 that x^{-1} cannot be 0.

Theorems 8.1 to 8.5 had only to do with addition, and consequently used only axioms I to IV. Using axioms V to VIII we can prove similar theorems about multiplication. Small but important changes must be made owing to the fact that, whereas axiom IV applies to *all* numbers, the analogous axiom VIII applies to all numbers *except* 0. We shall state the theorems, but we shall prove only the first one. The proofs of the others will be left as exercises.

Theorem 8.7 (Cancellation Law for Multiplication): *If a, x, and y are any numbers such that $ax = ay$, and if, further $a \neq 0$, then $x = y$.*

Proof: Since $a \neq 0$, by axiom VIII there is a number a^{-1} such that $a^{-1}a = 1$. Multiplying both sides of the given equality $ax = ay$ by a^{-1}, we obtain

$$a^{-1}(ax) = a^{-1}(ay).$$

Then applying the associativity axiom VI to both sides, we have

$$(a^{-1}a)x = (a^{-1}a)y.$$

By axiom VIII this gives us

$$1x = 1y,$$

and so applying axiom VII gives us $x = y$ as required. ∎

Observe that the proof of theorem 8.7 is just a repeat of the proof of theorem 8.1, except that addition has been replaced by multiplication and $-a$ has been replaced by a^{-1}. Since a^{-1} does not make sense for $a = 0$, we were forced to make the additional hypothesis that a be distinct from 0. If a is replaced by 0 in theorem 8.7, then the theorem is not longer true. The way one sees that a theorem is not true is to exhibit what we call a *counterexample;* that is, an instance for which the theorem does not hold. A counterexample in the present case is had by taking $x = 0$ and $y = 1$. Then we have $00 = 01$ since by theorem 8.6 they are both 0, but $0 \neq 1$ by axiom VII.

Corollary 8.8:   *If $xa = ya$ and $a \neq 0$, then $x = y$.* ∎

Theorem 8.9:   *If $xa = a$ and $a \neq 0$, then $x = 1$.* ∎

Theorem 8.10:   *If $xa = 1$, then $x = a^{-1}$.* ∎

(Notice that it is not necessary to assume that $a \neq 0$ in theorem 8.10, since if $a = 0$, then by theorem 8.6 we could not have $xa = 1$.)

Corollary 8.11:   *If $x \neq 0$, then $(x^{-1})^{-1} = x$.* ∎

Theorem 8.12:   *For any numbers a and b we have*

$$a(-b) = -(ab)$$
$$(-a)b = -(ab)$$
$$(-a)(-b) = ab.$$

Proof: To show that $a(-b) = -(ab)$, by theorem 8.4 it suffices to show that if we add $a(-b)$ to ab we get 0. We have (give the reasons)

$$a(-b) + ab = a((-b) + b) = a0 = 0$$

as required.

Now we have

$$(-a)b = b(-a) = -(ba) = -(ab)$$

where at the first and third equality we have used axiom V, and at the middle equality we have simply used the part of the theorem we have already proved with the roles of a and b interchanged.

Finally, using both parts of the theorem we have already proved, we have

$$(-a)(-b) = -(a(-b)) = -(-(ab)).$$

But by corollary 8.5 we have $-(-(ab)) = ab$, as required. ∎

EXERCISES

1. Prove theorems 8.8 to 8.11.
2. Use theorem 8.4 to show that $-0 = 0$. Likewise use theorem 8.10 to show that $1^{-1} = 1$.

3. Show that $(-1)a = -a$ and hence show that

$$-(a + b) = (-a) + (-b).$$

4. If a, b, and c are any numbers, prove that

$$(b + c)a = ba + ca.$$

(Observe that this is not the same as axiom IX. Axiom IX could be called the "left" distributive law and this one the "right" distributive law. To prove it you will use axiom IX and one other axiom.)

9. CONVERSES OF THEOREMS

It is interesting sometimes to take a statement which says that if one thing is true, then a second thing is true, and to turn it around so as to read that if the second thing is true, then the first thing is true. The latter statement is called the *converse* of the original statement. Even if a statement is true, it is seldom the case that the converse is true. For example, consider the statement which says, "If Lionel is a football player, then Lionel has two legs." This statement, we can be reasonably sure, is true. However, the converse statement "If Lionel has two legs, then Lionel is a football player" is not true. (Lionel may be a gorilla.)

In a few cases, nevertheless, it turns out that both a theorem and its converse are true. Consider, for example, theorem 8.6. That theorem could be stated, "If at least one of two numbers is zero, then their product is zero." The converse of this statement reads, "If the product of two numbers is zero then at least one of the two numbers is zero." This turns out to be a true statement as we see in the next theorem.

Theorem 9.1: *If $ab = 0$, then at least one of a and b is 0.*

Proof: We shall show that if $a \neq 0$, then $b = 0$. Since $a \neq 0$ we can use a^{-1}. We have

$$
\begin{aligned}
b &= 1b && \text{(axiom VII)} \\
&= (a^{-1}a)b && \text{(axiom VIII)} \\
&= a^{-1}(ab) && \text{(axiom VI)} \\
&= a^{-1}0 && \text{(hypothesis)} \\
&= 0 && \text{(theorem 8.6)}
\end{aligned}
$$

which is what is required. ∎

Notice that even though theorem 9.1 is the converse of theorem 8.6, the proofs of the theorems have nothing in common. This is not surprising, since they are entirely different theorems. Sometimes when it is the case that if one thing is true then a second thing is true, and also that if the second thing is true then the first thing is true, we combine the two statements into one by saying that the first thing is true *if and only if* the second thing is true. Thus we could have combined theorem 8.6 with theorem 9.1 to read, "$ab = 0$ if and only if at least one of a and b is 0." However, this does *not* mean that we would have any less work to do. There would still be two things to prove. All we would have done is to abbreviate the statements of the two theorems somewhat by combining them into one.

Before stating the next two theorems, we shall introduce two notational devices. The first is to write $a - b$ in the place of $a + (-b)$. This saves us writing a pair of parentheses and a plus sign. The reader is used to this notation in any case. However, he is probably not used to thinking of the "difference" $a - b$ as a sum. It must never be forgotten that the expression $a - b$ is simply a short way of writing the sum of the two numbers a and $(-b)$. Likewise in place of ab^{-1} we shall often write $\frac{a}{b}$ (or sometimes a/b to save space). Thus $\frac{a}{b}$ is nothing but a way of writing the product of the two numbers a and b^{-1}. Then another "if and only if" theorem is the rule for "cross multiplication" in arithmetic.

Theorem 9.2:   *Let a, b, c, and d be any numbers with b and d not 0. Then* $\frac{a}{b} = \frac{c}{d}$ *if and only if $ad = cb$.*

Proof: First let us suppose that $\frac{a}{b} = \frac{c}{d}$. By definition this is just another way of writing

$$ab^{-1} = cd^{-1}.$$

Multiplying both sides by bd and remembering that $bd = db$, we obtain

$$(ab^{-1})(bd) = (cd^{-1})(db).$$

Applying axiom VI to the three numbers (ab^{-1}), b, and d on the left side and the three numbers (cd^{-1}), d, and b on the right side gives us

$$((ab^{-1})b)d = ((cd^{-1})d)b.$$

Now applying the same axiom to the numbers a, b^{-1}, and b on the left side and c, d^{-1}, and d on the right side we obtain

$$(a(b^{-1}b))d = (c(d^{-1}d))b.$$

But since $b^{-1}b = 1$ and $d^{-1}d = 1$, this gives us $ad = cb$ as required.

Conversely, if we start by supposing that $ad = cb$, then multiplying both sides by $d^{-1}b^{-1}$ we can go through a similar argument and end up with $ab^{-1} = cd^{-1}$. The details are left as an exercise. ∎

The theorem for sums analogous to theorem 9.2 is the following theorem, which justifies the process of "taking numbers to the other side" in an equation. It is proved by replacing b^{-1} and d^{-1} by $-b$ and $-d$ and putting addition in the place of multiplication in the proof of theorem 9.2.

Theorem 9.3:   *Let a, b, c, and d be any numbers. Then $a - b = c - d$ if and only if $a + d = c + b$.* ∎

EXERCISES

1. Write out the details of the second half of the proof of theorem 9.2.
2. Prove theorem 9.3.
3. Prove the following equalities. (You will use exercise 2 of § 8 for two of them.)

$$a - 0 = a \qquad\qquad \frac{a}{1} = a$$

$$b - b = 0 \qquad\qquad \frac{b}{b} = 1 \text{ for } b \neq 0$$

$$0 - b = -b \qquad\qquad \frac{1}{b} = b^{-1} \text{ for } b \neq 0$$

$$\frac{a+c}{b} = \frac{a}{b} + \frac{c}{b} \text{ for } b \neq 0 \qquad\qquad \frac{0}{b} = 0 \text{ for } b \neq 0$$

4. Given any numbers a and b, use theorem 9.3 to show that $a - b$ is the only number x satisfying the equation $x + b = a$.

Likewise for any numbers a and b with $b \neq 0$, use theorem 9.2 to show that $\frac{a}{b}$ is the only number x satisfying the equation $xb = a$. How many such numbers are there if $b = 0$ and $a \neq 0$? How many are there if $b = 0$ and $a = 0$?

10. LEMMAS

A *lemma* is a theorem whose main purpose it is to help prove a more important theorem. Since it is just a matter of taste as to whether we call a statement a lemma or a theorem, the reader who does not like new words can simply call them all theorems.

Lemma 10.1: *If b and d are nonzero numbers, then $(bd)^{-1} = b^{-1}d^{-1}$.*

Proof: To show that $b^{-1}d^{-1}$ is the inverse of bd, by theorem 8.10 it suffices to show that the result of multiplying it by bd gives 1. We have (supply the reasons)

$$
\begin{aligned}
(b^{-1}d^{-1})(bd) &= (b^{-1}d^{-1})(db) \\
&= ((b^{-1}d^{-1})d)b \\
&= (b^{-1}(d^{-1}d))b \\
&= (b^{-1}1)b \\
&= b^{-1}b \\
&= 1
\end{aligned}
$$

as required. ∎

Theorem 10.2: *If a, b, c, and d are any numbers with b and d nonzero, then*

$$\frac{a}{b}\frac{c}{d} = \frac{ac}{bd}.$$

Proof: We have

$$\frac{a}{b}\frac{c}{d} = (ab^{-1})(cd^{-1}) \quad \text{(definition)}$$
$$= ((ab^{-1})c)d^{-1} \quad \text{(axiom VI)}$$
$$= (a(b^{-1}c))d^{-1} \quad \text{(axiom VI)}$$
$$= (a(cb^{-1}))d^{-1} \quad \text{(axiom V)}$$
$$= ((ac)b^{-1})d^{-1} \quad \text{(axiom VI)}$$
$$= (ac)(b^{-1}d^{-1}) \quad \text{(axiom VI)}$$
$$= (ac)(bd)^{-1} \quad \text{(lemma 10.1)}$$
$$= \frac{ac}{bd} \quad \text{(definition)}$$

which is what is required.   ∎

If we put $a = b$ in theorem 10.2 and use the fact that $\frac{b}{b} = 1$ (see § 9, exercise 3) we obtain:

Corollary 10.3:   *If b, c, and d are any numbers with b and d nonzero, then*

$$\frac{c}{d} = \frac{bc}{bd}. \quad ∎$$

Lemma 10.4:   *If c and d are nonzero, then*

$$\left(\frac{c}{d}\right)^{-1} = \frac{d}{c}.$$

Proof: We have

$$\left(\frac{c}{d}\right)^{-1} = (cd^{-1})^{-1} \quad \text{(definition)}$$
$$= c^{-1}(d^{-1})^{-1} \quad \text{(lemma 10.1)}$$
$$= c^{-1}d \quad \text{(corollary 8.11)}$$
$$= dc^{-1} \quad \text{(axiom V)}$$
$$= \frac{d}{c}. \quad \text{(definition)} \quad ∎$$

Theorem 10.5:   *If a, b, c, and d are any numbers with b, c, and d nonzero, then*

$$\frac{a/b}{c/d} = \frac{ad}{bc}.$$

Proof: We have

$$\frac{a/b}{c/d} = (a/b)(c/d)^{-1} \quad \text{(definition)}$$
$$= \frac{a}{b}\frac{d}{c} \quad \text{(lemma 10.4)}$$
$$= \frac{ad}{bc}. \quad \text{(theorem 10.2)} \quad ∎$$

Theorems 10.1 to 10.5 all have their counterparts for sums (see exercise 1). This is so whenever the proof of a theorem uses only axioms V to VIII or theorems which depend only on those axioms, for then we have only to replace multiplication by addition and use the corresponding axioms I to IV. It is only when we use the distributive axiom IX that we cannot interchange the roles of addition and multiplication in this mechanical way, since if we interchange addition and multiplication in axiom IX we do not get a true statement.

The following theorem justifies the process of "bringing to a common denominator."

Theorem 10.6: *If a, b, c, and d are any numbers with b and d nonzero, then*

$$\frac{a}{b} + \frac{c}{d} = \frac{ad + bc}{bd}.$$

Proof: We have

$$\frac{a}{b} + \frac{c}{d} = \frac{ad}{bd} + \frac{bc}{bd} \quad \text{(corollary 10.3)}$$

$$= \frac{ad + bc}{bd} \quad \text{(axiom IX)} \quad \blacksquare$$

EXERCISES

1. State and prove theorems for sums corresponding to theorems 10.1 to 10.5. Does theorem 10.6 have a counterpart for sums?

2. Prove that $\dfrac{(-a)}{b} = -\left(\dfrac{a}{b}\right)$. (Hint: Add the first number to $\dfrac{a}{b}$ and see if you get zero.) Prove also that $\dfrac{a}{(-b)} = -\left(\dfrac{a}{b}\right)$.

3. Prove that

$$(x - y) + (y - z) = x - z$$

for any three numbers x, y, and z. What does the corresponding statement for products say?

11. POSITIVE NUMBERS

One might begin to wonder if all the well known facts about the numbers follow from our nine axioms. However, it is easy to see that they do not. For on the basis of only these axioms, it is not even possible to prove that $1 + 1$ is not 0. (See § 7, exercise 1.) Therefore some more axioms are in order. They come from the notion of certain numbers being positive. We know that for each number x which is not 0, it is true that either x is positive or $-x$ is positive. Also we are familiar with the fact that the sum and the product of two positive numbers are again positive. Let us add these statements to our list of axioms.

X. There is a subset P of the numbers such that each number x has one and only one of the following properties:

$$x \in P, \quad x = 0, \quad \text{or} \quad -x \in P.$$

XI. If $x \in P$ and $y \in P$, then $x + y \in P$.

XII. If $x \in P$ and $y \in P$, then $xy \in P$.

If $x \in P$, then we shall call x a *positive* number, and if $-x \in P$ we shall call x a *negative* number. Notice that a negative number is *not* simply a number which can be written with a minus sign in front of it. Every number can be written with a minus sign in front of it, for if x is a number, then we can write $x = -y$, where y is the number $-x$.

According to axiom X, the set P of positive numbers has nothing in common with the set of negative numbers (that is, their intersection is empty), and neither one of them contains 0. On the other hand, according to the same axiom, every nonzero number is positive or negative.

The following theorem justifies the rule "two negatives make a positive." It is by no means the same as theorem 8.12, although it uses theorem 8.12 in its proof.

Theorem 11.1: *If x is negative and y is positive, then xy is negative. If x and y are both negative, then xy is positive.*

Proof: If x is negative and y is positive, then by definition we have $-x \in P$ and $y \in P$. Hence, by axiom XII, $(-x)y \in P$. But $(-x)y = -(xy)$ by theorem 8.12, and so $-(xy) \in P$. In other words, xy is negative.

The second statement is left as an exercise. ∎

Corollary 11.2: *If x is any nonzero number, then xx is positive.*

Proof: If x is positive, then xx is positive by axiom XII. If x is negative, then xx is positive by theorem 11.1. ∎

Corollary 11.3: 1 *is positive.*

Proof: This follows from corollary 11.2 in view of the fact that $1 = (1)(1)$. ∎

Corollary 11.4: *If x is positive, then x^{-1} is positive.*

Proof: If x^{-1} were negative, then since x is positive it would follow from 11.1 that the product $x^{-1}x$ would be negative. But $x^{-1}x = 1$, which we know to be positive by corollary 11.3. The only way out is to conclude that x^{-1} is positive. ∎

If x and y are two numbers, then we shall write $x < y$ (read "x is less than y") or equivalently $y > x$ (read "y is greater than x") if $y - x$ is a positive number. Since $-(y - x) = x - y$, it follows from axiom X that for every pair of numbers x and y, precisely one of the following statements is true:

$$x < y, \quad x = y, \quad \text{or} \quad x > y.$$

The relation $x < y$ is sometimes referred to as an *inequality*. Notice that since $x - 0 = x$, it follows that $x \in P$ if and only if $x > 0$.

If this definition of "less than" has anything to do with our usual idea of "less than," we shall certainly want the following theorem to be true.

Theorem 11.5: *If $x < y$ and $y < z$, then $x < z$.*

Proof: By definition, $x < y$ and $y < z$ mean that $y - x \in P$ and $z - y \in P$. Hence, by axiom XI, $(z - y) + (y - x) \in P$. But we have $(z - y) + (y - x) = z - x$. Hence $z - x \in P$, or in other words $x < z$. ∎

If $x < y$ and $y < z$, then we shall sometimes combine these two statements to read $x < y < z$. In this case we say that y is *between* x and z.

Theorem 11.6: *If $x < y$ and a is any number, then $a + x < a + y$.*

Proof: We have

$$(a + y) - (a + x) = y - x.$$

Since $y - x \in P$, this shows that $(a + y) - (a + x) \in P$, that is, that

$$a + x < a + y,$$

as required. ∎

Corollary 11.7: *If $x < y$ and $a < b$, then $a + x < b + y$.*

Proof: Applying theorem 11.6 we have $a + x < a + y$. But applying it again to the inequality $a < b$, we obtain $a + y < b + y$. Hence, combining the inequalities $a + x < a + y$ and $a + y < b + y$ and using theorem 11.5, we obtain $a + x < b + y$ as required. ∎

Theorem 11.6 says that we can add any number to both sides of an inequality without changing the inequality. The situation is not quite the same for multiplication, as we see from the following theorem.

Theorem 11.8: *If $x < y$ and a is positive, then $ax < ay$. If $x < y$ and a is negative, then $ax > ay$.*

Proof: If $x < y$ and $a > 0$, then both $y - x$ and a are positive. Hence by axiom XII, $a(y - x)$ is positive. But $a(y - x) = ay - ax$, and so $ax < ay$. The second statement is left as an exercise. ∎

If x and y are numbers, and if it is the case either that $x = y$ or that $x < y$, then we write $x \leq y$ (or equivalently, $y \geq x$). It is then an easy matter to check that each of theorems 11.5 to 11.8 is still true if "$<$" is replaced by "$\leq$" throughout.

EXERCISES

1. Prove the second half of theorem 11.1.
2. Prove the second half of theorem 11.8.
3. Show that each of theorems 11.5 to 11.8 is valid when $<$ is replaced by $\leq$.
4. If a and b are positive numbers, show that $a < b$ if and only if $\dfrac{1}{a} > \dfrac{1}{b}$.
5. Show that any positive number is greater than any negative number.
6. If $0 < x < y$ and $0 < a < b$, show that $ax < by$.

12. ABSOLUTE VALUES

If x is any nonzero number, then we let $|x|$ be whichever of the two numbers x and $-x$ is positive. Also we define $|0| = 0$. The number $|x|$ is called the *absolute value* of x. Notice that for any number x, we have $|-x| = |x|$.

Theorem 12.1:   *For all numbers x and y we have*

$$|xy| = |x|\,|y|.$$

Proof: If x and y are both ≥ 0, then so is xy, and so $|x| = x$, $|y| = y$, and $|xy| = xy$. Thus the equality is true in this case. If x and y are both negative, then xy is positive, and we have $|x| = -x$, $|y| = -y$, and $|xy| = xy$ But xy can be written $(-x)(-y)$, or in other words $|x|\,|y|$, and so again we have our result. Finally, if one of x and y is ≥ 0 and the other is < 0, say $x \geq 0$ and $y < 0$, then $xy \leq 0$, and we have $|x| = x$, $|y| = -y$, and $|xy| = -(xy)$. But $-(xy) = x(-y) = |x|\,|y|$, and so once more we have what is required. Since this exhausts all possibilities, we have proved the theorem. ∎

Lemma 12.2:   *For any number x, we have $x \leq |x|$ and $-x \leq |x|$.*

Proof: This is an immediate consequence of the fact that any negative number is less than any positive number. ∎

Theorem 12.3:   *For all numbers x and y, we have*

$$|x + y| \leq |x| + |y|.$$

Proof: By lemma 12.2, we have $x \leq |x|$ and $y \leq |y|$. Hence, by 11.7 we obtain $x + y \leq |x| + |y|$. A similar combination of 12.2 and 11.7 gives us $-x - y \leq |x| + |y|$. The first inequality gives us the desired result in the case where $x + y \geq 0$, and the second gives it in the case $x + y < 0$. ∎

Corollary 12.4:   *For all numbers a and b we have*

$$|a - b| \geq |a| - |b|.$$

Proof: This follows by taking $x = a - b$ and $y = b$ in 12.3. The details are left as an exercise. ∎

The inequality of theorem 12.3 is called the *triangle inequality*, for reasons which we shall see in chapter III.

EXERCISES

1. Prove theorem 12.3 in a straightforward way by breaking it up into the following four cases.

   Case 1: $x \geq 0$, $y \geq 0$.
   Case 2: $x < 0$, $y < 0$.
   Case 3: $x \geq 0$, $y < 0$ with $x + y \geq 0$.
   Case 4: $x \geq 0$, $y < 0$ with $x + y < 0$.

   (The cases where $x < 0$ and $y \geq 0$ follow by interchanging the roles of x and y in cases 3 and 4.)
       In which of the cases do we have $|x + y| = |x| + |y|$?

2. Prove corollary 12.4.

3. Let x and a be any numbers and let δ be a positive number. Show that $|x - a| < \delta$ if and only if $a - \delta < x < a + \delta$.

4. Prove that $\left|\dfrac{a}{b}\right| = \dfrac{|a|}{|b|}$ for any numbers a and b with b nonzero.

13. THE INTEGERS

By corollary 11.3 we know that 1 is positive, or in other words that $0 < 1$. By theorem 11.6 we can add 1 to both sides of this inequality to obtain $0 + 1 < 1 + 1$. If we denote $1 + 1$ by 2, then this last inequality becomes $1 < 2$. Adding 1 to both sides again gives us $1 + 1 < 2 + 1$, or, denoting $2 + 1$ by 3, $2 < 3$. Continuing in this way we obtain numbers

$$1 < 2 < 3 < 4 < 5 < 6 < 7 < 8 < 9 < \cdots$$

where each number in the list is the sum of the previous number and the number 1. If we continue the list indefinitely† we obtain what is known as the set of *positive integers*. We shall denote this set by J. Obviously we cannot invent a different symbol for each positive integer. A method for naming all of the positive integers in terms of the few we have named above will be given in § $(9 + 9)$.
    Suppose that S is a collection of positive integers which has the following two properties:

(1) $1 \in S$,
(2) If $n \in S$, then $n + 1 \in S$.

---

†Since the word "indefinitely" is rather vague, mathematicians usually prefer to extract the positive integers from the real numbers by another process which is described as follows. First define a subset S of the numbers to be *inductive* if $1 \in S$, and if $x + 1 \in S$ whenever $x \in S$. For example, the set of all numbers greater than or equal to 1 is inductive. A number n is then defined to be a *positive integer* if it is a member of every inductive set. The set J of all positive integers is easily seen to be itself inductive, and by its definition it is a subset of every other inductive set. In other words J is the smallest inductive set.

Then condition (1) together with condition (2) implies that $2 \in S$. But then again by the second condition, this implies in turn that $3 \in S$. Keeping this up we see that S must contain every positive integer. In other words, there is only one set of positive integers which has the two properties given above, and that is the set of *all* positive integers. This is known as the *principle of induction*. It is most often used in the following situation. Suppose that we have a theorem about a positive integer, and suppose that we know that the theorem is true when the integer is 1. Suppose also that for each positive integer n, the assumption that the theorem is true for n leads to a proof that the theorem is true for $n + 1$. Then the theorem is true for every positive integer. For if we let S be the set of all positive integers for which the theorem is true, then S satisfies conditions (1) and (2) given above, and so S must be all of the positive integers.

Let us prove as an example of induction that the sum of two positive integers is itself a positive integer.

Theorem 13.1:   *If $m \in J$ and $n \in J$, then $m + n \in J$.*

Proof: For a fixed positive integer m, let S be the set of all those positive integers n for which $m + n \in J$. In the first place, since $m \in J$, we must have $m + 1 \in J$ by very definition of J. In other words, $1 \in S$. Now let n be any member of S, so that $m + n \in J$. Then again the definition of J insures that $(m + n) + 1 \in J$. But $(m + n) + 1 = m + (n + 1)$ by axiom II, and so this proves that $n + 1 \in S$. Thus we have proved that $1 \in S$ and also that the assumption that $n \in S$ leads to the conclusion that $n + 1 \in S$. Hence, by the principle of induction we conclude that S is all of the positive integers, or in other words that $m + n \in J$ for all positive integers n. This argument was for a fixed m, but we need only observe that it did not depend on anything special about m to conclude that it works for every positive integer m. ∎

The following theorem is proved quite similarly to theorem 13.1, but uses theorem 13.1 as well. The proof is left as an exercise.

Theorem 13.2:   *If $m \in J$ and $n \in J$, then $mn \in J$.*

Theorem 13.3:   *If $m \in J$, $n \in J$, and $m > n$, then $m - n \in J$.*

Proof: Let S be the set of all those positive integers n with the property that whenever m is a positive integer such that $m > n$, we have $m - n \in J$. We first show that $1 \in S$. If $m > 1$ and m is a positive integer, then since each positive integer greater than 1 is obtained by adding 1 to the previous one, we can write $m = p + 1$ for some $p \in J$. Adding -1 to both sides we obtain $m - 1 = p$. In other words, $m - 1 \in J$, and so we have proved that $1 \in S$. Now suppose that $n \in S$, and let us show that $n + 1 \in S$. Suppose that $m \in J$ and $m > n + 1$. Adding $-n$ to both sides gives us $m - n > 1$. But since we are assuming that $n \in S$, we have $m - n \in J$, and so the relation $m - n > 1$ combined with what we have proved shows that $(m - n) - 1 \in J$. Since $(m - n) - 1 = m - (n + 1)$, this shows that $m - (n + 1) \in J$, or in other words, $n + 1 \in S$ as required. Therefore, by the principle of induction, S is the set of all positive integers, and so the theorem is proved. ∎

We say that a number n is a *negative integer* if $-n$ is a positive integer. A number is called simply an *integer* if it is either a positive or a negative integer or if it is 0. The set of all integers is denoted by Z.

Theorem 13.4: *If $m \in Z$ and $n \in Z$, then $m + n \in Z$.*

Proof: If one or both of m and n are zero, then this statement is trivial. Also, if both m and n are positive integers, then the result has already been proved in theorem 13.1. Now if m and n are both negative integers, then $-m$ and $-n$ are positive integers, and so by theorem 13.1 their sum

$$(-m) + (-n) = -(m + n)$$

is a positive integer. In other words, $m + n$ is a negative integer, and so this proves the case where m and n are both negative.

The only remaining case is where one of m and n is positive and the other negative, say m is positive and n is negative. There are three cases, namely $m > -n$, $m = -n$, and $m < -n$. If $m > -n$, then $m + n = m - (-n)$, which is a positive integer by theorem 13.3. If $m = -n$, then $m + n = 0$, hence again is an integer. If $m < -n$, then $-n - m$ is a positive integer by theorem 13.3. But $-n - m = -(m + n)$, and consequently $m + n$ is a negative integer. This handles all cases, and so the theorem is proved. ∎

The corresponding theorem for products, which is proved in a similar way by breaking it up into cases, is left as an exercise.

We shall say that an integer is *even* if it can be written as $2n$ for some integer n. We say that an integer is *odd* if it can be written as $2n + 1$ for some integer n. In particular, $0 = (2)(0)$, and so 0 is even. On the other hand, $1 = (2)(0) + 1$, and so 1 is odd. No integer can be both even and odd. For if it were, then it could be written as $2m$ for some integer m, and also $2n + 1$ for some integer n. This would give us $2m = 2n + 1$, or $m - n = \frac{1}{2}$. Since by theorem 13.4, $m - n$ is an integer, and also $\frac{1}{2} < 1$ (§ 11, exercise 4), this would give us a positive integer less than 1, contradicting the very definition of the positive integers. On the other hand, one can prove that every integer is either even or odd (exercise 3).

A number x is called a *rational* number if we can write $x = \dfrac{m}{n}$ where m and n are integers ($n \neq 0$). If p is any nonzero integer, then we have $\dfrac{pm}{pn} = \dfrac{m}{n}$; hence, there is nothing unique about the way a rational number can be written as a quotient of two integers. Using theorem 13.4 and exercise 2, it is easy to show that the sum and the product of two rational numbers is again a rational number (exercise 4). Moreover, using lemma 10.4, we see that the collection of rational numbers has a property that the collection of integers Z does not have: namely, if x is a nonzero rational number, then $\dfrac{1}{x}$ is also a rational number.

EXERCISES

1. Prove theorem 13.2.
2. Prove that if $m \in Z$ and $n \in Z$, then $mn \in Z$.
3. Show by induction that every positive integer is even or odd. Then using this, show that every negative integer is even or odd.
4. Show that the sum and the product of two rational numbers are also rational numbers. Then show that the collection of rational numbers satisfies each of the twelve axioms we have introduced so far. Which of the axioms is not satisfied by the set Z of integers?
5. If m and n are odd integers, show that mn is odd. If at least one of m and n is even, show that mn is even.
6. A number which is not rational is called an *irrational* number. Show that the sum of a rational and an irrational is irrational, and that the product of a nonzero rational and an irrational is irrational.
7. If x is an odd integer, show that there is only one integer n such that $x = 2n + 1$.

14. FINITE SETS

Let n be a positive integer, and let A be any set (not necessarily of numbers). Suppose that to each integer i such that $1 \leq i \leq n$ there is assigned a member a_i of A. Then

$$a_1, a_2, a_3, \ldots, a_{n-1}, a_n$$

is called a *finite sequence* of members of A. Thus a finite sequence is nothing but a function a from the set $\{1, 2, \ldots, n\}$ to the set A, where instead of denoting the member of A assigned to i by $a(i)$ as is customary with functions, it proves to be more convenient to write a_i.

If there is a sequence $a_1, a_2, \ldots, a_n$ which is actually a one to one correspondence from $\{1, 2, \ldots, n\}$ to A (that is, such that $a_1, a_2, \ldots, a_n$ are all different and, furthermore, include every member of A), then we say that *A has n members*. A set is said to be *finite* if either it is empty, or if it has n members for some positive integer n. Otherwise the set is said to be *infinite*. It is a fairly obvious fact that any subset of a finite set is also finite. However, as another illustration in the use of induction, let's prove it.

> **Theorem 14.1:**   *If A is a finite set and B is a subset of A, then B is also finite.*

Proof: We prove it by induction on the number of members of A. In the first place, it is clear that any subset of a set with only one member is finite, since the only subsets of such a set are either the empty set or the set itself. Now let us suppose that it is true that subsets of sets which have n members are finite, and suppose that A is a set with $n + 1$ members, say $a_1, a_2, \ldots,$ a_n, a_{n+1}. Let A' be the set A with a_{n+1} taken out, so that A' has n members and we can assume the theorem is true for it. Let B be any subset of A. We wish to show that B is finite. If $a_{n+1} \notin B$, then B is also a subset of A', and so by assumption B is finite. On the other hand, if $a_{n+1} \in B$, then let B' be B with a_{n+1} taken out. Then B' is a subset of A' and so by assumption B' is finite, say $B' = \{b_1, b_2, \ldots, b_k\}$. We can then define $b_{k+1} = a_{n+1}$ to obtain $B = \{b_1, b_2, \ldots, b_k, b_{k+1}\}$ as required. ∎

If A is a set of numbers (not necessarily finite), and if there is a number $x \in A$ such that $x < a$ for all other numbers $a \in A$, then x is called the *least* member of A. A set can have only one least member, for if x and y were distinct least members, then we would have $x < y$ since x is a least member and $y < x$ since y is a least member. In other words, we would have both $y - x \in P$ and $x - y \in P$, contradicting axiom X.

Theorem 14.2: *If A is any nonempty finite set of numbers, then A has a least member.*

Proof: We prove it by induction on the number of members of A. If A has only one member, then obviously that member is the least. Assuming that sets of numbers with n members all have least members, let us suppose that A is a set with $n + 1$ members, say $a_1, a_2, \ldots, a_n, a_{n+1}$. The set A' formed from A by taking out a_{n+1} is a set with n members, hence by assumption has a least member x. If $x < a_{n+1}$, then x is also a least member for A. On the other hand, if $a_{n+1} < x$, then since x is less than all other members of A except a_{n+1}, we see that a_{n+1} is the least member of A. ∎

Likewise we say that x is the *greatest member* of a set of numbers A if $x > a$ for all other members a of A. Now the condition $x > a$ is equivalent to the condition $-x < -a$. Hence, to say that x is the greatest member of a set A is equivalent to saying that $-x$ is the least member of the set A^* whose members are the negatives of the members of A. This simple trick frequently enables us to turn a theorem about least members into a theorem about greatest members without any work. For example, we have the following corollary of theorem 14.2.

Corollary 14.3: *If A is any nonempty finite set of numbers, then A has a greatest member.*

Proof: This could be proved in exactly the same way we proved theorem 14.2. However, it is easier to simply observe that the set A^* consisting of the negatives of members of A is also a finite set, hence has a least member x by theorem 14.2. Consequently $-x$ is the greatest member of A. ∎

Not all sets of numbers have least members. For example, the set of *all* numbers certainly has no least member. The same is true of the set of all negative numbers. Another such set is the set P of all positive numbers. (Remember that 0 is not a positive number.) To see this we prove the following lemma.

Lemma 14.4: *If a and b are any numbers such that $a < b$, then there is a number c such that $a < c < b$, namely $c = \dfrac{a + b}{2}$.*

Proof: To show that $\dfrac{a + b}{2} < b$, by definition we must show that $b - \dfrac{a + b}{2}$ is a member of P. We have

$$b - \frac{(a + b)}{2} = \frac{2b - a - b}{2} = \frac{b - a}{2}.$$

Since $a < b$, we have $b - a \in P$, and since $\frac{1}{2} \in P$, we have $\dfrac{b - a}{2} \in P$, as required. We leave it as an exercise to verify that $a < \dfrac{a + b}{2}$. ∎

Actually we can say a lot more than that there is simply one number between any two others. Namely:

Theorem 14.5: *If $a < b$, then the set of numbers between a and b is infinite.*

Proof: Suppose that there are only a finite number of numbers between a and b. Among these there must be a least, by theorem 14.2. Calling it x, and replacing b by x in lemma 14.4, we see that there is a number c between a and x. But then c would be a number between a and b smaller than x, contradicting the fact that x is supposed to be the least such. We conclude that there must be an infinite number of numbers between a and b. ∎

Frequently, in thinking of the numbers as something like a collection of clothes pegs strung out on a clothesline, people make the mistake of talking about "the number next to 2" or "the least positive number." Theorem 14.5 points out the fallacy in thinking this way. The fact is that the numbers do not at all resemble clothes pegs on a clothesline, for whereas between any two clothes pegs there is room for only a finite number of other clothes pegs, on the contrary between any two numbers there is room for, and in fact there are, an infinite number of other numbers.

Nevertheless, some infinite sets of numbers do have least members. For example, the set of nonnegative numbers has 0 as its least member. The set J of positive integers has 1 as its least member. The set of even positive integers has 2 as its least member. In fact, if one tries to think of a set of positive integers which does not have a least member, one soon becomes convinced that there aren't any. This is, in fact, a theorem.

Theorem 14.6: *If A is a nonempty set of positive integers, then A has a least member.*

Proof: Since A is nonempty, it has at least one member, say m. Let A' be the set of members of A which are less than or equal to m. Then A' is a subset of $\{1, 2, 3, \ldots, m\}$, and the latter being finite, by theorem 14.1 so is A'. Consequently by theorem 14.2, A' has a least member, say n. Now n being in A' must be $\leq m$, and since all members of A which are not in A' are $\geq m$, we see that n is a least member for all of A, as required. ∎

The following theorem shows that in proving a theorem by induction, not only can we assume that the theorem is true for the integer immediately preceding, but better still we may assume that it is true for *all* the preceding positive integers. This is called the *second principle of induction*.

Theorem 14.7: *Let S be a set of positive integers which contains each positive integer n for which it contains all the positive integers less than n. Then S is the set J of all positive integers.*

Proof: If S is not all of the positive integers, then the set A of positive integers which are not in S is nonempty. Consequently, by theorem 14.6, A has a least member, say n. But then all positive integers less than n must be in S, and so by hypothesis n also is in S. But then n cannot be in A, a contradiction. Therefore A must be empty, or in other words S is all of the positive integers. ∎

EXERCISES

1. Prove that $a < c$ in lemma 14.4.
2. Let A be the set $\{1, -3, \frac{8}{5}, 0, -\frac{8}{3}, 3, 7\}$. Write down the members of the set A^* of negatives of members of A. How does the least member of A compare with the greatest member of A^*? How does the greatest member of A compare with the least member of A^*?
3. Prove, using 11.5 and induction on n, that if

$$a_1 < a_2, a_2 < a_3, a_3 < a_4, \ldots, a_{n-1} < a_n, \text{ then } a_1 < a_n.$$

15. GENERALIZED LAWS

According to axiom VI, the expression $a_1 a_2 a_3$ is the same no matter which way we introduce parentheses, or in other words, in no matter which order we perform the multiplications. We are going to show that the same is true of a product of any finite number of terms. For definiteness, let us agree that $a_1 a_2 a_3$ is to mean $(a_1 a_2)a_3$, that $a_1 a_2 a_3 a_4$ is to mean $(a_1 a_2 a_3)a_4$, and in general that $a_1 a_2 a_3 \cdots a_n a_{n+1}$ is to mean $(a_1 a_2 a_3 \cdots a_n)a_{n+1}$. In other words, we have defined the meaning of a parenthesis-free expression by induction. Thus, for example, $a_1 a_2 a_3 a_4 a_5 a_6$ is just a short way of writing

$$((((a_1 a_2)a_3)a_4)a_5)a_6.$$

However, this is just one way of multiplying such an expression. Another way is $((a_1a_2)a_3)(a_4(a_5a_6))$. Still another is

$$a_1(a_2(a_3(a_4(a_5a_6)))).$$

Actually there are 42 ways. To start with, let us prove the following lemma.

Lemma 15.1: *If $a_1, a_2, \ldots, a_n$ are any numbers and k is any integer such that $1 \le k \le n - 1$, then*

$$(a_1a_2 \cdots a_k)(a_{k+1}a_{k+2} \cdots a_n) = a_1a_2 \cdots a_n.$$

Proof: The proof is by induction on the number of terms in the second group on the left side, or in other words on $n - k$. If this number is 1, then the left side is just $(a_1a_2 \cdots a_{n-1})(a_n)$, which equals the right side by definition. Now assume that the theorem is true when $n - k$ is replaced by $n - k - 1$, and let us prove the theorem for $n - k$. We have

$$
\begin{aligned}
(a_1a_2 \cdots a_k)&(a_{k+1}a_{k+2} \cdots a_n) \\
&= (a_1a_2 \cdots a_k)(a_{k+1}(a_{k+2} \cdots a_n)) \quad \text{(induction)} \\
&= ((a_1a_2 \cdots a_k)a_{k+1})(a_{k+2} \cdots a_n) \quad \text{(axiom VI)} \\
&= (a_1a_2 \cdots a_ka_{k+1})(a_{k+2} \cdots a_n) \quad \text{(definition)} \\
&= a_1a_2 \cdots a_n. \quad \text{(induction)}
\end{aligned}
$$

Hence, by induction the lemma is true for all values of $n - k$. ∎

It is now a simple matter to show that the product of n numbers a_1, $a_2, \ldots, a_n$ is the same no matter how we place parentheses (providing we do not change the order of the terms). In the first place, when we place parentheses, we start by choosing an integer k such that $1 \le k \le n - 1$, and then we put the terms $a_1, a_2, \ldots, a_k$ in one group and the terms $a_{k+1}, a_{k+2}, \ldots, a_n$ in another group. We then place parentheses in some way in the first group to obtain a number x, and then we place parentheses in some way in the second group to obtain a number y. Finally we take the product xy. For example, in the expression

$$((a_1a_2)a_3)(((a_4a_5)(a_6a_7))a_8)$$

we have $k = 3$, $x = (a_1a_2)a_3$, and $y = ((a_4a_5)(a_6a_7))a_8$.

Theorem 15.2: *The product of n numbers $a_1, a_2 \ldots, a_n$ is independent of the way in which parentheses are placed, providing the order of the terms is not changed.*

Proof: The proof is by induction on n. If $n = 1$, then there is no choice of introducing parentheses, and so the theorem in this case is trivial. Now assume that the theorem is true for all positive integers $< n$. (Thus we are going to use the second principle of induction. See theorem 14.7.) Let k, x, and y be as explained above. Then by assumption we can write $x = a_1a_2 \cdots a_k$ and $y = a_{k+1}a_{k+2} \cdots a_n$. Hence, by lemma 15.1 we have $xy = a_1a_2 \cdots a_n$.

Thus every way of placing parentheses gives the same result as the special way which the expression $a_1 a_2 \cdots a_n$ stands for. This proves the theorem. ▮

We are now going to show that even the order of the terms may be mixed up in performing a multiplication. To say precisely what this means, let $i_1, i_2, \ldots, i_n$ denote the integers from 1 to n written down in an order which is not necessarily the natural order $1, 2, 3, \ldots, n$. We wish to show that if $a_1, a_2, \ldots, a_n$ is any collection of n numbers, then

$$a_{i_1} a_{i_2} a_{i_3} \cdots a_{i_n} = a_1 a_2 a_3 \cdots a_n.$$

For example, in the expression $a_3 a_2 a_5 a_1 a_4$ we have $i_1 = 3$, $i_2 = 2$, $i_3 = 5$, $i_4 = 1$, and $i_5 = 4$.

Theorem 15.3: *If $a_1, a_2, \ldots, a_n$ are any numbers, then the product is independent of the order in which they are written down.*

Proof: We prove it by induction on the number n of terms. If $n = 1$, then there is no choice in the order, and so the theorem is trivial in this case. Now assume that the theorem is true for $n - 1$ terms, and let $i_1, i_2, \ldots, i_n$ be any ordering of the integers from 1 to n. Let us denote the integer i_n by k. Then we have

$$
\begin{aligned}
a_{i_1} a_{i_2} \cdots a_{i_n} &= (a_{i_1} a_{i_2} \cdots a_{i_{n-1}}) a_k && \text{(definition)} \\
&= (a_1 a_2 \cdots a_{k-1} a_{k+1} \cdots a_n) a_k && \text{(induction)} \\
&= (a_1 a_2 \cdots a_{k-1})((a_{k+1} \cdots a_n) a_k) && \text{(theorem 15.2)} \\
&= (a_1 a_2 \cdots a_{k-1})(a_k (a_{k+1} \cdots a_n)) && \text{(axiom VI)} \\
&= a_1 a_2 \cdots a_n. && \text{(theorem 15.2)} ▮
\end{aligned}
$$

In proving theorem 15.2 we used only axiom VI. This means that that theorem would be true if we replaced multiplication by any associative operation. In particular it is true for addition. In other words the expression

$$a_1 + a_2 + \cdots + a_n$$

is the same no matter how we introduce parentheses, and so we shall frequently just leave them out. Similarly, in proving theorem 15.3 we used only axiom V and theorem 15.2, or in other words only axioms V and VI. Therefore, the theorem is true for any operation which is both commutative and associative, and hence again, addition. We shall state the analogues of theorems 15.2 and 15.3 for addition in one theorem.

Theorem 15.4: *The sum of any numbers $a_1, a_2, \ldots, a_n$ is independent of the way in which parentheses are placed and also of the order in which they are written down.* ▮

It is theorem 15.4 which justifies the familiar process of "grouping" terms, when in taking a sum we collect together all those numbers having a certain feature in common. For example, if $a_1, a_2, \ldots, a_n$ and $b_1, b_2, \ldots, b_n$

are any numbers, then by theorem 15.4 we can write

$$(a_1 + a_2 + \cdots + a_n) + (b_1 + b_2 + \cdots + b_n)$$
$$= (a_1 + b_1) + (a_2 + b_2) + \cdots + (a_n + b_n). \qquad (1)$$

Theorem 15.2 *generalizes* axiom VI in the sense that if we state that theorem for the special case of $n = 3$, we obtain axiom VI. Similarly, theorem 15.3 generalizes axiom V, and theorem 15.4 generalizes axioms I and II. The following theorem is a generalization of axiom IX.

Theorem 15.5:   *If $a, b_1, b_2, \ldots, b_n$ are any numbers, then*

$$a(b_1 + b_2 + \cdots + b_n) = ab_1 + ab_2 + \cdots + ab_n.$$

Proof: Again the proof is by induction on n. If $n = 1$, then both sides of the equation are just ab_1. Assuming that the theorem is true with $n - 1$ in place of n, we have

$$a(b_1 + b_2 + \cdots + b_n)$$
$$= a((b_1 + b_2 + \cdots + b_{n-1}) + b_n)$$
$$= a(b_1 + b_2 + \cdots + b_{n-1}) + ab_n \qquad \text{(axiom IX)}$$
$$= (ab_1 + ab_2 + \cdots + ab_{n-1}) + ab_n \qquad \text{(induction)}$$
$$= ab_1 + ab_2 + \cdots + ab_n$$

as required. ∎

Another notation for the sum of n numbers $a_1 + a_2 + \cdots + a_n$ is the expression

$$\sum_{i=1}^{n} a_i.$$

Thus, for example, taking $n = 6$ and $a_i = i^2$, we can write

$$1 + 4 + 9 + 16 + 25 + 36 = \sum_{i=1}^{6} i^2.$$

More generally, if k is any integer $\leq n$, then we write

$$\sum_{i=k}^{n} = a_k + a_{k+1} + \cdots + a_n.$$

The lemma for sums corresponding to lemma 15.1 then reads

$$\sum_{i=1}^{k} a_i + \sum_{i=k+1}^{n} a_i = \sum_{i=1}^{n} a_i.$$

Also theorem 15.5 could be written

$$a\left(\sum_{i=1}^{n} b_i\right) = \sum_{i=1}^{n} (ab_i),$$

and equation (1) could be written

$$\sum_{i=1}^{n} a_i + \sum_{i=1}^{n} b_i = \sum_{i=1}^{n} (a_i + b_i).$$

EXERCISES

1. Without using theorem 15.2, but only repeated use of axiom VI, prove that

$$(((a_1a_2)a_3)a_4)a_5 = a_1(a_2(a_3(a_4a_5))).$$

2. Without using theorem 15.4, but only repeated use of axioms I and II, prove that

$$((a_1 + a_2) + a_3) + a_4 = (a_4 + a_1) + (a_3 + a_2).$$

3. Write out the following expressions in longhand

$$\sum_{i=1}^{4} i^3, \quad \sum_{i=1}^{n} i, \quad \sum_{i=-2}^{3} i^2, \quad \sum_{n=4}^{8} (n - 7).$$

4. Find abbreviations using the $\sum$ notation for the expressions

$$1 + 3 + 5 + 7 + 9 + 11 + 13, \text{ and}$$
$$2 + 4 + 8 + 16 + 32 + 64.$$

5. What must we take for k and n so that the expression

$$\sum_{i=k}^{n} (i - 3)^2$$

is the same as the expression

$$\sum_{i=1}^{15} i^2 \ ?$$

6. Prove, using theorem 12.3 and induction on n, that

$$|a_1 + a_2 + \cdots + a_n| \leq |a_1| + |a_2| + \cdots + |a_n|.$$

7. Prove, using theorem 12.1 and induction on n, that

$$|a_1a_2 \cdots a_n| = |a_1| \, |a_2| \cdots |a_n|.$$

8. Prove, using corollary 11.7 and induction on n, that if $a_i < b_i$ for $1 \leq i \leq n$, then

$$a_1 + a_2 + \cdots + a_n < b_1 + b_2 + \cdots + b_n.$$

9. The story runs that the schoolmaster of the German mathematician Karl Friedrich Gauss (1777–1855) gave the boys the task of adding up the first one hundred positive integers one afternoon to keep them busy so that he could write a letter to his mistress. (The last part of the story is probably invented, since schoolmasters did not have mistresses in those days.) Gauss, who happened to be a genius, called the sum S, and wrote it down twice, once forwards and once backwards, like so:

$$S = 1 + 2 + 3 + \cdots + 99 + 100$$
$$S = 100 + 99 + 98 + \cdots + 2 + 1.$$

(Which theorem was he assuming?) Then he added vertically to obtain

$$2S = 101 + 101 + 101 + \cdots + 101 + 101$$
$$= (100)(101),$$

or in other words, $S = (50)(101) = 5{,}050$, and handed the answer to his master before the latter had had time to write "Dear Annabelle."

Use Gauss's method to show that the sum of the first n positive integers is

$\dfrac{n(n+1)}{2}$ for any positive integer n. Then give another proof of this result by induction.

10. Show by induction that

$$1^2 + 2^2 + 3^2 + \cdots + n^2 = \frac{n(n+1)(2n+1)}{6}.$$

11. Prove that if $a_0, a_1, \ldots, a_n$ are any numbers, then

$$\sum_{i=1}^{n} (a_i - a_{i-1}) = a_n - a_0.$$

12. Let $f(n)$ denote the number of ways of multiplying the expression $a_1a_2a_3 \cdots a_n$. Show that

$$f(n) = f(n-1)f(1) + f(n-2)f(2) + f(n-3)f(3) + \cdots + f(1)f(n-1).$$

Hence deduce that $f(6) = 42$.

16. EXPONENTS

A product $a_1a_2 \cdots a_n$ where each of the numbers a_i is the same number x is denoted simply by x^n. Thus $x^1 = x$, and $x^{n+1} = x^n x$ for any positive integer n. The integer n in the expression x^n is called the *exponent*. The basic rules for exponents are proved in the following theorem.

Theorem 16.1: *If x is any number and m and n are positive integers, then*

$$x^m x^n = x^{m+n} \tag{1}$$

and

$$(x^m)^n = x^{mn}. \tag{2}$$

If x and y are any numbers and n is any positive integer, then

$$(xy)^n = x^n y^n. \tag{3}$$

Proof: Each rule is proved by induction on n.
To prove (1), we have for $n = 1$

$$x^m x^1 = x^m x = x^{m+1}.$$

Then, assuming the rule for n, we have

$$\begin{aligned}
x^m x^{n+1} &= x^m(x^n x) \\
&= (x^m x^n)x \\
&= x^{m+n}x \\
&= x^{(m+n)+1} \\
&= x^{m+(n+1)}
\end{aligned}$$

as required.

To prove (2) we observe that both sides are just x^m for $n = 1$. Then we have

$$
\begin{aligned}
(x^m)^{(n+1)} &= (x^m)^n x^m && \text{(definition)} \\
&= x^{mn} x^m && \text{(induction)} \\
&= x^{mn+m} && \text{(part (1))} \\
&= x^{m(n+1)}
\end{aligned}
$$

as required.

The proof of rule (3) is left as an exercise. ∎

Our definition of x^n makes sense only for n a positive integer. We would like to find definitions for x^0 and for x^{-n} in such a way that rules (1), (2), and (3) will still hold. In the first place, if (1) is to hold, then we must have

$$
x^0 x^1 = x^{0+1} = x^1
$$

and consequently we must take $x^0 = 1$. Similarly, for n a positive integer, we must have

$$
x^{-n} x^n = x^{(-n)+n} = x^0 = 1.
$$

Thus we must take $x^{-n} = \dfrac{1}{x^n}$. Since this does not make sense for $x = 0$, we leave 0^{-n} undefined. Notice that for $n = 1$, this becomes $x^{-1} = \dfrac{1}{x}$, so that our new meaning of x^{-1} agrees with our old meaning.

Now we must turn around and check that the definitions $x^0 = 1$ and $x^{-n} = \dfrac{1}{x^n}$ are actually such that the three rules (1), (2), and (3) are still satisfied. There are many cases, depending on whether the exponents are positive, negative, or zero. For example, let us prove rule (1) in the case where one exponent is positive and the other is negative. The other cases, as well as the proofs of (2) and (3) are left as exercises. Explicitly, we wish to show that

$$
x^m x^{-n} = x^{m-n} \tag{4}
$$

in the case where m and n are positive integers. If $m > n$, then $m - n$ is positive, and so using rule (1) applied to the two positive exponents $m - n$ and n, we obtain

$$
x^{m-n} x^n = x^{(m-n)+n} = x^m.
$$

Multiplying both sides by x^{-n} gives us (4) for the case $m > n$. Now if $n > m$, then we can interchange the roles of n and m in what we have already proved to obtain

$$
x^n x^{-m} = x^{n-m}.
$$

Taking inverses on both sides we get

$$
x^{-n} x^m = x^{-(n-m)} = x^{m-n}.
$$

This proves (4) for the case $n > m$. If $m = n$, then the left side of (4) is $x^n x^{-n}$, which is 1 by definition, and the right side is x^0, which is also 1 by definition. Thus we have proved (4) in all possible cases.

EXERCISES

1. Prove rule (3) for n a positive integer.
2. Prove rules (1), (2), and (3) for all exponents, positive, zero, or negative.
3. Prove by induction on m that

$$(x_1 x_2 \cdots x_m)^n = x_1^n x_2^n \cdots x_m^n.$$

4. If $0 < a_i < b_i$ for $1 \leq i \leq n$, prove by induction that

$$a_1 a_2 \cdots a_n < b_1 b_2 \cdots b_n.$$

Deduce a corollary about exponents.

17. THE BINOMIAL THEOREM

If n is a positive integer, then we define

$$n! = n(n - 1)(n - 2) \cdots (3)(2)(1). \tag{1}$$

Then $n!$ (read "n factorial") satisfies the rules

$$1! = 1, \quad (n + 1)! = (n + 1)n!. \tag{2}$$

Notice that formula (1) does not make any sense in the case $n = 0$. We would like to define $0!$ in such a way that (2) is still satisfied for the case $n = 0$. But writing $n = 0$ in (2), we obtain $1! = (1)0!$, or in other words $0! = 1$.

If k is an integer such that $0 \leq k \leq n$, then we define

$$\binom{n}{k} = \frac{n!}{(n - k)!k!}.$$

In particular this gives us $\binom{n}{0} = 1$ and $\binom{n}{n} = 1$. The number $\binom{n}{k}$ arises in the study of permutations and combinations as the number of combinations of n things taken k at a time.

Lemma 17.1: *If k and n are integers such that $1 \leq k \leq n$, then*

$$\binom{n}{k} + \binom{n}{k - 1} = \binom{n + 1}{k}.$$

Proof: Applying the definitions we have

$$\binom{n}{k} + \binom{n}{k - 1} = \frac{n!}{(n - k)!k!} + \frac{n!}{(n - k + 1)!(k - 1)!}$$

$$= \frac{(n - k + 1)n! + (k)n!}{(n - k + 1)!k!}$$

$$= \frac{(n + 1)n!}{(n - k + 1)!k!} = \binom{n + 1}{k},$$

where at the second step we have simply brought the fractions to a common denominator. ∎

Theorem 17.2 (The Binomial Theorem): *If a and b are any numbers and n is a positive integer, then*

$$(a + b)^n = \sum_{k=0}^{n} \binom{n}{k} a^{n-k}b^k. \tag{3}$$

Proof: The proof is by induction on n. If $n = 1$, then both sides of (3) are just $a + b$. Assuming the theorem true for n, we have

$$(a + b)^{n+1} = (a + b)(a + b)^n = a(a + b)^n + b(a + b)^n$$

$$= a \sum_{k=0}^{n} \binom{n}{k} a^{n-k}b^k + b \sum_{k=0}^{n} \binom{n}{k} a^{n-k}b^k$$

$$= \sum_{k=0}^{n} \binom{n}{k} a^{n-k+1}b^k + \sum_{k=0}^{n} \binom{n}{k} a^{n-k}b^{k+1}.$$

The sum of the exponents in every term of this last expression is $n + 1$. Collecting together the terms with the same distribution of exponents, we see that the coefficient of $a^{n+1}b^0$ is $\binom{n}{0} = 1$, the coefficient of a^0b^{n+1} is $\binom{n}{n} = 1$, and the coefficient of $a^{n+1-k}b^k$ for $1 \le k \le n$ is $\binom{n}{k} + \binom{n}{k-1}$. But by lemma 17.1, this is the same as $\binom{n+1}{k}$. Thus we can write

$$(a + b)^{n+1} = \sum_{k=0}^{n+1} \binom{n+1}{k} a^{n+1-k}b^k$$

which is just equation (3) with n replaced by $n + 1$. ∎

The binomial formula for the first few integers is as follows:

$$(a + b)^1 = a + b$$
$$(a + b)^2 = a^2 + 2ab + b^2$$
$$(a + b)^3 = a^3 + 3a^2b + 3ab^2 + b^3$$
$$(a + b)^4 = a^4 + 4a^3b + 6a^2b^2 + 4ab^3 + b^4$$
$$(a + b)^5 = a^5 + 5a^4b + 10a^3b^2 + 10a^2b^3 + 5ab^4 + b^5$$

Making a symmetrical diagram of the coefficients on the right side, we obtain the array which is known as *Pascal's triangle*, named after the French mathematician Blaise Pascal (1623–1662). In this diagram notice that every number is the sum of the two numbers immediately above it. This is precisely what lemma 17.1 says.

$$
\begin{array}{ccccccccccc}
 & & & & 1 & & 1 & & & & \\
 & & & 1 & & 2 & & 1 & & & \\
 & & 1 & & 3 & & 3 & & 1 & & \\
 & 1 & & 4 & & 6 & & 4 & & 1 & \\
1 & & 5 & & 10 & & 10 & & 5 & & 1 \\
\end{array}
$$

EXERCISES

1. Prove the relations $\binom{n}{0} = 1,\ \binom{n}{n} = 1,\ \binom{n}{1} = n,\ \binom{n}{n-1} = n.$

   Prove also that $\binom{n}{k} = \binom{n}{n-k}.$

2. Write out the proof of theorem 17.2 in longhand without using the $\sum$ notation.

3. Prove that $\dfrac{\binom{n}{k}}{\binom{n+1}{k+1}} = \dfrac{k+1}{n+1}.$

18. NAMES FOR THE INTEGERS

In this section we shall encounter expressions of the form

$$a_n r^n + a_{n-1} r^{n-1} + \cdots a_2 r^2 + a_1 r + a_0.$$

Since we have defined $r^0 = 1$ and $r^1 = r$, such an expression can more conveniently be written $\sum_{i=0}^{n} a_i r^i.$

When all the a_i's are the same, say a, then this expression becomes $\sum_{i=0}^{n} ar^i.$

This is just a geometric series with first term a and common ratio r. The reader is probably familiar with the following lemma which gives the sum of a geometric series.

Lemma 18.1: *If a and r are any real numbers with $r \neq 1$ and if n is any integer ≥ 0, then*

$$\sum_{i=0}^{n} ar^i = \frac{a(r^{n+1} - 1)}{r - 1}.$$

Proof: The proof is by induction on n, but we shall start things off with $n = 0$ instead of $n = 1$. If $n = 0$, then both sides are just a. Now assuming the theorem true for n, we have

$$\sum_{i=0}^{n+1} ar^i = ar^{n+1} + \sum_{i=0}^{n} ar^i$$

$$= ar^{n+1} + \frac{a(r^{n+1} - 1)}{r - 1}$$

$$= \frac{a(r^{n+2} - r^{n+1} + r^{n+1} - 1)}{r - 1}$$

$$= \frac{a(r^{n+2} - 1)}{r - 1},$$

which is the required formula with n replaced by $n + 1$. ∎

Theorem 18.2: *Let r be any integer > 1. Then every positive integer p can be written uniquely in the form*

$$p = a_n r^n + a_{n-1} r^{n-1} + \cdots + a_2 r^2 + a_1 r + a_0, \tag{1}$$

where each a_i is an integer such that $0 \le a_i \le r - 1$.

Proof: We first show by induction on p that every positive integer has at least one such representation. If $p = 1$, then we need only take $n = 0$ and $a_0 = 1$. Now assuming that p has a representation (1), let us show that $p + 1$ also has one. Suppose first that $a_0 < r - 1$. Then we can replace a_0 by $a_0 + 1$ and leave all the other a_i's the same to obtain such a representation for $p + 1$. On the other hand, if $a_0 = r - 1$, then let k be the first integer such that $a_k < r - 1$. (We can always add the term $a_{n+1} r^{n+1}$ with $a_{n+1} = 0$ to the representation for p so as to be able to assume that not all of the a_i's are $r - 1$.) Then we have

$$a_0 = a_1 = a_2 = \cdots = a_{k-1} = r - 1,$$

and so the representation for p can be written

$$\begin{aligned}
p &= \sum_{i=k}^{n} a_i r^i + \sum_{i=0}^{k-1} (r - 1) r^i \\
&= \sum_{i=k}^{n} a_i r^i + (r - 1) \frac{(r^k - 1)}{r - 1} \quad \text{(by lemma 18.1)} \\
&= \sum_{i=k}^{n} a_i r^i + r^k - 1.
\end{aligned}$$

Adding 1 to both sides and collecting the two terms on the right side involving r^k gives us

$$p + 1 = a_n r^n + a_{n-1} r^{n-1} + \cdots + a_{k+1} r^{k+1} + (a_k + 1) r^k.$$

This is a representation for $p + 1$ of the required form.

Suppose now that some integer p has two such representations, or in other words, that we have

$$\sum_{i=0}^{n} a_i r^i = \sum_{i=0}^{m} b_i r^i, \tag{2}$$

where $0 \le a_i \le r - 1$, $0 \le b_i \le r - 1$, and for at least one i we have $a_i \ne b_i$. We may assume that $m = n$ by adding zero terms to one of the sides if necessary. Also by canceling off equal terms on both sides of (2), we may assume that $a_n \ne b_n$, say $a_n > b_n$. Then adding $-b_n r^n$ to both sides of (2), we obtain

$$\sum_{i=0}^{n-1} a_i r^i + (a_n - b_n) r^n = \sum_{i=0}^{n-1} b_i r^i. \tag{3}$$

Now $a_n - b_n \ge 1$, and $\sum_{i=0}^{n-1} a_i r^i \ge 0$. Hence, using (3) and lemma 18.1, we can write

$$r^n \leq \sum_{i=0}^{n-1} b_i r^i \leq \sum_{i=0}^{n-1} (r-1)r^i = r^n - 1.$$

This is impossible, and so we must conclude that no integer has more than one representation in the form (1). ∎

In § 13 we invented symbols 0, 1, 2, ..., 8, 9 (which we call *digits*) for a few of the integers, but we postponed a more comprehensive naming until later. Let us give a name to one more integer, say X = 9 + 1. Replacing r by X in theorem 18.2, we see that every nonnegative integer has a unique representation in the form

$$a_n X^n + a_{n-1} X^{n-1} + \cdots + a_2 X^2 + a_1 X + a_0,$$

where each a_i is an integer such that $0 \leq a_i \leq 9$. For short we shall agree to call that integer

$$a_n a_{n-1} \cdots a_3, a_2 a_1 a_0,$$

where we put a comma after every group of three digits starting from the right so as to tell at a glance how many digits there are. For example, 304,297 is just an abbreviation for

$$3X^5 + 0X^4 + 4X^3 + 2X^2 + 9X + 7.$$

In particular X, which can be written as 1X + 0, will henceforth be known as 10. (With this notation we must use parentheses to denote multiplication so as to distinguish between a product such as (2)(3) = 6 and the integer 23 = 2X + 3.)

We see now that theorem 18.2 is what is taken for granted in our familiar decimal representation of the integers. However, there is nothing at all special about the integer ten in the above discussion. We could equally well have started with any integer $r > 1$ and based the names for the integers on r instead of on ten. Our names would then involve r digits instead of ten digits. For example, writing numbers in decimal notation we have

$$591 = (2)(4^4) + (1)(4^3) + (0)(4^2) + (3)(4) + 3,$$

and so the integer which goes under the name 591 in decimal notation has the name 21,033 in the notation based on four. In general, the smaller we take r, the longer the string of digits representing a given integer becomes. For practical purposes ten proves to be a good base to use, for it provides relatively short names for the integers which we tend to encounter in everyday experience, and at the same time it enables us to operate with not too many digits. Nevertheless, the electronic computing machines, which have no difficulty in writing down long names, prefer to operate with the base which uses the fewest number of digits possible, namely two. In this system, which is called the *binary* system, the representation of each integer is in terms of the digits 1 and 0 (which can therefore be produced by the making or the breaking of an electric circuit). For example, the integer whose decimal name is 147 has as its binary name

10,010,011. There is an interesting game which has become well known due to a certain French film, and which has a simple strategy based on the binary system (see exercise 7).

EXERCISES

1. In lemma 18.1 why did we have to assume $r \neq 1$? What is the sum of the geometric series when $r = 1$?

2. The name of a number based on eight is 7,607. Find its decimal name.

3. The decimal name of a number is 7,607. Find its name based on eight.

4. The name of a number based on five is 413. Find its name based on three.

5. Invent symbols for ten and eleven, and find the name based on twelve for the number whose decimal name is 6,778.

6. Consider the number whose name is 13 in the decimal system. Assuming that it is the number itself and not the name "13" which is unlucky, what is the name of this unlucky number based on four? On the other hand, assuming that it is the name "13" which is unlucky, what is the decimal name of the number which is unlucky when its name is based on four? (It is the latter assumption which is made in buildings where the thirteenth floor is called 14, since it is clear that although one can skip the name 13, one can't skip the floor.)

7. Consider m rows of matchsticks (m any positive integer), and suppose that in the ith row there are n_i matches (n_i any positive integer). For each i we consider the integer n_i in terms of its binary representation, and we put these representations in a list. For example, if $m = 4$, $n_1 = 1$, $n_2 = 3$, $n_3 = 5$, and $n_4 = 7$, we have the following situation.

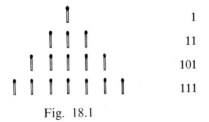

$$
\begin{aligned}
&1 \\
&11 \\
&101 \\
&111
\end{aligned}
$$

Fig. 18.1

We shall call the situation *special* if there are an even number of 1's in each column of the list of binaries. In the above example the situation is special.

Two players A and B are playing the following game. They play alternately, and at each turn a player has the right to take as many matches as he likes from any single row. (He may wipe out a whole row if he wishes, but he must take at least one match.) The object of the game is to force the other player to take the last match. Show that if at any time the situation is special, then no matter how one plays, after the play the situation will be nonspecial. On the other hand, show that if at any time the situation is nonspecial, then one can make the next move in such a way that the situation becomes special. Therefore, if one of the players, say A, has once played in such a way that the situation is special, then he can go on making it special after his turn for as long as he pleases.

Now, sooner or later the game must progress to the point where there is only one row left which has more than one match in it. Since such a situation is nonspecial it must be A's turn to play. What move can he make to win?

19. THE LINE

Few mathematicians are interested in taking a random collection of axioms and seeing what logical consequences they can deduce from them. There is almost always some intuitive picture, geometrical, physical, or otherwise, which guides them in their choice of systems to study, in their feeling for what theorems may be true for those systems, and in how to go about proving such theorems. Nevertheless, the proofs themselves never use any argument which depends on drawing a picture, or on making an analogy, or on some rule which has been memorized and repeated so often that one has come to accept it as self-evident. They use only the axioms which have been selected at the outstart and the theorems which have been previously proved from these axioms.

For example, a notion which has proved well worth studying because of the frequency with which it has arisen in both mathematics and physics is that of a *group*, which is simply a system with an operation satisfying axioms II, III, and IV of this chapter. The study of groups goes back as far as the French mathematician Evariste Galois (1811–1832). If one adds the additional axiom I, one obtains what is known as an *abelian* group, named after the Norwegian mathematician Niels Abel (1802–1829). (The life span of both of these mathematicians is worth remarking.) A system with two operations satisfying axioms I, II, III, IV, VI, IX, and also the rule $(b + c)a = ba + ca$ (whose proof depended on axiom V, which we are dropping from the list) is called a *ring*. A system satisfying axioms I–IX is called a *field*. There are many fields besides the field of real numbers. Up until § 11 we were doing more than simply establishing facts about the real numbers. We were establishing theorems which are valid for any field.

As far as the real numbers are concerned, the guiding picture is that of the points (whatever those are) on a straight line (whatever that is). We select any point on the line and label it 0. Then we select any other point and we label it 1. The direction traveled on the line in going from 0 to 1 is then called the *positive* direction and the other direction the *negative* direction. If n is a positive integer, then we lay off the interval from 0 to 1 n times in the positive direction from 0, and we label the point so arrived at n. More generally, if p and q are positive integers, then the rational number $\frac{p}{q}$ is located by dividing up the interval from 0 to 1 into q equal parts, and then laying off one of those parts p times in the positive direction from 0. The negative rational number $\frac{-p}{q}$ is located by traveling in the negative direction from 0 instead of the positive direction. The points labeled $\frac{12}{5}$ and $\frac{-12}{5}$ have been located in the accompanying picture (figure 19.1).

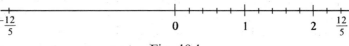

Fig. 19.1

The sum of two numbers x and y is given geometrically by laying off the interval from 0 to y in the positive direction from x if y is positive (figure 19.2), in the negative direction from x if y is negative (figure 19.3).

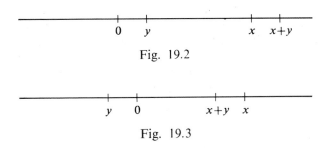

Fig. 19.2

Fig. 19.3

The product of two numbers x and y can be located as follows. We draw another line through 0, and on it we mark points P and Q such that the length of the segment joining 0 to P is 1 and the length of the segment joining 0 to Q is y (figure 19.4). Through Q we draw the line parallel to the line joining P to x, and we call the point where it cuts our first line z. Then from similar triangles we see that $\dfrac{x}{1} = \dfrac{z}{y}$, or in other words $z = xy$, so that z gives us the point representing the product of the two numbers x and y.

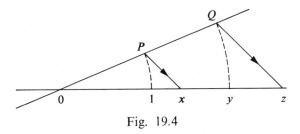

Fig. 19.4

The *distance* between two numbers x and y is defined as $|x - y|$. Thus if $x = y$, then the distance between x and y is 0, whereas if $x \neq y$, then whether $x > y$ or $x < y$, the distance is a positive number. In everyday language we have the notion of "large" distances and "small" distances. However, these notions are completely relative and do not apply to the numbers. For example, what criterion should we apply to determine if 100 is a large number or not? If we locate the point corresponding to 100 on the line, then we go a long distance from 0 if we have chosen the mile as our unit of measure (that is, if the point labeled 1 is one mile from the point labeled 0). However, if we have chosen a sixteenth of an inch as our unit, then 100 does not seem very big. Moreover, even if we were to decide on a unit of measure once and for all, say the inch, then 100 would not seem like a very large number to a man, but for a snail it represents a considerable walk. The moral is that as far as the numbers are concerned, although we have the relative notion of "greater than" between two numbers, we do not have the absolute notion of "great" for a single number.

It may seem that if we took all points on the line corresponding to rational numbers, we would get such a dense population that there would be no room for any other points. A question we may therefore ask is the following: Are there any numbers besides the rational numbers? Since the rational numbers by themselves satisfy all of the twelve axioms we have so far stated (see exercise 4 of § 13), it follows that we are not going to be able to demonstrate that there are any more numbers unless we introduce another axiom. The need for such an axiom is seen from the following geometrical evidence.

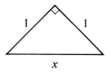

Fig. 19.5

Consider the right angled triangle in figure 19.5, where two of the sides have length one, and we are calling the length of the hypotenuse x. By the pythagorean theorem, we must have $x^2 = 1^2 + 1^2$, or in other words $x^2 = 2$. Thus we have shown geometrically the existence of a number x whose square is 2. We now show that there is no rational number whose square is 2.

Suppose to the contrary that $\left(\dfrac{p}{q}\right)^2 = 2$ where p and q are integers. By canceling off factors of 2 from numerator and denominator, we may assume that not both p and q are even. Now we have $p^2 = 2q^2$, so that p^2 is even. Therefore p must be even, say $p = 2r$. Then the relation $p^2 = 2q^2$ becomes $(2r)^2 = 2q^2$, or $2r^2 = q^2$. But then by the same reasoning as for p, q must be even. Thus we have shown that both p and q are even, contrary to assumption. Hence we are forced to conclude that there is no rational number whose square is 2.

Of course we could simply add to our list of axioms one which says that there is a number whose square is 2. But this would not guarantee the existence of a number whose square is 3, or a number whose cube is 13, or a number whose 49th power is 50. It turns out that there is a simple axiom which guarantees the existence of all these numbers, and of many other numbers besides. We shall not need this axiom in chapter II, and so we shall postpone its statement until the beginning of chapter III. After that we shall require no more axioms. It then turns out that the rational numbers are a very small minority of all the real numbers, in a perfectly definite sense of the word "minority" which we shall not go into in this book.

EXERCISES

1. Consider the diagram of figure 19.6, where a, b, and x are the distances of R, S, and T respectively from P using PQ as a unit of measure. Then the distances from R to S and from R to T using PQ as unit of measure are $b - a$ and $x - a$

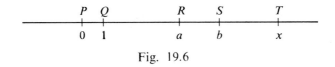

Fig. 19.6

respectively. Hence the distance from R to T using RS as unit of measure is $\dfrac{x - a}{b - a}$. In other words, if instead of labeling P by 0 and Q by 1, we label R by 0 and S by 1, then the number we attach to T is $\dfrac{x - a}{b - a}$.

Now draw the above diagram in the case where PQ is one inch, a is 2, b is $\frac{8}{3}$, and x is 4. By looking at the diagram, estimate approximately what T should be labeled if R is labeled 0 and S is labeled 1. Then see how close this comes to $\dfrac{x - a}{b - a}$.

2. Suppose that we label two points on a line 0 and 1 so as to give us one way of naming the points on the line, and then we take two points so named a and b and rename them 0 and 1 respectively, thus giving us a new way of naming the points on the line. Using exercise 1, find what a and b must be so that the new name x' of any point is related to the old name x by the relation $x' = 3x + 5$.

20. THE PLANE

The guiding picture for the ordered pairs of numbers (that is, the set $R \times R$) is the plane. Explicitly, we choose two perpendicular lines meeting at a point O which we shall call the *origin*, and we call one of the lines the *first axis* and the other line the *second axis*. On each axis we pick a direction which we shall call the *positive direction*. The other direction is called the *negative direction*.

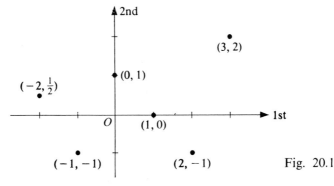

Fig. 20.1

Also we pick a unit of length. Given an ordered pair of numbers (x, y), we travel a distance $|x|$ from O along the first axis in the positive direction if x is positive, in the negative direction if x is negative. Then we travel a distance $|y|$ parallel to the second axis in the positive direction if y is positive, in the negative direction if y is negative. We then label the point so reached (x, y), and we call x and y the *first* and *second coordinates* respectively of that point. A few points have been assigned coordinates in figure 20.1.

The idea of thinking of ordered pairs of numbers as points on the plane is particularly useful in helping us visualize functions. Given a function f from A to B where A and B are sets of numbers, we can think of f as the collection of all points on the plane whose coordinates are of the form $(x, f(x))$ where $x \in A$. This collection is called the *graph* of f. For example, if f is the function whose domain is the set R of all numbers and such that $f(x) = x^2$ for all $x \in R$, then the graph of f is the set of all points whose coordinates are of the form (x, x^2). It can be drawn by locating a few points on it, such as $(0, 0)$, $(1, 1)$, $(2, 4)$, $(3, 9)$, $(-1, 1)$, $(-2, 4)$, $(-3, 9)$, $(\frac{1}{2}, \frac{1}{4})$, and by filling in the rest of the graph so as to obtain a smooth curve (figure 20.2). It is one of the purposes of the calculus to pin down exactly what we mean by the word "smooth," and to show that a function such as the one above is smooth. Another purpose of the calculus is to find better methods for drawing the graph of a function than simply by locating a few points on it as we have done here.

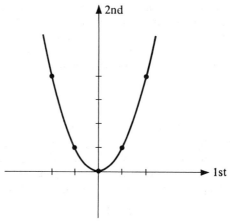

Fig. 20.2

If we take the restriction of the above function f to the set A of those numbers x satisfying $-1 \leq x \leq 2$, (see § 4) we obtain the function with the graph shown in figure 20.3.

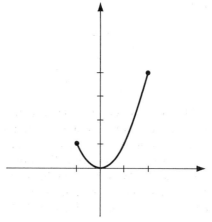

Fig. 20.3

The majority of funtions are not as smooth as the function of figure 20.2, and in fact most of them are so far from being smooth that we cannot even attempt to draw their graphs. This makes it doubly important that our proofs should not depend in any way on looking at graphs. A function which is not as smooth as the function of figure 20.2, but whose graph nevertheless we can draw, is what is known as "the greatest integer" function. It is defined for all numbers x by taking $f(x)$ to be the greatest integer $\leq x$. For example, $f(\frac{5}{2}) = 2$, $f\left(\dfrac{-8}{3}\right) = -3$, and $f(7) = 7$. Its graph is given in figure 20.4.

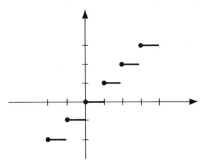

Fig. 20.4

EXERCISES

1. Is any collection of points in the plane the graph of some function? If not, state the condition which such a collection must satisfy before it is the graph of a function.

2. Draw the graph of the function f such that $f(x) = x^3$ for all numbers x. Then draw the restriction of this function to the set of numbers x satisfying either $-2 \leq x \leq -1$ or $\frac{1}{2} \leq x \leq \frac{3}{2}$.

3. Let m and b be fixed numbers, and let $f(x) = mx + b$ for all x. What is the graph of f?

4. Let $f(x) = |x|$ for all numbers x. Draw the graph of f.

5. Let $f(x) = \dfrac{1}{x}$ for all $x \neq 0$. Draw the graph of f.

6. Let $f(x) = \dfrac{1}{x - 2}$ for all $x \neq 2$. Draw the graph of f.

7. Let f be defined by

$$f(x) = x^2 \qquad \text{for } -2 \leq x < 0$$
$$f(x) = 1 \qquad \text{for } 0 \leq x \leq 1$$
$$f(x) = x - 2 \quad \text{for } 1 < x \leq 3.$$

Draw the graph of f.

8. Let $f(x) = |x| + x$ for all numbers x. Draw the graph of f.

9. (a) Consider the set of all points in the plane of the form $(x, 2)$. Is this the graph of some function?
   (b) Consider the set of all points in the plane of the form $(2, y)$. Is this the graph of some function?

21. WAYS OF DEFINING FUNCTIONS

Henceforth when we use the word "function," we shall mean a function f whose domain is a set of numbers and whose values $f(x)$ are numbers. Given two such functions f and g, we can define another function $f + g$ whose value at a number x is given by the rule

$$(f + g)(x) = f(x) + g(x)$$

for all those x for which the right side makes sense, or in other words, for all x which are simultaneously in the domains of f and g. Similarly, we can define the product fg by the rule

$$(fg)(x) = f(x)g(x),$$

where again the domain of fg is the intersection of the domains of f and g. When $g = f$, then we shall denote the product by f^2. Also we can define the quotient function $\dfrac{f}{g}$ by the rule

$$\left(\frac{f}{g}\right)(x) = \frac{f(x)}{g(x)}$$

for all those x which are simultaneously in the domains of both f and g *and* for which $g(x) \neq 0$.

For example, if $f(x) = \dfrac{1}{x}$ for $x \neq 0$, and $g(x) = \dfrac{x + 2}{(x - 1)(x - 3)}$ for $x \neq 1$ or 3, then

$$(f + g)(x) = \frac{1}{x} + \frac{x + 2}{(x - 1)(x - 3)} \qquad \text{for } x \neq 0, 1, \text{ or } 3$$

$$(fg)(x) = \frac{x + 2}{x(x - 1)(x - 3)} \qquad \text{for } x \neq 0, 1, \text{ or } 3$$

and

$$\left(\frac{f}{g}\right)(x) = \frac{1/x}{(x + 2)/(x - 1)(x - 3)} \qquad \text{for } x \neq 0, 1, 3, \text{ or } -2.$$

If n is an integer ≥ 0, then a function f is called a *polynomial function of degree n* (or more simply, a *polynomial*) if there are numbers $a_0, a_1, a_2, \ldots, a_n$ such that $a_n \neq 0$, and such that

$$f(x) = a_n x^n + a_{n-1} x^{n-1} + \cdots + a_2 x^2 + a_1 x + a_0$$

for all numbers x. We then call a_n the *leading coefficient* of the polynomial. Using our summation notation we could write more briefly

$$f(x) = \sum_{i=0}^{n} a_i x^i.$$

For example, if

$$f(x) = 7x^4 - \tfrac{2}{3}x^3 + x - \tfrac{1}{2} \text{ for all } x,$$

then f is a polynomial function of degree 4 with leading coefficient 7. The other coefficients are $a_3 = -\frac{2}{3}$, $a_2 = 0$, $a_1 = 1$, and $a_0 = -\frac{1}{2}$.

Special cases of polynomial functions are the following.

(1) Let c be any number, and let f be the function such that $f(x) = c$ for all numbers x. Then f is called a *constant function* (or more simply, a *constant*). The graph of f is in figure 21.1. We shall frequently denote f simply by c. Strictly speaking this is not correct notation, since there is a vast difference between the number c, and the function whose value is c for every x. However, this is just a case of two different things having the same name, and it will always be clear whether it is the number c or the function c which is in question. If $c \neq 0$, then f is just a polynomial function of degree 0. We shall also consider f a polynomial in the case where $c = 0$, although in this case there is no degree.

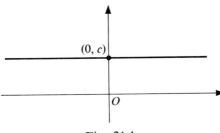

Fig. 21.1

(2) Consider any straight line which is not parallel to the second axis. Let f be the function which assigns to each number x the number y such that (x, y) is on the line. To find an explicit expression for $f(x)$, take any pair of distinct points (x_1, y_1) and (x_2, y_2) on the line. Then from similar triangles (figure 21.2), we see that (x, y) is on the line if and only if

$$\frac{y - y_1}{x - x_1} = \frac{y_2 - y_1}{x_2 - x_1}. \tag{1}$$

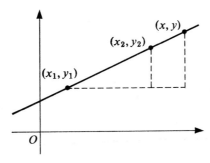

Fig. 21.2

The number $\dfrac{y_2 - y_1}{x_2 - x_1}$ is called the *slope* of the line.

Denoting it by a_1, equation (1) becomes

$$y = a_1 x + (y_1 - a_1 x_1).$$

Therefore, if we let $a_0 = y_1 - a_1 x_1$, we obtain

$$f(x) = a_1 x + a_0$$

for all numbers x. If $a_1 \neq 0$ (that is, if the line is not parallel to the first axis), then we see that f is just a polynomial function of degree 1.

Conversely, suppose that we start with a polynomial function of degree 1, say $f(x) = a_1 x + a_0$. Then, taking (x_1, y_1) and (x_2, y_2) to be $(0, a_0)$ and $(1, a_1 + a_0)$ in the above discussion, we see that the graph of f is just the straight line joining these two points. In other words, the polynomial functions of degree 1 are precisely those functions which have as their graphs straight lines parallel to neither axis.

(3) A polynomial of degree 2 is called a *quadratic* function. Its graph can be shown to be a parabola. For example, if $f(x) = x^2 - 4x + 5$, then (x, y) lies on the graph if and only if $y = x^2 - 4x + 5$, which can be rewritten

$$y - 1 = (x - 2)^2. \tag{2}$$

If we take a new origin at $(2, 1)$ and new axes parallel to the old axes, then the new coordinates (x', y') of a point are related to the old coordinates (x, y) by the formulas $x' = x - 2$ and $y' = y - 1$. Thus equation (2) becomes $y' = x'^2$, and this we recognize as a parabola. Therefore we see that the graph of the original function f is as given in figure 21.3.

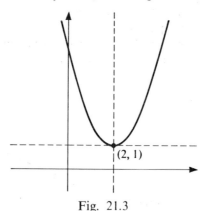

$(2, 1)$

Fig. 21.3

The sum and the product of two polynomials are again polynomials. For example, if $f(x) = 2x^2 - 3x + 1$ and $g(x) = 3x^3 + x^2 - x + 5$, then

$$(f + g)(x) = (2x^2 - 3x + 1) + (3x^3 + x^2 - x + 5)$$
$$= 3x^3 + 3x^2 - 4x + 6$$

and

$$(fg)(x) = (2x^2 - 3x + 1)(3x^3 + x^2 - x + 5)$$
$$= 6x^5 - 7x^4 - 2x^3 + 14x^2 - 16x + 5.$$

The quotient of two polynomial functions is what we call a *rational function*. For example, if f is defined by

$$f(x) = \frac{x^3 - 4x + 2}{x^2 - 1} \quad \text{for } x \neq 1 \text{ and } x \neq -1,$$

then f is a rational function. In the same way that an integer may be considered as a rational number with the number 1 in the denominator, a polynomial may be considered as a rational function with the function 1 in the denominator.

If f is a function with the property that $f(-x) = f(x)$ for all x in its domain, then f is called an *even* function. The graph of f on the negative side of O is thus obtained by placing a mirror along the second axis and taking the reflection of the graph on the positive side of O. An example of an even function is given by the polynomial function $f(x) = x^2$. On the other hand, we say that f is an *odd* function if $f(-x) = -f(x)$ for all x in the domain of f. An example is given by $f(x) = x^3$.

EXERCISES

1. Give the degree and the leading coefficient of each of the following polynomials:

$$f(x) = \frac{x^5 - 2x^2 + x}{8}, \quad g(x) = 7x, \quad h(x) = -x^{99} + 2x - 2.$$

Find the sum and the product of each pair of them.

2. How does the degree of the product fg of two polynomials compare with the degrees of f and g? What is the leading coefficient of fg in terms of the leading coefficients of f and g? Can the degree of the sum $f + g$ be larger than the degrees of both f and g? Can it be smaller? If either answer is yes, illustrate with an example.

3. What is the distinction between the polynomial function $f(x) = x^2 + 1$, and the rational function $g(x) = \dfrac{(x - 1)(x^2 + 1)}{(x - 1)}$? Is either function the restriction of the other to some set?

4. Give appropriate definitions for the sum and the product of any number of functions $f_1, f_2, \ldots, f_n$. Show by induction that the sum and the product of any number of polynomials are again polynomials.

5. Show that the composition $g \circ f$ of any two polynomials is also a polynomial. (You will have to use exercise 4.)

6. Show that the sum and product of any two rational functions are again rational functions.

7. (a) If $f(x) = cx^n$, show that f is an even function or an odd function depending on whether n is an even integer or an odd integer.
   (b) Show that the sum of two even functions is an even function, and the sum of two odd functions is an odd function.

(c) Use parts (a) and (b) to show that if

$$f(x) = a_n x^n + a_{n-1} x^{n-1} + \cdots + a_1 x + a_0$$

where $a_i = 0$ whenever i is odd, then f is even. On the other hand, if $a_i = 0$ whenever i is even, then f is odd.

(d) Prove that the product of two even or two odd functions is even. Prove that the product of an even function with an odd function is odd. Show that $\dfrac{1}{f}$ is even or odd depending on whether f is even or odd.

(e) If f is odd and $f(0)$ is defined, show that $f(0) = 0$.

8. Sketch the graph of f in each of the following cases.

(a) $f(x) = 2x + 1$
(c) $f(x) = x/2$
(e) $f(x) = x^2 + 2$
(g) $f(x) = x^2 - 2x + 3$
(b) $f(x) = 1 - x$
(d) $f(x) = -2$
(f) $f(x) = 1 - x^2$
(h) $f(x) = x - x^2$

9. If $f(x)$ is a polynomial of degree 2, show that the graph of f is a parabola. Distinguish between the case where the leading coefficient is positive and the case where it is negative.

22. FACTORS OF POLYNOMIALS

Consider a polynomial

$$f(x) = a_n x^n + a_{n-1} x^{n-1} + \cdots + a_1 x + a_0. \tag{1}$$

We call a polynomial p a *factor* of f if there is another polynomial q such that $f = pq$. For example, if $f(x) = 3x^3 - 6x^2 + x - 2$ and $p(x) = 3x^2 + 1$, then we can write

$$(3x^3 - 6x^2 + x - 2) = (3x^2 + 1)(x - 2)$$

for all x, and so p is a factor of f. Obviously, any nonzero constant c is a factor of every polynomial. For if f is the polynomial function given by (1), then we can write

$$f(x) = c\left(\frac{a_n}{c} x^n + \frac{a_{n-1}}{c} x^{n-1} + \cdots + \frac{a_1}{c} x + \frac{a_0}{c} \right).$$

If p is a factor of f, then obviously the degree of p must be $\le$ the degree of f. However, if we start out with two random polynomials p and f where the degree of p is $\le$ the degree of f, there is not much chance of p being a factor of f. For instance, if we take $f(x) = 7x^5 - 5x^4 + 2x^3 - 4x + 1$ and $p(x) = x^3 - 2x^2 + 4x + 1$, let us write down the expression

$$(7x^5 - 5x^4 + 2x^3 - 4x + 1) = (x^3 - 2x^2 + 4x + 1)(\qquad)$$

and try to fill in the blank. First, since the coefficient of x^5 on the left side is 7, we must insert $7x^2$ in the blank so that the same will be true on the right side. But this will give us $-14x^4$ on the right side, whereas we want $-5x^4$. To rectify the situation we add $9x$ in the blank, and now the coefficients of

x^4 agree. But with $7x^2 + 9x$ in the blank, we obtain $10x^3$ on the right side, whereas we want $2x^3$. Therefore we add -8 in the blank and this gives us the right cofficient of x^3. But now there is nothing more we can add in the blank since we are down to the term of degree 0. On the right side we have

$$(x^3 - 2x^2 + 4x + 1)(7x^2 + 9x - 8)$$
$$= 7x^5 - 5x^4 + 2x^3 + 59x^2 - 23x - 8,$$

which is not the same as the left side. What we can write is

$$7x^5 - 5x^4 + 2x^3 - 4x + 1$$
$$= (x^3 - 2x^2 + 4x + 1)(7x^2 + 9x - 8) - 59x^2 + 19x + 9.$$

Now although we have not been able to perform the factorization, we notice that the polynomial $-59x^2 + 19x + 9$ which we had to add at the end, and which is called the *remainder*, has degree less than the polynomial $x^3 - 2x^2 + 4x + 1$ which we originally tried to write as a factor. This process can be applied to any pair of polynomials f and p where $p \neq 0$ to obtain polynomials q and r such that

$$f(x) = p(x)q(x) + r(x) \tag{2}$$

and such that r is either 0 (in the case where p happens to be a factor of f) or its degree is less than the degree of p. In exercise 6 you are challenged to write down a formal proof of this.

If we divide both sides of (2) by $p(x)$, we obtain

$$\frac{f(x)}{p(x)} = q(x) + \frac{r(x)}{p(x)}. \tag{3}$$

Thus we see that any rational function can be written as the sum of a polynomial function and a rational function whose numerator has degree less than that of its denominator. The latter is called a *proper* rational function.

The following lemma is an easy exercise in the distributive law. The proof is left to the reader. ▫

Lemma 22.1: *If x and c are any numbers and n is any positive integer, then*

$$x^n - c^n = (x - c)(x^{n-1} + cx^{n-2} + c^2x^{n-3} + \cdots + c^{n-1}).$$

Hence $x - c$ is a factor of $x^n - c^n$. ∎

A number c is called a *root* of a polynomial f if $f(c) = 0$. Geometrically, this means that at c the graph of f crosses the first axis.

Theorem 22.2: *The number c is a root of the polynomial f if and only if $x - c$ is a factor of f.*

Proof: If $x - c$ is a factor of f, say $f(x) = (x - c)q(x)$, then

$$f(c) = (c - c)q(c) = 0.$$

Conversely, suppose that $f(c) = 0$, or in other words that

$$a_n c^n + \cdots + a_1 c + a_0 = 0. \tag{4}$$

Then we can write

$$\begin{aligned} f(x) &= f(x) - 0 = (a_n x^n + \cdots + a_1 x + a_0) - (a_n c^n + \cdots + a_1 c + a_0) \\ &= a_n(x^n - c^n) + a_{n-1}(x^{n-1} - c^{n-1}) + \cdots + a_1(x - c). \end{aligned}$$

Now by lemma 22.1, $x - c$ is a factor of every term in the last expression. Hence by the distributive law, $x - c$ is a factor of the whole expression, or in other words of $f(x)$. ∎

Theorem 22.3: *A polynomial of degree n has no more than n roots.*

Proof: The proof is by induction on n. If $n = 0$, then the polynomial must be a nonzero constant function, and so has no roots. Now suppose that all polynomials of degree $n - 1$ have at most $n - 1$ roots, and let f be a polynomial of degree n(where $n \geq 1$). If f has no roots, then we are certainly justified in saying that it has no more than n roots. If f has some root, say c, then by theorem 17.2 we can write $f(x) = (x - c)q(x)$, where, since f has degree n, q must have degree $n - 1$. Now a root d of f must satisfy $(d - c)q(d) = 0$, and so if $d \neq c$, then $q(d) = 0$. In other words, the roots of f other than c must be roots of q, and since, by induction, there are no more than $n - 1$ roots of q, this means that there are no more than n roots of f. This is what is required. ∎

Corollary 22.4: *If two polynomials*

$$a_n x^n + a_{n-1} x^{n-1} + \cdots + a_1 x + a_0 \tag{5}$$

and

$$b_m x^m + b_{m-1} x^{m-1} + \cdots + b_1 x + b_0 \tag{6}$$

have the same value for an infinite number of x's, then $a_i = b_i$ for every i, and consequently the polynomials must have the same value for every x.

Proof: To say that the two polynomials have the same value for an infinite number of x's is to say that their difference, which is also a polynomial, has an infinite number of roots. But by theorem 22.3, the only way this can happen is to have all the coefficients of this difference polynomial equal to zero. Since these coefficients are just the numbers $a_i - b_i$, this proves the corollary. ∎

Corollary 22.4 says in particular that a function cannot be written in more than one way as a polynomial. For if it could be, then we would have two different expressions (5) and (6) which would have the same value for every x, contradicting the corollary.

If c is a root of a polynomial f, then by theorem 22.2, $x - c$ must be a factor of f. The greatest integer m such that $(x - c)^m$ is a factor of f is called the *multiplicity* of the root c. Once we know a number c is a root of f, then it is a straightforward process to find its multiplicity. For we can write

$$f(x) = (x - c)q_1(x) \tag{7}$$

where $q_1(x)$ can be found by the method illustrated earlier. If $q_1(c) = 0$, then $x - c$ is a factor of q_1, so that we can write $q_1(x) = (x - c)q_2(x)$. Substituting in (7) we obtain

$$f(x) = (x - c)^2 q_2(x).$$

We can continue this process until we obtain a factorization

$$f(x) = (x - c)^m q_m(x) \tag{8}$$

where $q_m(c) \neq 0$. Then m must be the multiplicity of f. For if it weren't, then there would have to be an integer $n > m$ such that $(x - c)^n$ is a factor of f, say

$$f(x) = (x - c)^n q(x) \tag{9}$$

for some polynomial q. From (8) and (9) we have

$$(x - c)^m q_m(x) = (x - c)^n q(x) \tag{10}$$

for every number x. Since $n > m$, we can cancel $(x - c)^m$ from each side of (10) whenever $x \neq c$, obtaining

$$q_m(x) = (x - c)^{n-m} q(x) \tag{11}$$

for all x save possibly $x = c$. But by corollary 22.4, the polynomials on either side of (11) must be identical, which means that they must be the same even when $x = c$. However, the right side evaluated at c is 0, whereas the left side is $q_m(c)$ which we assumed not to be 0. This contradiction shows that m must be the multiplicity.

In general it is not an easy matter to find the roots of a polynomial, even when we know that some exist. They may be located approximately by a number of methods, one of which is to plot a graph of the polynomial and see where it crosses the first axis. Methods for plotting graphs will be discussed in chapter III.

EXERCISES

1. Find polynomials $q(x)$ and $r(x)$ such that $f(x) = p(x)q(x) + r(x)$ in each of the following cases:

   (a) $f(x) = 6x^6 - 4x^4 + x^3 - 2x^2 - 1,\ p(x) = 3x^4 + 2x$
   (b) $f(x) = 2x^4 + 2x^3 + 2x^2 + 4x - 4,\ p(x) = x^2 + x - 1$

2. Express the following rational function as a polynomial plus a proper rational function:

   $$f(x) = \frac{5x^4 - 3x^3 + 4x^2 - x + 2}{x^3 - 2x^2 + 7}.$$

3. Given that -1 is a root of $x^6 + 8x^5 + 4x^4 - 4x^3 - 11x^2 - 8x + 2$, find its multiplicity. What is the multiplicity of the only root of $x^7 + x^5$?

4. Use the fact that two polynomials which have the same value for every x must have the same coefficients to show that a polynomial which is an even function must have the coefficients of all of its odd powers zero, and that a polynomial which is an odd function must have the coefficients of all of its even powers zero.

5. Let a_1, a_2, and a_3 be three distinct numbers, and let b_1, b_2, and b_3 be any numbers. Show that the polynomial defined by

$$f(x) = b_1 \frac{(x - a_2)(x - a_3)}{(a_1 - a_2)(a_1 - a_3)} + b_2 \frac{(x - a_1)(x - a_3)}{(a_2 - a_1)(a_2 - a_3)} + b_3 \frac{(x - a_1)(x - a_2)}{(a_3 - a_1)(a_3 - a_2)}$$

is such that $f(a_1) = b_1$, $f(a_2) = b_2$, and $f(a_3) = b_3$.

   More generally, given distinct numbers a_1, a_2, ..., a_n, and any numbers b_1, b_2, ..., b_n, find a polynomial $f(x)$ of degree $n - 1$ such that $f(a_i) = b_i$ for each i. How many such polynomials are there? (This result is known as *Lagrange's interpolation formula*, after the French mathematician Joseph Louis Lagrange (1736–1813).)

6. If f and p are polynomials of degrees n and m respectively, show that there are polynomials q and r such that $f = pq + r$, and such that r is either 0 or has degree less than m. (Hint: If $n < m$, take $q = 0$. Otherwise use induction on n, starting with $n = m$. Observe that if a_n is the leading coefficient of f and b_m is the leading coefficient of p, then

$$f(x) - \frac{a_n}{b_m} x^{n-m} p(x)$$

is a polynomial of degree less than n.)

7. By taking $q(x) = x - c$ in exercise 6, give another proof of theorem 22.2.

23. TRIGONOMETRY

In this section we shall depart from the program of using only our axioms in order to give geometrical definitions of the trigonometric functions. In chapter VI we shall give a treatment of these functions which depends only on our axioms and not on pictures. Our reason for introducing them at this point is twofold. First, we wish to have some functions other than rational functions at our disposal so as to provide more variety in our examples. Second, we wish to provide motivation for the definitions we shall make in chapter VI. Nevertheless, the material done here will be used in the rest of the book only in examples and exercises. Our theorems will continue to depend only on our axioms.

   Let us select any unit of length, say

———— ,   (1)

and consider any other length, say

———— .   (2)

Suppose that the second length is R using the first length as unit. We draw two circles having a common center O, one with radius 1 (or the *unit* circle, as

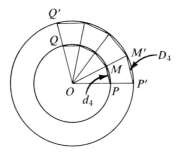

Fig. 23.1

we say) and the other with radius R. We pick any two points P and Q on the unit circle, and we let P' and Q' be the points on the circle of radius R such that OPP' and OQQ' are straight lines (figure 23.1). Let n be any positive integer, and divide the sector $OP'Q'$ into n equal parts. (In figure 23.1, $n = 4$.) Let M and M' be the points indicated in the figure. Let d_n and D_n be the straight line distances (using (1) as unit of measure) from P to M and from P' and M' respectively. The distance traveled along the polygonal path from P to Q is then nd_n. As we take larger and larger values of n, this polygonal distance will approach the length s of the arc PQ of the unit circle. In symbols we write

$$nd_n \rightarrow s. \tag{3}$$

Similarly, if S represents the length of the arc $P'Q'$ of the circle of radius R, then we have $nD_n \rightarrow S$, so that

$$\frac{nD_n}{R} \rightarrow \frac{S}{R}. \tag{4}$$

But by similar triangles we have

$$\frac{D_n}{R} = \frac{d_n}{1} \tag{5}$$

and so from (3) and (4) we see that $s = S/R$. But S/R is the length of the arc $P'Q'$ using (2) as unit of length instead of (1). Thus we see that the number s is a number which depends only on the relative position of the lines OP and OQ and not on the size of the unit circle.

In particular, let Q be halfway around the unit circle. In this case we denote the number s by π. This number is equal to neither 180 nor $\frac{22}{7}$, although it comes much closer to being the latter than the former. It can be shown to be an irrational number. By looking at the unit circle, π can be seen to be somewhere around 3. In chapter VI we shall be able to compute it more accurately.

If Q is one quarter of the way around, then s is $\pi/2$, whereas if Q is 3/4 of the way around, then $s = 3\pi/2$. If Q is all the way around, then $s = 2\pi$. The relation $S = sR$ then shows that the circumference of a circle of radius R is $2\pi R$.

We now wish to find the area of the sector $OP'Q'$ in terms of s. Recall first that the area of a triangle is given by one half the base times the altitude. Let R_n denote the altitude, measured from O, of the triangle $OP'M'$ in figure 23.1. Then the area of this triangle is $\frac{1}{2}D_nR_n$, which, using (5), becomes $\frac{1}{2}d_nRR_n$. Hence, the total area of the n inscribed triangles is $\frac{1}{2}nd_nRR_n$. As n gets larger and larger, this total area will approach the area of the sector $OP'Q'$. But $nd_n \to s$ and $R_n \to R$, and so we have

$$\tfrac{1}{2}nd_nRR_n \to \tfrac{1}{2}sR^2.$$

In other words, the area of the sector is $sR^2/2$. In particular, the area of the whole circle, given by taking $s = 2\pi$, is πR^2.

In what follows, it will be convenient to distinguish between a *counterclockwise* coordinate system, which is one which requires a counterclockwise motion in rotating the positive 1st axis through a right angle into the positive 2nd axis (figure 23.2), and a *clockwise* coordinate system, where this rotation is clockwise (figure 23.3). (It is true that if we have drawn a counterclockwise coordinate system, a person on the other side of the plane will see a clockwise system. However, we shall all agree to stay on the same side of the plane so as to avoid confusion.)

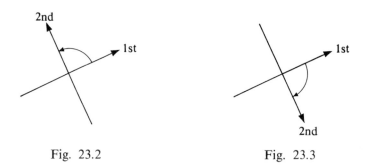

Fig. 23.2   Fig. 23.3

We now select a counterclockwise coordinate system, and we draw the unit circle with center at the origin (figure 23.4). Given a number x, we start at the point P with coordinates $(1, 0)$ and travel along the circle a distance $|x|$ in the counterclockwise direction if x is positive and in the clockwise direction if x is negative. Let Q be the point arrived at in this way. (It may be necessary to travel around the circle a number of times before arriving at Q.) Then we define $\cos x$ as the first coordinate of Q and $\sin x$ as the second coordinate. Thus in the picture, where x is a positive number somewhat less than 1, $\cos x$ is the length OM and $\sin x$ is the length QM.

Referring to figure 23.4, by the Pythagorean theorem we must have $QM^2 + OM^2 = OQ^2$. In other words, we have

$$\sin^2 x + \cos^2 x = 1 \tag{6}$$

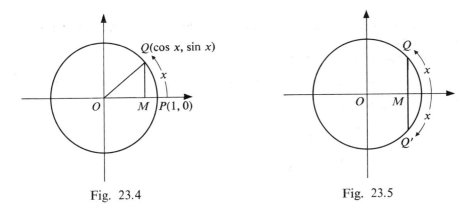

Fig. 23.4   Fig. 23.5

for all numbers x. Another formula arises from the fact that if we travel around the unit circle a distance $2n\pi$ (n any integer) we get back to where we started from. This gives us

$$\cos (x + 2n\pi) = \cos x, \qquad \sin (x + 2n\pi) = \sin x.$$

Also take any number x, and consider figure 23.5. The points Q and Q' have the same first coordinate, but the second coordinate of Q' is the negative of the second coordinate of Q. This gives us

$$\cos (-x) = \cos x, \qquad \sin (-x) = -\sin x. \qquad (7)$$

In other words cos is an even function, whereas sin is an odd function.

To draw the graph of sin, we observe that as x increases from 0 to $\dfrac{\pi}{2}$, $\sin x$ increases from 0 to 1; then as x increases from $\dfrac{\pi}{2}$ to π, $\sin x$ decreases from 1 to 0; then as x increases from π to $3\pi/2$, $\sin x$ decreases from 0 to -1; and finally as x increases from $3\pi/2$ to 2π, $\sin x$ increases from -1 to 0. After that the situation repeats itself. The graph for negative values of x can be obtained using the fact that sin is odd. Consequently the graph looks like that in figure 23.6.

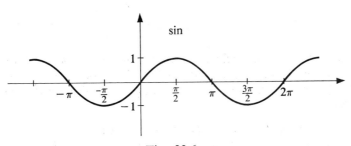

Fig. 23.6

The graph of cos looks the same, only shifted to the left a distance $\dfrac{\pi}{2}$ (exercise 1).

We shall now prove the sum rule for cos:

$$\cos (a + b) = \cos a \cos b - \sin a \sin b. \tag{8}$$

First recall the formula

$$d^2 = (x - x_1)^2 + (y - y_1)^2 \tag{9}$$

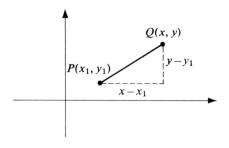

Fig. 23.7

for the square of the distance d between two points P and Q with coordinates (x_1, y_1) and (x, y) respectively. In view of the diagram (figure 23.7), this formula is a simple consequence of the Pythagorean theorem. Now, given two numbers a and b, we pick any unit of length OP and we draw the unit circle with center O. Starting at P we travel a distance $|a|$ along the circle in the counterclockwise or clockwise direction depending on whether a is positive or negative, arriving at a point P', say. Then, starting at P' we travel a distance $|b|$ along the circle in the counterclockwise or clockwise direction, again depending on whether b is positive or negative, arriving at a point Q, say. In figure 23.8, both a and b are positive.

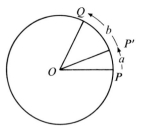

Fig. 23.8

Relative to the counterclockwise coordinate system with OP as positive first axis, P has coordinates $(1, 0)$ and Q has coordinates $(\cos (a + b), \sin (a + b))$. Hence, the square of the straight line distance d from P to Q is given by

$$\begin{aligned} d^2 &= (\cos (a + b) - 1)^2 + (\sin (a + b) - 0)^2 \\ &= \cos^2 (a + b) - 2 \cos (a + b) + 1 + \sin^2 (a + b) \\ &= 2 - 2 \cos (a + b), \end{aligned} \tag{10}$$

where at the last step we have simply used relation (6). On the other hand, relative to the counterclockwise coordinate system with OP' as positive first axis, P has coordinates $(\cos(-a), \sin(-a))$, or $(\cos a, -\sin a)$ in view of (7), and Q has coordinates $(\cos b, \sin b)$. Hence, we have

$$d^2 = (\cos b - \cos a)^2 + (\sin b + \sin a)^2$$
$$= 2 - 2 \cos a \cos b + 2 \sin a \sin b. \tag{11}$$

Equating the two expressions (10) and (11) for d^2 then gives us the desired formula (8).

Now, if we put $b = -\dfrac{\pi}{2}$ in (8), we obtain

$$\cos\left(a - \frac{\pi}{2}\right) = \sin a. \tag{12}$$

Setting $a = \dfrac{\pi}{2} - b$ in (12) and recalling that $\cos b = \cos(-b)$, we find

$$\cos b = \sin\left(\frac{\pi}{2} - b\right). \tag{13}$$

Consequently, using (8), (12), and (13) we obtain

$$\sin(a + b) = \cos\left(a + b - \frac{\pi}{2}\right)$$
$$= \cos a \cos\left(b - \frac{\pi}{2}\right) - \sin a \sin\left(b - \frac{\pi}{2}\right)$$
$$= \cos a \sin b + \sin a \sin\left(\frac{\pi}{2} - b\right)$$
$$= \cos a \sin b + \sin a \cos b.$$

The other trigonometric functions are defined as follows:

$$\tan = \frac{\sin}{\cos}, \qquad \cot = \frac{\cos}{\sin},$$

$$\sec = \frac{1}{\cos}, \qquad \csc = \frac{1}{\sin}.$$

EXERCISES

1. Draw the graph of cos.
2. Give the domains of each of the functions tan, cot, sec, and csc, and draw their graphs.
3. Prove that $\sin(2a) = 2 \sin a \cos a$. Also show that $\cos(2a) = 2\cos^2 a - 1 = 1 - 2\sin^2 a$. Hence prove the formulas $\cos^2 a = \dfrac{1 + \cos(2a)}{2}$ and $\sin^2 a = \dfrac{1 - \cos(2a)}{2}$.

4. Show that

$$\sin a \cos b = \frac{\sin (a + b) + \sin (a - b)}{2}$$

$$\cos a \cos b = \frac{\cos (a + b) + \cos (a - b)}{2}$$

and

$$\sin a \sin b = \frac{\cos (a - b) - \cos (a + b)}{2}.$$

5. Show that

$$\tan (a + b) = \frac{\tan a + \tan b}{1 - \tan a \tan b}.$$

For what values of a and b is this valid?

LIMITS and DERIVATIVES

II

1. INTERVALS

If a and b are two numbers such that $a < b$, then the set of numbers x satisfying $a \leq x \leq b$ is called the *closed interval* from a to b, and is denoted by $[a, b]$. If $a < b$, then the set of numbers satisfying $a < x < b$ is called the *open interval* from a to b, and we denote it by (a, b). (Do not confuse this with the ordered pair consisting of a and b, which has the same notation.) Thus the open interval is just the closed interval with the endpoints a and b taken out. It is sometimes useful also to talk about intervals where just one endpoint is taken out. These are denoted by $[a, b)$ when it is b that is taken out and $(a, b]$ when it is a that is taken out, and are called *half open intervals*. For any of the intervals just defined, the number $b - a$ is called the *length* of the interval.

The above are known as finite intervals. On the other hand, given a number a, we frequently wish to talk about the set of numbers x satisfying $x \geq a$. This set is denoted by $[a, \infty)$. If we take out a, the resulting set is denoted by (a, ∞). Similarly $(-\infty, a]$ denotes the set of numbers $\leq a$, and $(-\infty, a)$ denotes the set of numbers $< a$. These are known as *infinite intervals*. The set R of all numbers (which we could denote by $(-\infty, \infty)$) is also considered as an infinite interval.

It must be remarked that the symbol ∞ has no meaning all by itself. In particular it does not represent any number. It arises frequently in mathematics, but only as a notational device for shortening certain expressions which themselves make no reference to "infinity."

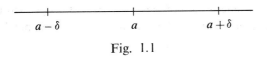

Fig. 1.1

Let a be any number, and let δ be a positive number. (δ is the Greek letter for d, and is called delta.) Consider the set of numbers x satisfying the relation $|x - a| < \delta$. By considering the two separate cases $x - a \geq 0$ and $x - a < 0$, we see that this set of numbers is just the open interval $(a - \delta, a + \delta)$. We shall call such an open interval a *neighborhood* of a. Thus there are as many neighborhoods of a as there are positive numbers δ. Suppose also

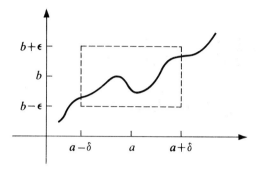

Fig. 1.2

that b and ϵ are numbers with $\epsilon > 0$. We shall frequently encounter the situation where a function f is such that for all x satisfying $|x - a| < \delta$, we have $|f(x) - b| < \epsilon$. The situation is represented in figure 1.2. Thus the geometrical meaning of the condition is that for x in the interval $(a - \delta, a + \delta)$ the graph of f lies entirely between the two horizontal lines of height $b - \epsilon$ and $b + \epsilon$ above the 1st axis. The function in figure 1.3 does not satisfy the given condition. However, for the same ϵ, the condition would be satisfied if we picked a smaller δ. (Pick one.)

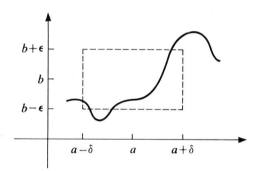

Fig. 1.3

EXERCISES

1. (a) Is the union of the two intervals $(-2, 1]$ and $(\frac{1}{2}, 8]$ an interval?
    (b) Is the union of the two intervals $(-2, 1]$ and $(3, 7)$ an interval?
    (c) What is the intersection of the two intervals $(3, \infty)$ and $[-5, 4]$?
    (d) What is the intersection of the two intervals $(-\infty, 4]$ and $(4, 11)$?

2. Find two intervals whose union is the set of those numbers x satisfying
$$\frac{x^2 - 1}{3} > 1.$$

3. In figure 1.2, using the same δ, mark a smaller ϵ for which it is no longer true that $|f(x) - b| < \epsilon$ whenever $|x - a| < \delta$.

4. In figure 1.3, using the same ϵ, mark a smaller δ for which it is true that $|f(x) - b| < \epsilon$ whenever $|x - a| < \delta$. Then mark another ϵ so small that no matter what we take as δ, it will never be true that $|f(x) - b| < \epsilon$ whenever $|x - a| < \delta$.

2. LIMITS

Consider the function f defined by $f(x) = x^3$ for all numbers x. Its graph is given in figure 2.1. Now, it is clear from the picture that the values $f(x)$ approach 0 as x approaches 0 from either side. By this we do not mean that $f(0) = 0$. This fact, although true, does not interest us for the moment. What is in question is the values $f(x)$ for x near 0, but not equal to 0 itself. Of course the word "approaches" is a vague one. If we want to give a precise meaning to the statement "$f(x)$ approaches 0 as x approaches 0" we could say that given any positive number ϵ, there is always a positive number δ such that $|f(x)| < \epsilon$ whenever $|x| < \delta$. In figure 2.1 we have located the biggest possible δ corresponding to the given ϵ.

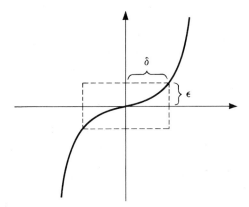

Fig. 2.1

Now consider the function g defined by $g(x) = |x|/x$ for all $x \neq 0$. For $x > 0$ we have $g(x) = x/x = 1$, whereas for $x < 0$ we have $g(x) = -x/x = -1$. Consequently the graph of g is as shown in figure 2.2. It is understood, of course, that there is no point on the graph above or below $x = 0$, since 0 is not in the domain of g. Now the function g differs basically from the function f near $x = 0$ in that, whereas the values $f(x)$ approach a definite number as x approaches 0, we cannot claim that the values $g(x)$ are approaching anything as x approaches 0. For example, we cannot claim that $g(x)$ approaches 1,

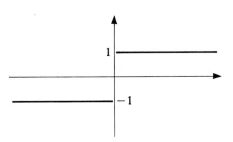

Fig. 2.2

for there are x's as close as we please to 0 such that $g(x)$ differs from 1 by as much as 2. (Take any x to the left of 0.) Likewise, we cannot claim that $g(x)$ approaches -1, for there are x's as close as we please to 0 such that $g(x)$ differs from -1 by as much as 2. (Take any x to the right of 0.) Nor can we claim that $g(x)$ approaches 0, for there are x's as close as we please to 0 such that $g(x)$ differs from 0 by as much as 1. (Take any x to the left or to the right of 0.)

This leads to the following definition. Let f be a function, and let a be a number. Suppose that there is a number L which has the property that for each positive number ϵ, there is a positive number δ such that for all x in the domain of f satisfying $0 < |x - a| < \delta$ we have $|f(x) - L| < \epsilon$. Then L is called the *limit of f at a*, and is denoted by $\lim_{x \to a} f(x)$.

Notice that in the example $f(x) = x^3$ considered above, we had $a = 0$ and $L = 0$. That is why the condition involving ϵ and δ was simpler to state in that example than in the general case. Notice also that we didn't prove anything in that example. We simply allowed ourselves to be guided by the picture so as to give a precise meaning to the idea of $f(x)$ approaching a number as x approaches a number.

The definition of limit calls for several remarks.

(1) The condition $0 < |x - a|$ simply says that x is not a itself. Thus, even if a is in the domain of f, the value $f(a)$ plays no role in determining the limit.

(2) Instead of saying "for all x in the domain of f satisfying $0 < |x - a| < \delta$" we shall usually say simply "for all x satisfying $0 < |x - a| < \delta$," it being understood that x must be in the domain of f in order that it make sense to write $f(x)$. Likewise, in dealing with a theorem in which two or more functions are involved, we shall always consider only those x's which are simultaneously in the domains of all the functions, without explicitly saying so each time.

(3) The definition of limit requires that there be a δ for *every* positive number ϵ, although it will usually be necessary to take smaller δ's the smaller we take ϵ. In the case of the function g of figure 2.2, the number 1 failed to be the limit at 0 because there was no δ relative to $\epsilon = 2$ (and consequently there was no δ relative to any ϵ less than 2). Nevertheless relative to $\epsilon = 3$ we could take δ to be any positive number we please. The number 0 failed to be the limit since there was no δ relative to $\epsilon = 1$. In general, no matter what number we had tested for L, it would have sufficed to take $\epsilon = 1$ to see that that number could not be the limit. Thus we must simply say in this case that g has no limit at 0. (Nevertheless, it has limits at all numbers other than 0. See exercise 1.)

(4) If it is true that $|f(x) - L| < \epsilon$ whenever $0 < |x - a| < \delta$, and if δ_1 is a positive number less than δ, then it will certainly be true that $|f(x) - L| < \epsilon$ whenever $0 < |x - a| < \delta_1$. In other words, once a number δ satisfies the required condition relative to some given ϵ, then any positive number smaller than δ also satisfies the condition. Thus there is nothing unique about the number δ corresponding to a given ϵ.

EXERCISES

1. Let g be the function of figure 2.2, and suppose that $a > 0$. Prove that $\lim_{x \to a} g(x) = 1$ by showing that given any number $\epsilon > 0$, it suffices to take $\delta = a$. Show similarly if $a < 0$ that $\lim_{x \to a} g(x) = -1$.

2. Let f be the greatest integer function defined in § 20 of chapter I. At what points does f fail to have a limit? What is the limit of f at all other points? Prove your assertions.

3. EXAMPLES OF LIMITS

We shall consider here four examples of limits. The first two are quite trivial, but will be important, nevertheless, in our subsequent theory of limits. The other two examples will seem more difficult. However, they too will become easy after we have proved some theorems about limits.

Example 1: Let f be a constant function, say $f(x) = c$ for all x. If a is any number, then $\lim_{x \to a} f(x) = c$. For we have $|f(x) - c| = |c - c| = 0$ for all x, and so given $\epsilon > 0$ we can take δ to be any positive number we wish in order to have $|f(x) - c| < \epsilon$ whenever $0 < |x - a| < \delta$.

Example 2: Let f be the identity function for the numbers; that is, $f(x) = x$ for all x. If a is any number, then $\lim_{x \to a} f(x) = a$. For we have $|f(x) - a| = |x - a|$, and so given $\epsilon > 0$ we need only take $\delta = \epsilon$ in order to insure that $|f(x) - a| < \epsilon$ whenever $0 < |x - a| < \delta$.

Example 3: Let $f(x) = x^3 - 3x^2 + 4x - 1$ for all numbers x. Then $f(2) = 3$. We are going to show that $\lim_{x \to 2} f(x) = 3$ also. The definition of limit requires that we try to make $|f(x) - 3|$ less than any prescribed positive number by taking x close enough to 2. First we do some algebra on the expression $|f(x) - 3|$. We have

$$
\begin{aligned}
|f(x) - 3| &= |(x^3 - 3x^2 + 4x - 1) - 3| \\
&= |x^3 - 3x^2 + 4x - 4| \\
&= |(x - 2)(x^2 - x + 2)| \\
&= |x - 2| \, |x^2 - x + 2| \quad \text{(by I, theorem 12.1)} \\
&\leq |x - 2|(|x|^2 + |x| + 2). \quad \text{(by I, theorem 12.3)}
\end{aligned}
$$

Now in the last expression, we can make the first term as small as we like by taking x close enough to 2. However, in doing so the second term may conceivably become large, so that the whole expression would not be small after all. To get around this difficulty, let us first consider only those x for which $|x - 2| < 1$, or in other words, for which $1 < x < 3$. Then for such x, we have $|x| < 3$, and so $|x|^2 + |x| + 2 < 14$. Now given $\epsilon > 0$, suppose that δ is the smaller of the two numbers 1 and $\dfrac{\epsilon}{14}$. (For example, if $\epsilon = 15$, then

$\delta = 1$, whereas if $\epsilon = 3$, then $\delta = \frac{3}{14}$.) Then for $|x - 2| < \delta$, we have simultaneously $|x - 2| < \frac{\epsilon}{14}$ and $|x|^2 + |x| + 2 < 14$, and so, using the algebra we did above, we obtain

$$|f(x) - 3| \leq |x - 2|(|x|^2 + |x| + 2)$$
$$< \frac{\epsilon}{14} \, 14 = \epsilon.$$

In other words, we have produced the required positive number δ as in the definition of limit.

Remark 1:   You may wonder why the above method would not work if we started with some number other than 3 as the candidate for the limit.   The reason is that if we had started with anything but 3, then $x - 2$ wouldn't have factored out in the nice way that it did above (see chapter I, theorem 22.2).

Remark 2:   When we restricted ourselves to $|x - 2| < 1$ as a first step, there was nothing special about 1 (other than the fact that it is an easy number to work with).   We could have restricted ourselves, for example, to $|x - 2| < 2$, or in other words, $0 < x < 4$.   In this case, for such x we have $|x| < 4$, so that $|x|^2 + |x| + 2 < 22$, and consequently as our δ we could take the smaller of 2 and $\frac{\epsilon}{22}$.   This is a different δ than the one we found the first time through. However, this is not surprising since, as we pointed out in the last section, if there is one number δ which satisfies the required condition, then there are an infinite number of other δ's which also satisfy the condition.

Example 4:   Let $f(x) = \dfrac{x^2 + 3}{x - 2}$ for all numbers $x \neq 2$.   Then we have $f(1) = -4$.   We shall show also that $\lim\limits_{x \to 1} f(x) = -4$.   By definition of limit we must show that given $\epsilon > 0$, there is a number δ such that $|f(x) - (-4)| < \epsilon$ whenever $0 < |x - 1| < \delta$.   As before, we first do some algebra on the expression $|f(x) - (-4)|$.   We have

$$|f(x) - (-4)| = \left| \frac{x^2 + 3}{x - 2} + 4 \right|$$
$$= \left| \frac{x^2 + 4x - 5}{x - 2} \right|$$
$$= \left| (x - 1) \frac{(x + 5)}{(x - 2)} \right|$$
$$= |x - 1| \left| \frac{x + 5}{x - 2} \right|.$$

Again we must first restrict ourselves to some neighborhood of 1 in which the term $\left| \dfrac{x + 5}{x - 2} \right|$ does not get too big.   In particular, we must stay clear of $x = 2$

if this is to be true. Therefore, let us restrict ourselves to $|x - 1| < \frac{1}{2}$, say, or in other words, $\frac{1}{2} < x < \frac{3}{2}$. Then the biggest that $|x + 5|$ can be for such x's is $\frac{13}{2}$, whereas the smallest that $|x - 2|$ can be is $\frac{1}{2}$. Consequently for such x's we will certainly have $\dfrac{|x + 5|}{|x - 2|} < \dfrac{13/2}{1/2} = 13$, and so we need only take δ to be the smaller of the two numbers $1/2$ and $\epsilon/13$ in order to guarantee that $|f(x) - (-4)| < \epsilon$ whenever $|x - 1| < \delta$.

EXERCISES

1. Prove that $\lim\limits_{x \to -2} (3x) = -6$.

2. Prove that $\lim\limits_{x \to -1} (2x^3 - x^2 - 1) = -4$.

3. Prove that $\lim\limits_{x \to 0} \dfrac{2x^2 + 1}{x + 1} = 1$.

4. Let f be the function defined by $f(x) = \dfrac{x^2 - 4x + 3}{x - 1}$ for all x except $x = 1$.
   Show that even though $f(1)$ is not defined, we have $\lim\limits_{x \to 1} f(x) = -2$.

5. Show that $\lim\limits_{x \to 0} |x| = 0$.

4. RULES FOR LIMITS

The study of limits would be very tedious indeed if, every time we confronted one, we were to be put to as much work as we were in the previous section. The thing to do when one reaches such a conclusion is to prove some theorems, and thereby take care of the work all at once. This we now proceed to do.

Theorem 4.1 (Sum Rule for Limits): *If f and g are functions such that* $\lim\limits_{x \to a} f(x) = L$ *and* $\lim\limits_{x \to a} g(x) = M$, *then*

$$\lim_{x \to a} (f(x) + g(x)) = L + M.$$

Proof: By definition of limit we must show that given $\epsilon > 0$, there is a $\delta > 0$ such that

$$|(f(x) + g(x)) - (L + M)| < \epsilon \tag{1}$$

whenever $0 < |x - a| < \delta$. As usual, we first do some algebra on the left side of (1). We have

$$\begin{aligned} |(f(x) + g(x)) - (L + M)| &= |(f(x) - L) + (g(x) - M)| \\ &\leq |f(x) - L| + |g(x) - M|. \end{aligned} \tag{2}$$

Now, in order to make (2) less than ϵ, it suffices to make each of the two terms less than $\dfrac{\epsilon}{2}$. But if ϵ is a positive number, then $\dfrac{\epsilon}{2}$ is a perfectly good positive number, and so since $\lim\limits_{x \to a} f(x) = L$, we can find $\delta_1 > 0$ such that $|f(x) - L| <$ $\frac{\epsilon}{2}$ whenever $0 < |x - a| < \delta_1$. Likewise, since $\lim\limits_{x \to a} g(x) = M$, we can find $\delta_2 > 0$ such that $|g(x) - M| < \frac{\epsilon}{2}$ whenever $0 < |x - a| < \delta_2$. Then, if we let δ be the smaller of the two numbers δ_1 and δ_2, (2) will be less than $\frac{\epsilon}{2} + \frac{\epsilon}{2} = \epsilon$ whenever $0 < |x - a| < \delta$, which is what is required. ∎

Lemma 4.2: *If* $\lim\limits_{x \to a} f(x) = L$ *and c is any number, then*

$$\lim_{x \to a} (cf(x)) = cL. \tag{3}$$

Proof: We must show that, given $\epsilon > 0$, there is a number $\delta > 0$ such that $|cf(x) - cL| < \epsilon$ whenever $0 < |x - a| < \delta$. We have

$$|cf(x) - cL| = |c(f(x) - L)|$$
$$= |c| \, |f(x) - L|. \tag{4}$$

Now $\epsilon/(|c| + 1)$ is a perfectly good positive number, and so since $\lim\limits_{x \to a} f(x) = L$, there is a number $\delta > 0$ such that $|f(x) - L| < \epsilon/(|c| + 1)$ whenever $0 < |x - a| < \delta$. For these x's, (4) will then be less than $|c| \dfrac{\epsilon}{|c| + 1}$, which in turn is less than ϵ, as required. ∎

Remark: The reason we used $\epsilon/(|c| + 1)$ and not $\epsilon/|c|$ in the above proof is that we had to allow for the possibility of c being 0.

Taking $c = -1$ in lemma 4.2, we see that if $\lim\limits_{x \to a} f(x) = L$, then
$$\lim_{x \to a} (-f(x)) = -L.$$

Hence, applying the sum rule (theorem 4.1), we obtain:

Corollary 4.3: *If* $\lim\limits_{x \to a} f(x) = L$ *and* $\lim\limits_{x \to a} g(x) = M$, *then*

$$\lim_{x \to a} (f(x) - g(x)) = L - M. \quad ∎$$

Lemma 4.4: *We have* $\lim\limits_{x \to a} f(x) = L$ *if and only if* $\lim\limits_{x \to a} (f(x) - L) = 0$.

Proof: First assume that $\lim\limits_{x \to a} f(x) = L$. Then, applying corollary 4.3 with the constant function L playing the role of g, we obtain

$$\lim_{x \to a} (f(x) - L) = \lim_{x \to a} f(x) - \lim_{x \to a} L$$
$$= L - L = 0.$$

This proves one half of the lemma.

Now assume that $\lim_{x \to a} (f(x) - L) = 0$.

Then, using the sum rule, we have

$$\lim_{x \to a} f(x) = \lim_{x \to a} ((f(x) - L) + L)$$

$$= \lim_{x \to a} (f(x) - L) + \lim_{x \to a} L$$

$$= 0 + L = L,$$

which proves the other half of the lemma. $\blacksquare$

Lemma 4.5: *If* $\lim_{x \to a} f(x) = L$, *then there is a number* $\delta > 0$ *such that* $|f(x)| < |L| + 1$ *whenever* $0 < |x - a| < \delta$.

Proof: Taking $\epsilon = 1$ in the definition of limit, there must be a number $\delta > 0$ such that $|f(x) - L| < 1$ whenever $0 < |x - a| < \delta$. Using corollary 12.4 of chapter I, we then have for such x,

$$|f(x)| - |L| \le |f(x) - L| < 1,$$

or in other words, $|f(x)| < |L| + 1$, as required. $\blacksquare$

Theorem 4.6 (The Product Rule for Limits): *If* $\lim_{x \to a} f(x) = L$ *and* $\lim_{x \to a} g(x) = M$, *then*

$$\lim_{x \to a} (f(x)g(x)) = LM.$$

Proof: First consider the case where $\lim_{x \to a} g(x) = 0$. We wish to show that given $\epsilon > 0$, there is a number $\delta > 0$ such that $|f(x)g(x)| < \epsilon$ whenever $0 < |x - a| < \delta$. Now we have $|f(x)g(x)| = |f(x)| |g(x)|$, and we know by lemma 4.5 that there is a number $\delta_1 > 0$ such that $|f(x)| < |L| + 1$ whenever $0 < |x - a| < \delta_1$. Also since $\lim_{x \to a} g(x) = 0$, there is a number $\delta_2 > 0$ such that $|g(x)| < \dfrac{\epsilon}{|L| + 1}$ whenever $0 < |x - a| < \delta_2$. Consequently, if we let δ be the smaller of δ_1 and δ_2, we have

$$|f(x)| |g(x)| < (|L| + 1) \frac{\epsilon}{|L| + 1} = \epsilon$$

whenever $0 < |x - a| < \delta$, as required.

Now suppose that $\lim_{x \to a} g(x) = M$, where M is not necessarily zero. Then by lemma 4.4, we have $\lim_{x \to a} (g(x) - M) = 0$, and so, applying what we have already proved, we have $\lim_{x \to a} (f(x)(g(x) - M)) = 0$. Consequently, writing $f(x)g(x) = f(x)(g(x) - M) + f(x)M$ and using the sum rule and lemma 4.2, we obtain

$$\lim_{x \to a} (f(x)g(x)) = \lim_{x \to a} (f(x)(g(x) - M) + f(x)M)$$

$$= \lim_{x \to a} (f(x)(g(x) - M)) + \lim_{x \to a} (f(x)M)$$
$$= 0 + LM = LM,$$

which is what is required. ∎

EXERCISES

1. Prove the difference rule (corollary 4.3) directly in the same way we proved the sum rule, without any appeal to lemma 4.2.

2. Give another, more direct proof of the product rule (theorem 4.6) by observing the following inequality:

$$|f(x)g(x) - LM| = |f(x)(g(x) - M) + (f(x) - L)M|$$
$$\leq |f(x)| |g(x) - M| + |f(x) - L| |M|.$$

(You will have to use lemma 4.5 but you will not have to use any of the other results proved in this section.)

   Then explain why lemma 4.2 would follow as a corollary of theorem 4.6 in this case, whereas it did not follow as a corollary of theorem 4.6 with the proof given in the text.

3. Suppose that we have n functions $f_1, f_2, \ldots, f_n$, and that $\lim_{x \to a} f_i(x) = L_i$ for $1 \leq i \leq n$. Use the sum and product rules for limits and induction on n to prove that

$$\lim_{x \to a} (f_1(x) + f_2(x) + \cdots + f_n(x)) = L_1 + L_2 + \cdots + L_n$$

and

$$\lim_{x \to a} (f_1(x)f_2(x) \cdots f_n(x)) = L_1 L_2 \cdots L_n.$$

4. By example 2 of § 3 we know $\lim_{x \to a} x = a$. Show how it follows from exercise 3 that $\lim_{x \to a} x^n = a^n$, so that by lemma 4.2, $\lim_{x \to a} (cx^n) = ca^n$. Then show how it follows from exercise 3 that for a polynomial function

$$f(x) = c_n x^n + c_{n-1} x^{n-1} + \cdots + c_1 x + c_0$$

we have

$$\lim_{x \to a} f(x) = c_n a^n + c_{n-1} a^{n-1} + \cdots + c_1 a + c_0,$$

or in other words, $\lim_{x \to a} f(x) = f(a)$.

5. Let $f(x) = \dfrac{1}{x}$ for $x \neq 0$. Show that, given any number $c > 0$, we have $|f(x)| > c$ whenever $0 < |x| < 1/c$. Hence, use lemma 4.5 to show that f cannot have a limit at 0.

6. Let $f(x) = \dfrac{x}{|x|}$ for $x \neq 0$, and let $g(x) = \dfrac{-x}{|x|}$ for $x \neq 0$. Then as we saw in § 2, f has no limit at 0, and similarly, g has no limit at 0. Show nevertheless that

$$\lim_{x \to 0} (f(x) + g(x)) = 0 \quad \text{and} \quad \lim_{x \to 0} (f(x)g(x)) = -1.$$

Thus a sum or a product of two functions may have a limit without either of the functions having a limit.

7. Suppose that there is a number B and a neighborhood of a such that $|f(x)| < B$ for all x in that neighborhood. Then, if $\lim_{x \to a} g(x) = 0$, show also that $\lim_{x \to a} (f(x)g(x)) = 0$.

5. MORE RULES

Now that we have sum, difference, and product rules for limits, it is natural to ask for a quotient rule. Such a rule will be necessary, for example, in dealing with rational functions. Since in taking a quotient we must worry about the denominator being 0, we shall first prove a lemma which says that a function with a nonzero limit at a point "keeps its distance" from 0 in a neighborhood of that point.

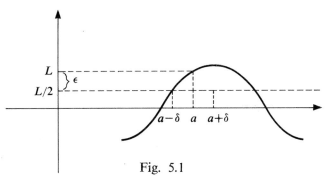

Fig. 5.1

Lemma 5.1: *Suppose that* $\lim_{x \to a} f(x) = L$. *If* $L > 0$, *then there is a positive number* δ *such that* $f(x) > L/2$ *whenever* $0 < |x - a| < \delta$. *Likewise, if* $L < 0$, *then there is a positive number* δ *such that* $f(x) < L/2$ *whenever* $0 < |x - a| < \delta$.

Proof: Suppose that $L > 0$. This case is illustrated in figure 5.1. Taking $\epsilon = L/2$ in the definition of limit, we know there is a number $\delta > 0$ such that $|L - f(x)| < L/2$ whenever $0 < |x - a| < \delta$. Hence, for such x we have

$$L - f(x) \le |L - f(x)| < \frac{L}{2},$$

and so adding $f(x) - \dfrac{L}{2}$ to both sides we obtain $L/2 < f(x)$, as required.

If $L < 0$, then

$$\lim_{x \to a} (-f(x)) = -L > 0.$$

Therefore applying what we have already proved, we know there is a positive number δ such that whenever $0 < |x - a| < \delta$ we have $-f(x) > -L/2$. But since this last inequality is equivalent to $f(x) < L/2$, this is what is required. ∎

The two cases in lemma 5.1 can be combined to say simply that if $\lim_{x \to a} f(x) = L$ and $L \neq 0$, then there is a number $\delta > 0$ such that $|f(x)| > |L|/2$ whenever $0 < |x - a| < \delta$. We shall use this remark in the proof of the following theorem.

Theorem 5.2:   *If* $\lim_{x \to a} f(x) = L$ *and* $L \neq 0$, *then*

$$\lim_{x \to a} \frac{1}{f(x)} = \frac{1}{L} \cdot$$

Proof: Given $\epsilon > 0$ we must find a $\delta > 0$ such that $|1/f(x) - 1/L| < \epsilon$ whenever $0 < |x - a| < \delta$. We have

$$\left| \frac{1}{f(x)} - \frac{1}{L} \right| = \frac{|L - f(x)|}{|f(x)L|}$$

$$= \frac{|L - f(x)|}{|f(x)|\,|L|} \cdot \tag{1}$$

We must first have some guarantee that the denominator of (1) does not get too close to 0 for x near a. But this is provided by lemma 5.1 which says that there is a number δ_1 such that $|f(x)| > \dfrac{|L|}{2}$ whenever $0 < |x - a| < \delta_1$. Since $\lim_{x \to a} f(x) = L$, we can find a number $\delta_2 > 0$ such that $|L - f(x)| < \epsilon|L|^2/2$ whenever $0 < |x - a| < \delta_2$. Then, taking δ to be the smaller of the two numbers δ_1 and δ_2, we see that (1) becomes less than

$$\frac{\epsilon|L|^2/2}{(|L|/2)|L|} = \epsilon$$

whenever $0 < |x - a| < \delta$. This is what is required.   ∎

Writing $\dfrac{f(x)}{g(x)}$ as $f(x)\dfrac{1}{g(x)}$ and using the product rule, we now obtain:

Corollary 5.3 (The Quotient Rule for Limits):   *If* $\lim_{x \to a} f(x) = L$ *and* $\lim_{x \to a} g(x) = M$, *and if* $M \neq 0$, *then*

$$\lim_{x \to a} \frac{f(x)}{g(x)} = \frac{L}{M} \cdot \quad ∎$$

Theorem 5.4:   *Suppose that* $\lim_{x \to a} f(x) = L$ *and* $\lim_{x \to a} g(x) = M$, *and suppose further that every neighborhood of* a *contains at least one number* x *(other than* a *itself) such that* $f(x) \leq g(x)$. *Then* $L \leq M$.

Proof: We shall obtain a contradiction by assuming that $L > M$. If $L > M$, then $\dfrac{L - M}{2}$ is a positive number, and so, taking $\epsilon = \dfrac{L - M}{2}$ in the definition of limit, we must have a number $\delta_1 > 0$ such that $f(x) > L - \epsilon$

whenever $0 < |x - a| < \delta_1$. Likewise, there must be a $\delta_2 > 0$ such that $g(x) < M + \epsilon$ whenever $0 < |x - a| < \delta_2$. But $L - \epsilon = M + \epsilon$ since they are both $\dfrac{L + M}{2}$, and consequently it follows that if we take δ to be the smaller of the two numbers δ_1 and δ_2, we will have $g(x) < f(x)$ whenever $0 < |x - a| < \delta$. But this contradicts the hypothesis, which tells us that there must be at least one such x such that $f(x) \le g(x)$. The only way out is to conclude that $L \le M$. ∎

Remark: If we replace the hypothesis $f(x) \le g(x)$ by the hypothesis $f(x) < g(x)$, we cannot conclude necessarily $L < M$. For example, if $f(x) = 0$ for all x and $g(x) = x^2$ for all x, then $f(x) < g(x)$ for all $x \ne 0$. But $\lim_{x \to 0} f(x) = 0$ and also $\lim_{x \to 0} g(x) = 0$ and so in this case we have $L = M$.

There is nothing in the definition of limit which immediately rules out the possibility of a function having two different limits at the same point. Nevertheless, using theorem 5.4 we can now prove the following.

Corollary 5.5: *Let f be a function such that every neighborhood of a number a contains at least one member of the domain of f other than a itself. If L and M are both limits for f at a, then $L = M$.*

Proof: Taking $f = g$ in theorem 5.4, we see that $L \le M$. But for the same reason we have $M \le L$. Consequently $L = M$. ∎

Theorem 5.6 (The Squeeze Rule): *If $\lim_{x \to a} f(x) = L$ and also $\lim_{x \to a} h(x) = L$, and if there is a neighborhood of a for which $f(x) \le g(x) \le h(x)$ for all x in that neighborhood (except possibly a itself), then $\lim_{x \to a} g(x) = L$ as well.*

Proof: We must show that given $\epsilon > 0$, there is a $\delta > 0$ such that $|g(x) - L| < \epsilon$ whenever $0 < |x - a| < \delta$. We have for x in the given neighborhood,

$$
\begin{aligned}
|g(x) - L| &= |(g(x) - f(x)) + (f(x) - L)| \\
&\le |g(x) - f(x)| + |f(x) - L| \\
&= (g(x) - f(x)) + |f(x) - L| \\
&\le (h(x) - f(x)) + |f(x) - L| \\
&= (h(x) - L) + (L - f(x)) + |f(x) - L| \\
&\le |h(x) - L| + |L - f(x)| + |f(x) - L|. \tag{2}
\end{aligned}
$$

Now (2) will be less than ϵ if each of the three terms is less than $\dfrac{\epsilon}{3}$. The remainder of the proof is left as an exercise. ∎

If we restrict a function f to the set of numbers x in the domain of f satisfying $x > a$, then the limit at a of the restricted function is what we call the *right-hand limit of f at a*, and we denote it by $\lim_{x \to a+} f(x)$. Thus $\lim_{x \to a+} f(x)$

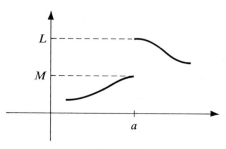

Fig. 5.2

denotes a number L with the property that for each $\epsilon > 0$ there is a $\delta > 0$ such that $|f(x) - L| < \epsilon$ whenever $a < x < a + \delta$ (see figure 5.2). Likewise, the *left-hand limit of f at a*, $\lim_{x \to a-} f(x)$, is a number M with the property that for each $\epsilon > 0$ there is a $\delta > 0$ such that $|f(x) - M| < \epsilon$ whenever $a - \delta < x < a$.

If $\lim_{x \to a} f(x) = L$ and $\overline{f}$ is the restriction of f to some subset of the domain of f, then it is clear from the definition of limit that $\lim_{x \to a} \overline{f}(x) = L$ also. In particular, we must have $\lim_{x \to a+} f(x) = L$ and $\lim_{x \to a-} f(x) = L$. On the other hand, if f has both right- and left-hand limits at a, *and if these are the same number L*, then L is the limit of f at a.

For example, consider the function g defined by $g(x) = \dfrac{x}{|x|}$ for $x \neq 0$ (see figure 2.2 of § 2). Here we have $\lim_{x \to 0+} g(x) = 1$, whereas $\lim_{x \to 0-} g(x) = -1$. The function g fails to have a limit at 0 because its right- and left-hand limits are different.

EXERCISES

1. Complete the proof of theorem 5.6.

2. Use exercise 4 of § 4 and the quotient rule to show that if f is a rational function whose domain includes a, then $\lim_{x \to a} f(x) = f(a)$. Explain why we would have no work to do if we were now to attack example 4 of § 3.

3. What is wrong with the following "proof" of theorem 5.2?

   Set $\lim_{x \to a} \left(\dfrac{1}{f(x)}\right) = M$. Then, since $f(x) \dfrac{1}{f(x)} = 1$, using the product rule we have

   $$LM = \lim_{x \to a} \left(f(x) \frac{1}{f(x)}\right) = \lim_{x \to a} (1) = 1.$$

   Therefore $M = \dfrac{1}{L}$.

4. What is wrong with the following "proof" of theorem 5.6?

> Set $\lim_{x \to a} g(x) = M$. Then, since $f(x) \leq g(x)$ in a neighborhood of a, by theorem 5.4 we have $L \leq M$. But also, since $g(x) \leq h(x)$ in that neighborhood, for the same reason we have $M \leq L$. Therefore $L = M$.

5. Show that $\lim_{x \to a-} f(x) = L$ if and only if $\lim_{x \to (-a)+} f(-x) = L$.

6. Show that if $\lim_{x \to a-} f(x) = L$ and $\lim_{x \to a+} f(x) = L$, then $\lim_{x \to a} f(x) = L$.

7. Let $f(x) = [x]$ (the greatest integer $\leq x$). Does f have right- and left-hand limits at all points? If so, what are they?

8. Show that if f is an even function (chapter I, § 21) and if $\lim_{x \to 0+} f(x) = L$, then $\lim_{x \to 0-} f(x) = L$ also, and consequently $\lim f(x) = L$.

   On the other hand, show that if f is an odd function and $\lim_{x \to 0+} f(x) = L$, then $\lim_{x \to 0-} f(x) = -L$. Hence, if $\lim_{x \to 0} f(x)$ exists, then we must have $L = -L$; that is, $L = 0$.

6. CONTINUOUS FUNCTIONS

Suppose that a number a is in the domain of a function f. Then we say that f is *continuous at a* if it has a limit at a, and if, furthermore, the limit is the same as the value of f at a. In symbols, f is continuous at a if

$$\lim_{x \to a} f(x) = f(a).$$

By definition of limit, this means that f is continuous at a if and only if for each $\epsilon > 0$, there is a $\delta > 0$ such that $|f(x) - f(a)| < \epsilon$ whenever $|x - a| < \delta$. (We do not have to bother to write $0 < |x - a| < \delta$ here, for if $0 = |x - a|$, or in other words if $x = a$, then we have $|f(x) - f(a)| = 0$, which is less than ϵ in any case.)

The function f as a whole is said to be continuous if it is continuous at every number in its domain.

If f is not continuous at a (or is *discontinuous* at a, as we say), then one of the following must be true:

(1) $\lim_{x \to a} f(x)$ does not exist.

(2) $\lim_{x \to a} f(x)$ exists, but is not the same as $f(a)$.

Case (1) is illustrated by the function f defined for $x \neq 0$ by $f(x) = \dfrac{|x|}{x}$, and for $x = 0$ by $f(0) = 0$. As we saw in § 2, f fails to have a limit at $x = 0$, hence cannot be continuous at $x = 0$. (See figure 6.1.)

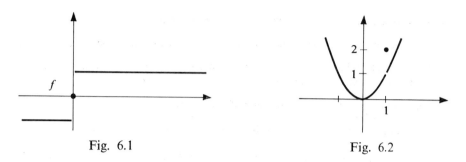

Fig. 6.1   Fig. 6.2

Case (2) is illustrated by the function f defined for $x \neq 1$ by $f(x) = x^2$, and for $x = 1$ by $f(1) = 2$. Here we have $\lim_{x \to 1} f(x) = 1$, whereas $f(1) = 2$. (See figure 6.2.)

By exercise 2 of § 5 we see that every rational function is continuous. Also the sin function is continuous. To see this, consider the graph in figure 6.3. (Since we used a picture to define sin, it is not surprising that we must use a picture to show that it is continuous.) The difference $|\sin x - \sin a|$ is just the distance from P to R, which is certainly less than the distance from Q to P along the circle. But this last is just $|x - a|$. Hence, give a positive number ϵ, we need only take $|x - a| < \epsilon$ to insure that $|\sin x - \sin a| < \epsilon$, and so sin is continuous at a. Since this argument works for any number a, this proves that sin is continuous. In a similar way we see that cos is continuous.

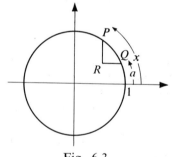

Fig. 6.3

Theorem 6.1: *If f and g are continuous at a, then $f + g$ and fg are continuous at a. Furthermore, if $g(a) \neq 0$, then $\dfrac{f}{g}$ is also continuous at a.*

Proof: To show that $f + g$ is continuous at a, we must show that
$$\lim_{x \to a} (f + g)(x) = (f + g)(a).$$

We have
$$\lim_{x \to a} (f + g)(x) = \lim_{x \to a} (f(x) + g(x)) \qquad \text{(definition of } f + g)$$

$$= \lim_{x \to a} f(x) + \lim_{x \to a} g(x) \quad \text{(sum rule for limits)}$$

$$= f(a) + g(a) \quad \text{(continuity of } f \text{ and } g)$$

$$= (f + g)(a) \quad \text{(definition of } f + g)$$

The proofs of continuity for fg and $\dfrac{f}{g}$ are left as an exercise. ∎

Theorem 6.2: *If* $\lim\limits_{x \to a} f(x) = b$ *and* g *is continuous at* b*, then*

$$\lim_{x \to a} g(f(x)) = g(b).$$

Proof: We must show that given $\epsilon > 0$, there is a $\delta > 0$ such that $|g(f(x)) - g(b)| < \epsilon$ whenever $0 < |x - a| < \delta$. Now since g is continuous at b, we know there is a $\delta_1 > 0$ such that

$$|g(u) - g(b)| < \epsilon \tag{1}$$

whenever $|u - b| < \delta_1$. Since $\lim\limits_{x \to a} f(x) = b$ and δ_1 is a perfectly good positive number, there must be a number δ such that $|f(x) - b| < \delta_1$ whenever $0 < |x - a| < \delta$. This means that for such x, $f(x)$ may play the role of u in (1), giving us $|g(f(x)) - g(b)| < \epsilon$ as required. ∎

Corollary 6.3: *If* f *is continuous at* a *and* g *is continuous at* $f(a)$*, then the composition* $g \circ f$ *is continuous at* a*.*

Proof: We must show that $\lim\limits_{x \to a} g(f(x)) = g(f(a))$. But since f is continuous at a we have $\lim\limits_{x \to a} f(x) = f(a)$, and so the result follows from theorem 6.2 with $f(a)$ playing the role of b. ∎

EXERCISES

1. Given n functions $f_1, f_2, \ldots, f_n$, use exercise 3 of § 4 to show that if each of the functions is continuous at a, then so is the sum.

2. Repeat exercise 1 with "sum" replaced by "product."

3. If $f(x) = x^3 - 3x^2 + 1$ for $x \neq 2$ and $f(2) = 0$, is f continuous at 2? If not, what would we have to take as $f(2)$ in order to make it continuous?

4. Let $f(x) = \sin x$ for $x < \dfrac{\pi}{2}$ and let $f(x) = x + 1 - \dfrac{\pi}{2}$ for $x > \dfrac{\pi}{2}$. Draw a rough graph of f. Is there a number we could take as $f\left(\dfrac{\pi}{2}\right)$ in order to make f continuous at $\dfrac{\pi}{2}$?

5. Explain how corollary 6.3 enables us to conclude that the function f defined by $f(x) = \sin(x^3 + 3x)$ is continuous.

6. Let $f(x) = x^2 + 1$ for $x < -1$ and $f(x) = x + 1$ for $x > -1$. Draw a graph of f. What are $\lim\limits_{x \to (-1)-} f(x)$ and $\lim\limits_{x \to (-1)+} f(x)$? Is there a number we can take as $f(-1)$ so as to make f continuous at -1?

7. What theorem enables us to conclude that tan, sec, csc, and cot are continuous functions?

8. Complete the proof of theorem 6.1.

7. DERIVATIVES

Before giving a precise definition of derivative, we shall give two illustrations, the first geometrical and the second physical.

Consider a function f, and let P be the point on the graph of f corresponding to a point a on the first axis. Also let Q be the point corresponding to some other point $a + h$. If h is positive, then Q will be to the right of P, as in figure 7.1. If h is negative, then Q will be to the left of P. The coordinates of P are $(a, f(a))$, and those of Q are $(a + h, f(a + h))$. Consequently the expression for the slope of the straight line joining P to Q is

$$\frac{f(a + h) - f(a)}{h}. \tag{1}$$

Now, unless the graph of f happens to be a straight line, (1) will have different values for different values of h, and so it will not make sense to define (1) as the "slope" of the graph at P. Nevertheless, if the graph is smooth enough at P, then as we take smaller and smaller values of h, it is reasonable to suppose that the line PQ will approach a certain line, called the *tangent* to the graph at P. Furthermore, if this tangent line is not parallel to the second axis, then the expression (1) will approach the slope of the tangent line.

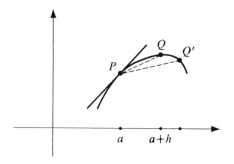

Fig. 7.1

Now consider the following physical situation. Suppose that a small object is moving along a straight line with a velocity which may not always be the same. Choose a point O on the line, a positive direction along the line, and a unit of length, say the foot. Also choose a unit of time, say the second. For each number t, let $f(t)$ denote the distance (in feet) of the object from the point O after t seconds have gone by. ($f(t)$ is positive if the object is in the positive direction from O, and is negative otherwise.) For example, it can be shown experimentally that if an object is dropped near the surface of the earth, then t seconds after it is released it will have fallen $\frac{1}{2}gt^2$ feet, where g is a constant which is approximately equal to 32. Now, if we wish to find the velocity of the object at a certain time a, we can take the distance traveled by the object between time a and some other time $a + h$, and divide by the difference h in the two times. Once again this gives us the expression

$$\frac{f(a + h) - f(a)}{h}.$$

Of course, this expression will not in general give us the exact velocity at time a, since the object may speed up or slow down between times a and $a + h$. However, as we take smaller and smaller values of h, our expression will come closer and closer to the true velocity at time a.

The above illustrations lead us to the following definition. Let f be a function, and let a be a number such that there is an entire neighborhood $(a - \delta, a + \delta)$ in the domain of f. If the limit

$$\lim_{h \to 0} \frac{f(a + h) - f(a)}{h} \tag{2}$$

exists, then f is said to be *differentiable* at a, and the number (2), which we shall denote more briefly by $f'(a)$, is called the *derivative* of f at a. The function as a whole is said to be differentiable if it is so at every point in its domain. The process of finding a derivative is called *differentiation*.

Notice that our definition of derivative, although motivated geometrically, depends in no way upon drawing a picture. It depends only on our previous notion of limit, which in turn was defined in terms of numbers and not pictures.

If the domain of f is a closed interval $[a, b]$ where $a < b$, then the end-points a and b do not have neighborhoods which lie entirely within the domain of f, and so strictly speaking our definition of derivative does not apply at these points. However, we shall agree to call the numbers

$$f'(a) = \lim_{h \to 0+} \frac{f(a + h) - f(a)}{h}$$

$$f'(b) = \lim_{h \to 0-} \frac{f(b + h) - f(b)}{h}$$

the derivatives in these cases.

Example 1: Let f be a constant function, say $f(x) = c$ for all x. Then for any number a we have

$$\frac{f(a + h) - f(a)}{h} = \frac{c - c}{h} = 0,$$

and so

$$f'(a) = \lim_{h \to 0} 0 = 0.$$

Example 2: Let f be the identity function for the numbers, so that $f(x) = x$ for all x. Then for any number a we have

$$\frac{f(a + h) - f(a)}{h} = \frac{(a + h) - a}{h} = \frac{h}{h} = 1,$$

and so

$$f'(a) = \lim_{h \to 0} 1 = 1.$$

Example 3: Let $f(x) = x^2$ for all numbers x, and let us find the derivative of f at 1. We have

$$\frac{f(1 + h) - f(1)}{h} = \frac{(1 + h)^2 - 1^2}{h} = \frac{2h + h^2}{h} = 2 + h.$$

Consequently,

$$f'(1) = \lim_{h \to 0} (2 + h) = 2.$$

Geometrically this means that the tangent line to the graph of f at the point $(1, 1)$ has slope 2 (figure 7.2).

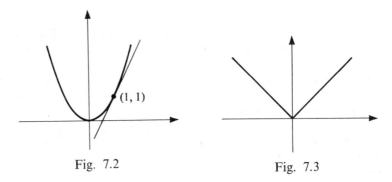

Fig. 7.2   Fig. 7.3

Example 4: Let $f(x) = |x|$ for all x, so that the graph of f is that shown in figure 7.3. At $x = 0$, the graph of f has a sharp corner, and consequently does not have a tangent line. Let us see what happens if we try to compute the derivative at 0. We have

$$\frac{f(0 + h) - f(0)}{h} = \frac{|h| - |0|}{h} = \frac{|h|}{h}.$$

But as we saw in §2, the expression $\dfrac{|h|}{h}$ has no limit at 0, and so f has no derivative at 0. Observe, nevertheless, that f is continuous at 0. Consequently, a function may be continuous at a point without having a derivative there. One is then led to ask if a function which has a derivative at a point is continuous at the point. This turns out to be true. Before proving it, we take another look at what continous means.

By definition, a function f is continuous at a if and only if for each $\epsilon > 0$ there exists a $\delta > 0$ such that $|f(x) - f(a)| < \epsilon$ whenever $|x - a| < \delta$.

Let us call $x - a = h$, or in other words $x = a + h$. Then the condition for continuity reads: For each $\epsilon > 0$ there is a $\delta > 0$ such that $|f(a + h) - f(a)| < \epsilon$ whenever $|h| < \delta$. Thus we see that f is continuous at a if and only if $\lim_{h \to 0} f(a + h) = f(a)$.

Lemma 7.1: *If f is differentiable at a, then f is continuous at a. In other words, if f is differentiable at a, then*

$$\lim_{h \to 0} f(a + h) = f(a).$$

Proof: For $h \neq 0$, we can certainly write

$$f(a + h) = h \frac{(f(a + h) - f(a))}{h} + f(a).$$

Hence, using the sum and product rules for limits we have

$$\lim_{h \to 0} f(a + h) = \lim_{h \to 0} h \lim_{h \to 0} \frac{f(a + h) - f(a)}{h} + \lim_{h \to 0} f(a)$$
$$= 0 f'(a) + f(a) = f(a),$$

as required. ∎

It should be remarked that the derivative of a function is itself a function, namely the function f' which assigns to x the number $f'(x)$ whenever the latter makes sense. The domain of f' is thus a subset of the domain of f. In example 4 above we saw that 0 is not in the domain of f'. Nevertheless, all other numbers are in the domain of f' (exercise 4). Thus, in this case the domain of f' is a proper subset of the domain of f.

EXERCISES

1. Find $f'(3)$ where $f(x) = x^3 - 2x + 1$ for all x.
2. Find $f'(a)$ where $f(x) = 3x^2 + 2x + 2$ for all x.
3. Find $f'(x)$ where $f(x) = \dfrac{x^2 - 1}{x^2 + 1}$ for all x.
4. If $f(x) = |x|$ for all x, show that $f'(x) = 1$ for $x > 0$, whereas $f'(x) = -1$ for $x < 0$.
5. If f is an even function and f has a derivative at a, show that $f'(-a) = -f'(a)$. On the other hand, if f is odd, show that $f'(-a) = f'(a)$.
6. If $f(x) = x^n$ where n is a positive integer, show that $f'(x) = nx^{n-1}$. (Hint: Use the binomial theorem in dealing with $f(x + h)$.)

8. DERIVATIVES OF SIN AND COS

To find the derivative of the function sin at the number a, by definition we must find the limit of the expression

$$\frac{\sin (a + h) - \sin a}{h}$$

as h approaches 0. Using the sum rule for sin, we have

$$\frac{\sin (a + h) - \sin a}{h} = \frac{\sin a \cos h + \cos a \sin h - \sin a}{h}$$

$$= \cos a \frac{\sin h}{h} - \sin a \frac{(1 - \cos h)}{h}.$$

Thus we have

$$\sin' (a) = \cos a \lim_{h \to 0} \left(\frac{\sin h}{h}\right) - \sin a \lim_{h \to 0} \left(\frac{1 - \cos h}{h}\right) \tag{1}$$

providing the two limits on the right exist. Notice that the limit of the numerator and the denominator of each expression is 0, so that the quotient rule for limits does not help us. First we consider $\dfrac{\sin h}{h}$. Let us restrict ourselves for the minute to $0 < h < \dfrac{\pi}{2}$. We draw two circles centered at the origin, one with

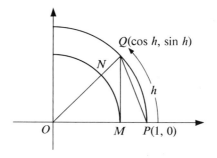

$Q(\cos h, \sin h)$

Fig. 8.1

radius 1 and the other with radius $\cos h$ (figure 8.1). The area of the sector OMN is less than the area of the triangle OPQ, which in turn is less than the area of the sector OPQ. Recalling the formula for the area of the sector of a circle (chapter I, § 23), this gives us

$$\tfrac{1}{2} h \cos^2 h < \tfrac{1}{2} \sin h < \tfrac{1}{2} h. \tag{2}$$

Multiplying each expression in (2) by the positive number $\dfrac{2}{h}$ gives us

$$\cos^2 h < \frac{\sin h}{h} < 1 \tag{3}$$

for $0 < h < \pi/2$. Since $\lim_{h \to 0} \cos^2 h = 1$, applying the squeeze rule (theorem 5.6) to (3), we see that

$$\lim_{h \to 0+} \frac{\sin h}{h} = 1.$$

Since

$$\frac{\sin (-h)}{-h} = \frac{\sin h}{h},$$

it then follows that $\lim\limits_{h \to 0-} \dfrac{\sin h}{h} = 1$ also, and consequently

$$\lim_{h \to 0} \frac{\sin h}{h} = 1. \tag{4}$$

For the other limit in equation (1), we write

$$\frac{1 - \cos h}{h} = \frac{1 - \cos^2 h}{h(1 + \cos h)} = \frac{\sin^2 h}{h(1 + \cos h)} = \frac{\sin h}{h} \cdot \frac{\sin h}{1 + \cos h}.$$

From (4) and the product rule for limits, we then find

$$\lim_{h \to 0} \frac{1 - \cos h}{h} = \lim_{h \to 0} \frac{\sin h}{h} \lim_{h \to 0} \frac{\sin h}{1 + \cos h} = 1 \left(\frac{0}{2}\right) = 0. \tag{5}$$

Substituting (4) and (5) in equation (1) now gives us

$$\sin'(a) = \cos a.$$

Using the same limits (4) and (5), the derivative of cos may be shown in a similar way to be

$$\cos'(a) = -\sin a.$$

EXERCISES

1. Prove that $\cos'(a) = -\sin a$.
2. Use the sum rule for tan (chapter I, § 23, exercise 5) to show that

$$\frac{\tan(a + h) - \tan a}{h} = \frac{\sin h}{h} \left(\frac{1 + \tan^2 a}{\cos h(1 - \tan a \tan h)}\right).$$

Hence show that $\tan'(a) = 1 + \tan^2 a$.

9. RULES FOR DERIVATIVES

In our study of limits we found it expedient to prove a few rules so as to avoid reverting to the definition of limit every time we confront one. We now prove some rules which will facilitate our work with derivatives.

Theorem 9.1 (The Sum Rule for Derivatives):   *If f and g are differentiable at a, then f + g is differentiable at a, and*

$$(f + g)'(a) = f'(a) + g'(a).$$

Proof: We have

$$\frac{(f + g)(a + h) - (f + g)(a)}{h} = \frac{(f(a + h) + g(a + h)) - (f(a) + g(a))}{h}$$

$$= \frac{f(a + h) - f(a)}{h} + \frac{g(a + h) - g(a)}{h}.$$

Consequently, using the sum rule for limits and the definition of derivative, we obtain

$$(f + g)'(a) = \lim_{h \to 0} \frac{f(a + h) - f(a)}{h} + \lim_{h \to 0} \frac{g(a + h) - g(a)}{h}$$
$$= f'(a) + g'(a). \ \blacksquare$$

On the basis of former experience we may suspect now that the derivative of a product is given by $(fg)'(a) = f'(a)g'(a)$. This rule turns out to be wrong. The right rule is the following.

Theorem 9.2 (The Product Rule for Derivatives): *If f and g are differentiable at a, then fg is differentiable at a, and*

$$(fg)'(a) = f'(a)g(a) + f(a)g'(a).$$

Proof: We have

$$\frac{(fg)(a + h) - (fg)(a)}{h}$$
$$= \frac{f(a + h)g(a + h) - f(a)g(a)}{h}$$
$$= \frac{f(a + h)g(a + h) - f(a)g(a + h) + f(a)g(a + h) - f(a)g(a)}{h}$$
$$= \frac{f(a + h) - f(a)}{h} g(a + h) + f(a) \frac{g(a + h) - g(a)}{h}.$$

Consequently, using the sum and product rules for limits, we obtain

$$(fg)'(a)$$
$$= \lim_{h \to 0} \frac{f(a + h) - f(a)}{h} \lim_{h \to 0} g(a + h) + f(a) \lim_{h \to 0} \frac{g(a + h) - g(a)}{h}$$
$$= f'(a)g(a) + f(a)g'(a),$$

where we are justified in writing $\lim_{h \to 0} g(a + h) = g(a)$ by theorem 7.1. $\blacksquare$

Recalling that the derivative of a constant function c is always 0 (§ 7, example 1) and replacing f by c in theorem 9.2, we get:

Corollary 9.3:   *If g is differentiable at a and c is any number, then cg is differentiable at a, and*

$$(cg)'(a) = cg'(a). \ \blacksquare$$

Corollary 9.4:   *If n is any positive integer and $f(x) = x^n$ for all numbers x, then $f'(x) = xn^{n-1}$ for all numbers x.*

Proof: The proof is by induction on n. For $n = 1$, we must show that if $f(x) = x$, then $f'(x) = 1$ for all x. But this has been shown in example 2 of § 7. Now assuming the result valid for n, take $f(x) = x^{n+1}$, and write $x^{n+1} = x^n x$. Then, using the product rule and our induction assumption, we have

$$f'(x) = (nx^{n-1})x + x^n 1$$
$$= nx^n + x^n$$
$$= (n + 1)x^n,$$

as required. ∎

From corollaries 9.3 and 9.4 we see that if $f(x) = cx^n$ where c is any number and n is a positive integer, then $f'(x) = cnx^{n-1}$. Since a polynomial function is by definition just a sum of such functions f, and since the sum rule 9.1 is valid for the sum of any number of·functions (exercise 1), we see that a polynomial function has a derivative at all numbers x, and furthermore the derivative function is again a polynomial function.

Example 1:   Let

$$f(x) = 5x^6 - 2x^4 + \tfrac{1}{2}x^3 + 3x^2 - 7x + 11.$$

Then

$$f'(x) = 30x^5 - 8x^3 + \tfrac{3}{2}x^2 + 6x - 7.$$

Example 2:   Let

$$f(x) = (x^3 - 2x + 1) \sin x + x^2 \cos x.$$

Applying the sum and product rules, we obtain

$$f'(x) = (3x^2 - 2) \sin x + (x^3 - 2x + 1) \cos x + 2x \cos x - x^2 \sin x$$
$$= (2x^2 - 2) \sin x + (x^3 + 1) \cos x.$$

Theorem 9.5:   *If g is differentiable at a and if, furthermore, $g(a) \neq 0$, then $1/g$ is differentiable at a, and*

$$(1/g)'(a) = \frac{-g'(a)}{g^2(a)}.$$

Proof: We have

$$\frac{(1/g)(a + h) - (1/g)(a)}{h} = \frac{1/g(a + h) - 1/g(a)}{h}$$

$$= -\left(\frac{g(a + h) - g(a)}{h}\right) \frac{1}{g(a + h)g(a)}.$$

Since g is differentiable at a, we have $\lim_{h \to 0} g(a + h) = g(a)$ by theorem 7.1. Consequently, using the product and quotient rules for limits, we obtain

$$(1/g)'(a) = -\lim_{h \to 0} \frac{g(a + h) - g(a)}{h} \lim_{h \to 0} \frac{1}{g(a + h)g(a)}$$

$$= -g'(a) \cdot \frac{1}{g(a)g(a)}$$

as required. ∎

Corollary 9.6 (The Quotient Rule for Derivatives): *If f and g are differentiable at a and if g(a) ≠ 0, then f/g is differentiable at a, and*

$$(f/g)'(a) = \frac{f'(a)g(a) - f(a)g'(a)}{g^2(a)}.$$

Proof: Regard f/g as the product of the two functions f and $1/g$. Then, using the product rule for derivatives and theorem 9.5, we have

$$(f/g)'(a) = f'(a)(1/g)(a) + f(a)(1/g)'(a)$$

$$= f'(a)\frac{1}{g(a)} - f(a)\frac{g'(a)}{g^2(a)}$$

$$= \frac{f'(a)g(a) - f(a)g'(a)}{g^2(a)}$$

as required. ∎

In particular corollary 9.6 shows us how to handle the derivative of any rational function. Recalling that a rational function is just the quotient of two polynomial functions, and that the derivative of a polynomial function is again a polynomial function, we see that the derivative of a rational function is a rational function with the same domain as the original function.

Example 3:   Consider

$$f(x) = \frac{x^2 + 3x - 1}{2x^3 + 1}.$$

Using the quotient rule we have

$$f'(x) = \frac{(2x + 3)(2x^3 + 1) - (x^2 + 3x - 1)(6x^2)}{(2x^3 + 1)^2}$$

$$= \frac{-2x^4 - 12x^3 + 6x^2 + 2x + 3}{4x^6 + 4x^3 + 1}.$$

Example 4:   Let us find the derivative of $\tan = \sin/\cos$. We have, using the quotient rule,

$$\tan'(x) = \frac{\cos x \cos x - \sin x \, (-\sin x)}{\cos^2 x}$$

$$= 1 + \tan^2 x.$$

Using the relation $\sin^2 + \cos^2 = 1$, we could equally well write $\tan'x = \sec^2 x$.

Example 5:   Let n be a positive integer, and let $f(x) = x^{-n}$. Remembering that x^{-n} is just $1/x^n$, and using theorem 9.5, we have

$$f'(x) = \frac{-nx^{n-1}}{(x^n)^2} = (-n)x^{-n-1}.$$

In other words, corollary 9.4 is valid for negative integers as well as for positive integers.

EXERCISES

1. Show, using theorem 9.1 and induction on n, that if $f_1, f_2, \ldots, f_n$ are functions with derivatives at a, then the sum function has a derivative at a given by

$$(f_1 + f_2 + \cdots + f_n)'(a) = f_1'(a) + f_2'(a) + \cdots + f_n'(a).$$

2. Use theorem 9.2 and induction to show that if $f_1, \ldots, f_n$ have derivatives at a, then the derivative of the product is given by

$$(f_1 f_2 \cdots f_n)'(a) = f_1'(a) f_2(a) f_3(a) \cdots f_n(a)$$
$$+ f_1(a) f_2'(a) f_3(a) \cdots f_n(a)$$
$$\vdots$$
$$+ f_1(a) f_2(a) f_3(a) \cdots f_n'(a).$$

3. Use exercise 2 to show that if f has a derivative at a and n is a positive integer, then f^n has a derivative at a given by

$$(f^n)'(a) = n f^{n-1}(a) f'(a).$$

Then use the quotient rule to show that this result is valid also when n is a negative integer providing $f(a) \neq 0$.

4. Find $f'(x)$ in each of the following cases:

(a) $f(x) = 2x^2 - 3x + 4$

(b) $f(x) = 7x^9 - 3x^5 - 8$

(c) $f(x) = x + \dfrac{1}{x}$

(d) $f(x) = \dfrac{x-1}{x+1}$

(e) $f(x) = (x^2 + 2) \sin x$

(f) $f(x) = \dfrac{x}{\tan x}$

(g) $f(x) = \dfrac{\sin x}{x^3 + x \cos x}$

(h) $f(x) = \dfrac{x-1}{x+1} \sin x \tan x$

(i) $f(x) = (x - 1)^4$

(j) $f(x) = \sin^2 x$

5. Find $f'(x)$ when $f(x) = (x^3 + x)^5$

(a) by expanding the expression for $f(x)$ into a polynomial of degree 15 using the binomial theorem;
(b) by using exercise 3.

Show that your two answers are the same.

6. Use the quotient rule to show each of the following:

$$\sec'(x) = \tan x \sec x$$
$$\csc'(x) = -\cot x \csc x$$
$$\cot'(x) = -(1 + \cot^2 x) = -\csc^2 x$$

10. THE CHAIN RULE

Consider the function F defined by

$$F(x) = \sin(x^3 + x)$$

for all numbers x. Although we know what the derivative of sin is, and also we know how to find the derivative of the function f given by $f(x) = x^3 + x$, as yet we have no rule which will enable us to find the derivative of F. Now observe that F is just the composition of the two functions sin and f. Therefore we shall be able to find the derivative of F once we have settled the more general problem of finding the derivative of the composition $g \circ f$ of two functions. By definition, the derivative of $g \circ f$ at a number a is given by the limit at 0 of the expression

$$\frac{(g \circ f)(a + h) - (g \circ f)(a)}{h} = \frac{g(f(a + h)) - g(f(a))}{h}, \tag{1}$$

providing this limit exists. Let us define

$$k(h) = f(a + h) - f(a),$$

or equivalently,

$$f(a + h) = f(a) + k(h),$$

so that (1) becomes

$$\frac{g(f(a) + k(h)) - g(f(a))}{h}. \tag{2}$$

If it were true that for all values of h different from 0 we had $k(h) \neq 0$, then we could multiply both numerator and denominator of (2) by $k(h)$, in which case (2) would become

$$\frac{g(f(a) + k(h)) - g(f(a))}{k(h)} \frac{k(h)}{h}. \tag{3}$$

To allow for the possibility of $k(h)$ being 0 for some values of h, we define a function φ by the rule

$$\varphi(t) = \frac{g(f(a) + t) - g(f(a))}{t}$$

for $t \neq 0$. If g has a derivative at $f(a)$, then by definition of derivative we have

$$g'(f(a)) = \lim_{t \to 0} \varphi(t).$$

Consequently, if we take $\varphi(0) = g'(f(a))$, then φ will be a continuous function at 0. The expression (3), which makes sense when $k(h) \neq 0$, now becomes

$$\varphi(k(h)) \frac{k(h)}{h}, \tag{4}$$

and so (4) is the same as (2) when $k(h) \neq 0$. But (4) is the same as (2) even when $k(h) = 0$, since in this case both (4) and (2) are just 0. Hence, the problem reduces to finding the limit of (4). To this end we prove the following lemma.

Lemma 10.1:   *Let g be a function with a derivative at b, and let φ be the function defined by*

$$\varphi(t) = \frac{g(b + t) - g(b)}{t} \quad \text{for } t \neq 0,$$

$$\varphi(0) = g'(b).$$

If k is any function such that $\lim\limits_{h \to 0} k(h) = 0$, *then we have*

$$\lim_{h \to 0} \varphi(k(h)) = g'(b).$$

Proof: The function φ is defined at 0 so as to make it continuous there. Therefore, since $\lim\limits_{h \to 0} k(h) = 0$, it follows from theorem 6.2 that

$$\lim_{h \to 0} \varphi(k(h)) = \varphi(0) = g'(b)$$

as required. ∎

Now returning to (4), let us suppose that f has a derivative at a. Then by lemma 7.1 we have $\lim\limits_{h \to 0} f(a + h) = f(a)$, or in other words, $\lim\limits_{h \to 0} k(h) = 0$. Therefore, using lemma 10.1 (with $f(a)$ playing the role of b) and the product rule for limits, the limit of (4) is given by

$$\lim_{h \to 0} \varphi(k(h)) \lim_{h \to 0} \frac{k(h)}{h} = g'(f(a)) \lim_{h \to 0} \frac{f(a + h) - f(a)}{h}$$

$$= g'(f(a))f'(a).$$

Thus we have proved:

Theorem 10.2 (The Chain Rule): *If f has a derivative at a and g has a derivative at f(a), then g ∘ f has a derivative at a given by*

$$(g \circ f)'(a) = g'(f(a))f'(a). \quad \blacksquare$$

Example 1: We can now find the derivative of the function F given by $F(x) = \sin(x^3 + x)$ considered at the beginning of the section. For if we take $g(u) = \sin u$ and $f(x) = x^3 + x$, then we have $F(x) = g(f(x))$ and consequently

$$F'(x) = g'(f(x)) \cdot f'(x)$$
$$= (\cos(x^3 + x))(3x^2 + 1).$$

Example 2: Let $F(x) = \tan^3(x^4)$. Here we can write $F(x) = g(f(x))$ where $g(u) = u^3$ and $f(x) = \tan(x^4)$. Since $g'(u) = 3u^2$, we have

$$F'(x) = g'(f(x))f'(x)$$
$$= 3 \tan^2(x^4) \cdot f'(x). \quad (5)$$

To find $f'(x)$ we must again apply the chain rule. We take $h(u) = \tan u$ and $k(x) = x^4$ so that $f(x) = h(k(x))$. Then we have

$$f'(x) = h'(k(x))k'(x)$$
$$= \sec^2(x^4) \cdot 4x^3.$$

Substituting this in (5) we obtain finally,

$$F'(x) = 3 \tan^2(x^4) \cdot \sec^2(x^4) \cdot 4x^3.$$

EXERCISES

1. If f has a derivative at x and n is any positive integer, use the chain rule to show that $(f^n)'(x) = nf^{n-1}(x)f'(x)$.

2. Find F' in each of the following cases:

   (a) $F(x) = (4x^3 - 2x^2 + 1)^{15}$
   (b) $F(x) = \sin(\tan x)$
   (c) $F(x) = \cos(x^2 \sin^5 x)$
   (d) $F(x) = (x^2 + x)^4 \sec^5(x^2 - 1)$
   (e) $F(x) = \cos^3(\sin^2(x^3 - x^2))$
   (f) $F(x) = \dfrac{\csc^2(x^3)}{\tan^3(x^2)}$.

3. Let $F(x) = |x^3 - x|$ for all x. Use exercise 4 of § 7 and the chain rule to find $F'(x)$ when $x \neq 0, 1$, or -1. Explain why the chain rule does not apply when $x = 0, 1$, or -1. Plot a rough graph of F.

4. Let $g(u) = u^2$ for $u \neq 1$, and take $g(1) = 0$. Also let $f(x) = [x - 1]$ (the greatest integer $\leq x - 1$) for all x. Show that f is not continuous at 2 and hence has no derivative there, and that g is not continuous at $f(2)$ and hence has no derivative there. On the other hand, show that $g(f(x)) = 0$ for every x in the interval $[1, 3)$, and consequently $(g \circ f)'(2) = 0$.

11. HIGHER DERIVATIVES

Given a function f, the derivative f' is a function which in general has a smaller domain than f. If we take its derivative $(f')'$, we obtain what is known as the *second* derivative of f. It is denoted by f''. Similarly the *third* derivative f''' is defined as $(f'')'$. Continuing in this way we define the $(n + 1)$st derivative $f^{(n+1)}$ as $(f^{(n)})'$, where the superscript (n) is supposed to represent n prime signs. (With this notation we could equally well write $f = f^{(0)}, f' = f^{(1)}, f'' = f^{(2)}$, etc.)

Example 1: Let us find f''' in the case where $f(x) = \dfrac{x}{2x + 1}$. Using the quotient rule for derivatives we have

$$f'(x) = \frac{1}{(2x + 1)^2},$$

$$f''(x) = \frac{-4}{(2x + 1)^3},$$

$$f'''(x) = \frac{24}{(2x + 1)^4}.$$

Since the derivative of a rational function is another rational function with the same domain as the original function (see § 9), repeating this principle n times (which really means using induction) we see that the nth derivative of a rational function is also a rational function with the same domain. However, for general functions it will be the case that each derivative has a smaller domain than the preceding one.

The computation of higher derivatives can get very messy in some cases. However, there is a rule which sometimes helps us simplify matters. It is due to the German mathematician Gottfried Wilhelm Leibniz (1646–1716), who at about the same time as (but independently of) the English mathematician Isaac Newton (1642–1727) began the study of the calculus.

Let us start with two functions f and g, each defined on some common interval, and each having a derivative at every point in that interval. Then the product rule for derivatives gives

$$(fg)' = f'g + fg'. \tag{1}$$

If each of f' and g' have derivatives throughout the interval, then we can apply the sum and product rules to (1) to obtain

$$(fg)'' = f''g + f'g' + f'g' + fg''$$
$$= f''g + 2f'g' + fg''.$$

Similarly, if each function has a second derivative throughout the interval, we obtain

$$(fg)''' = f'''g + 3f''g' + 3f'g'' + fg'''.$$

This is a familiar pattern, and we are led to suspect the following theorem.

Theorem 11.1 (Leibniz's Rule for the Derivatives of a Product): *If each of f and g has n derivatives throughout some interval, then the product fg has an nth derivative throughout the interval, given by*

$$(fg)^{(n)} = \sum_{k=0}^{n} \binom{n}{k} f^{(n-k)} g^{(k)}. \tag{2}$$

Proof: The proof proceeds, needless to say, by induction. If $n = 1$, then equation (2) is just the ordinary product rule for derivatives. Now assume that equation (2) is true for some n, and that each of f and g has $n + 1$ derivatives throughout the interval. Then applying the sum and product rules for derivatives to (2), we obtain

$$(fg)^{(n+1)} = \sum_{k=0}^{n} \binom{n}{k} (f^{(n-k+1)} g^{(k)} + f^{(n-k)} g^{(k+1)}). \tag{3}$$

On the right side of (3) the coefficients of $f^{(n+1)} g^{(0)}$ and $f^{(0)} g^{(n+1)}$ are both 1. For values of k such that $1 \leq k \leq n$, the coefficient of $f^{(n+1-k)} g^{(k)}$ is $\binom{n}{k} + \binom{n}{k-1}$, which is the same as $\binom{n+1}{k}$ by lemma 17.1 of chapter I. Consequently, (3) can be written

$$(fg)^{(n+1)} = \sum_{k=0}^{n+1} \binom{n+1}{k} f^{(n+1-k)} g^{(k)},$$

which is just equation (2) with n replaced by $n + 1$. ∎

Example 2: Let us find $F^{(5)}(x)$ where $F(x) = x^9 \sin x$. We take $f(x) = x^9$ and $g(x) = \sin x$. Then Leibniz's rule gives us

$$
\begin{aligned}
F^{(5)}(x) = {}& (9)(8)(7)(6)(5)x^4 \sin x + 5(9)(8)(7)(6)x^5 \cos x \\
& + 10(9)(8)(7)x^6(-\sin x) + 10(9)(8)x^7(-\cos x) \\
& + 5(9)x^8 \sin x + x^9 \cos x.
\end{aligned}
$$

Notice that the rule enables us to write down the derivative of fg without even computing the derivatives of f and g beforehand. For we can first write down the binomial coefficients (leaving lots of space after each of them). Then starting at the last one and working back toward the first we insert $f(x)$, $f'(x)$, $f''(x)$, ..., $f^{(n)}(x)$. In other words, we insert after each coefficient the derivative of what we have just inserted after the previous one. Then, starting at the first term and working toward the last, we do the same thing with g.

The second derivative has a physical interpretation which we shall now discuss briefly. Suppose that a small object moving along a straight line is at a distance $f(t)$ feet from a point O after t seconds have elapsed. Then as we saw in § 7, the velocity of the object at any time a is $f'(a)$ feet per second. Now, if we wish to find the acceleration of the object at time a, we take the difference in the velocities between time a and some other time $a + h$, and divide by the difference h in the two times. This yields the expression

$$
\frac{f'(a + h) - f'(a)}{h}. \tag{4}
$$

This does not give us the exact acceleration at time a, but rather only an approximation to the acceleration which becomes more and more accurate as we take smaller and smaller values of h. The true acceleration is given by the limit of the expression (4) as h approaches 0, or in other words,

$$
\lim_{h \to 0} \frac{f'(a + h) - f'(a)}{h} = f''(a).
$$

In chapter III, § 11 we shall consider a geometrical interpretation of the second derivative.

EXERCISES

1. For any positive integer n, prove by induction on n that $\sin^{(4n)} = \sin$, $\sin^{(4n+1)} = \cos$, $\sin^{(4n+2)} = -\sin$, and $\sin^{(4n+3)} = -\cos$. Similarly, find the higher derivatives of cos.

2. (a) Let $f(x) = x^n$ where n is a positive integer. What is $f^{(k)}(x)$ when $0 < k < n$? What is $f^{(n)}(x)$? What is $f^{(k)}(x)$ when $k > n$?
   (b) Let $f(x) = x^{-n}$ where n is a positive integer and let k be any positive integer. What is $f^{(k)}(x)$?

3. Find $f^{(4)}(x)$ when $f(x) = 3x^7 - 6x^5 + 2x^4 - x^3 + x$.

4. Find $f'''(x)$ when

$$
f(x) = \frac{x^2 - x}{x^2 + 1}.
$$

5. Find $\tan^{(4)}$ and $\sec^{(4)}$.

6. Find $F^{(2)}(x)$ when $F(x) = \sin^3 (3x^2 - 1)$.

7. Use Leibniz's rule to find

   (a) $F^{(4)}(x)$ when $F(x) = (x^6 + 3x^2 - 1) \tan x$.

   (Use exercise 5 for the derivatives of tan.)

   (b) $F^{(6)}(x)$ when $F(x) = \dfrac{\cos x}{x^2}$.

8. Let $f(x) = x |x|^n$ where n is odd. Show that $f^{(n)}(0) = 0$, whereas $f^{(n+1)}(0)$ does not exist.

12. TYPES OF DISCONTINUITY

So far, in giving examples of functions which are not continuous at some point, we have used what are known as jump discontinuities. A function f is said to have a *jump discontinuity from the right* at a number a in its domain if there are positive numbers ϵ and δ such that $|f(x) - f(a)| > \epsilon$ whenever $a < x < a + \delta$. This is illustrated in figure 12.1.

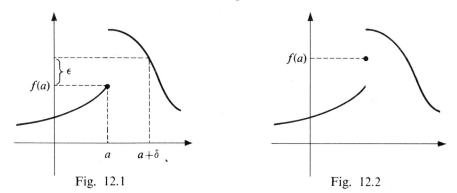

Fig. 12.1   Fig. 12.2

Similarly, if there are positive numbers ϵ and δ such that $|f(x) - f(a)| > \epsilon$ whenever $a - \delta < x < a$, then we say that f has a *jump discontinuity from the left* at a. In figure 12.2 the function has jump discontinuities at a from both the left and the right.

A discontinuity which is not a jump discontinuity is called a *discontinuity due to oscillation*. This is illustrated in example 1.

Example 1: Let $f(x) = \sin\left(\dfrac{1}{x}\right)$ for $x \neq 0$, and let us take $f(0) = 0$ so as to have f defined at all x. For the values $x = \dfrac{1}{\pi}, \dfrac{1}{2\pi}, \dfrac{1}{3\pi}, \ldots$, we have $f(x) = 0$. Similarly, we see that for the values $x = \dfrac{2}{\pi}, \dfrac{2}{5\pi}, \dfrac{2}{9\pi}, \ldots$ we have $f(x) = 1$, and for the values $x = \dfrac{2}{3\pi}, \dfrac{2}{7\pi}, \dfrac{2}{11\pi}, \ldots$, we have $f(x) = -1$.

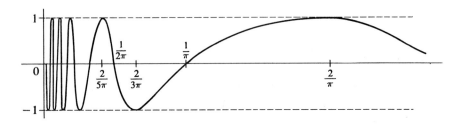

Fig. 12.3

Consequently, for positive values of x the graph of f looks something like that in figure 12.3. (For convenience of drawing, we use a much smaller unit of length along the second axis than we do along the first axis.)

The graph is such that no matter how small a positive number δ we take, there are an infinite number of oscillations for x between 0 and δ. Thus for any $\delta > 0$ the function takes on both the values 1 and -1 between 0 and δ. Hence, $\lim\limits_{x \to 0+} f(x)$ does not exist. Using the fact that f is an odd function, we see that a similar situation prevails for negative values of x, so that $\lim\limits_{x \to 0-} f(x)$ does not exist either.

Using the chain rule, the derivative of f is given by $f'(x) = -\dfrac{1}{x^2} \cos\left(\dfrac{1}{x}\right)$ for $x \neq 0$. However, f does not have a derivative at 0 since it is not even continuous there.

Example 2: Let $f(x) = x \sin\left(\dfrac{1}{x}\right)$ for $x \neq 0$, and let $f(0) = 0$. Since the values $\sin\left(\dfrac{1}{x}\right)$ are all between -1 and 1, the values $x \sin\left(\dfrac{1}{x}\right)$ are between $-x$ and x. Also f is an even function. Thus the graph of f looks like that in figure 12.4.

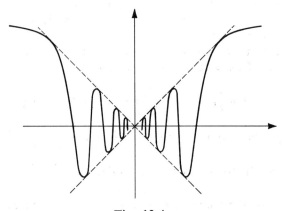

Fig. 12.4

Again there are an infinite number of oscillations in any interval around 0. Nevertheless, f is continuous at 0. For we have

$$|f(x) - f(0)| = \left| x \sin\left(\frac{1}{x}\right) - 0 \right| \leq |x|$$

and so, given $\epsilon > 0$, we need only take $\delta = \epsilon$ to insure that $|f(x) - f(0)| < \epsilon$ whenever $|x - 0| < \delta$.

For $x \neq 0$, we have, using the product rule for derivatives,

$$f'(x) = \sin\left(\frac{1}{x}\right) - \frac{1}{x}\cos\left(\frac{1}{x}\right).$$

However, for $x = 0$ we cannot use the product rule, since one of the terms, namely $\sin\left(\frac{1}{x}\right)$, does not have a derivative at 0. To investigate the derivative at 0, we must go back to the definition of derivative. We have

$$\frac{f(0 + h) - f(0)}{h} = \frac{h \sin\left(\frac{1}{h}\right) - 0}{h} = \sin\left(\frac{1}{h}\right)$$

for $h \neq 0$. But in example 1 we saw that $\lim\limits_{h \to 0} \sin\left(\frac{1}{h}\right)$ does not exist, and consequently f does not have a derivative at 0.

Example 3:   Let $f(x) = x^2 \sin\left(\frac{1}{x}\right)$ for $x \neq 0$, and let $f(0) = 0$. The values of f are between $-x^2$ and x^2, and so since f is odd its graph looks something like the one in figure 12.5. For $x \neq 0$, we have

$$f'(x) = 2x \sin\left(\frac{1}{x}\right) - \cos\left(\frac{1}{x}\right). \tag{1}$$

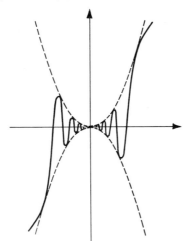

Fig. 12.5

We claim that $\lim_{x\to 0} f'(x)$ does not exist. For suppose that it exists, and rewrite (1) as

$$\cos\left(\frac{1}{x}\right) = 2x \sin\left(\frac{1}{x}\right) - f'(x). \tag{2}$$

Then, since each term on the right side of (2) has a limit at 0, by the sum rule for limits $\cos\left(\frac{1}{x}\right)$ also has a limit. But $\cos\left(\frac{1}{x}\right)$ behaves like $\sin\left(\frac{1}{x}\right)$ near 0 (exercise 1) and so does not have a limit. This contradiction shows that $\lim_{x\to 0} f'(x)$ does not exist. Nevertheless, $f'(0)$ does exist. For we have

$$\frac{f(0+h)-f(0)}{h} = \frac{h^2 \sin(1/h) - 0}{h} = h \sin(1/h),$$

and consequently, using example 2, we have

$$f'(0) = \lim_{h\to 0} h \sin(1/h) = 0.$$

This example shows that a function may have a derivative at all numbers x without the derivative being continuous. Nevertheless, in the following chapter we shall prove that a derivative cannot have any jump discontinuities. In other words, any discontinuity of a derivative must be due to oscillation.

EXERCISES

1. Rework the three examples of this section with sin replaced by cos in each case.
2. Let $f(x) = x^3 \sin(1/x)$ for $x \neq 0$, and let $f(0) = 0$. Find $f'(x)$ for all values of x including $x = 0$. Also find $f''(x)$ for $x \neq 0$, and show that $f''(0)$ does not exist.
3. Repeat exercise 2 with $f(x) = x^4 \sin(1/x)$, except show in this case that $f''(0) = 0$.

13. INFINITE LIMITS

Consider the function f defined by $f(x) = 1/x$ for $x > 0$. Its graph is shown in figure 13.1. Consider also the function g defined by $g(x) = \frac{1}{x}\sin\left(\frac{1}{x}\right)$ for

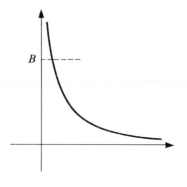

B

Fig. 13.1

all $x > 0$. The $\sin\left(\dfrac{1}{x}\right)$ term causes the same kind of oscillation that we en-

countered in the examples of the previous section. The $\dfrac{1}{x}$ term forces the

oscillations to go from the graph of $\dfrac{1}{x}$ to the graph of $-\dfrac{1}{x}$. Consequently the

graph of g is that shown in figure 13.2. Again we are prevented from drawing the graph close to 0 since there are an infinite number of oscillations in any neighborhood of 0.

Now the functions f and g have one thing in common. Namely, each function takes on values as large as we like for x near 0. To be more precise,

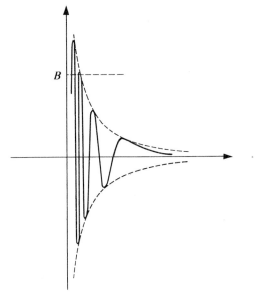

Fig. 13.2

we can say that given any number B, there are values $f(x)$ and $g(x)$ which exceed B for x arbitrarily close to 0. However, the functions differ in one important aspect, and that is that the values of f eventually become greater than any prescribed number B and *stay* that way as x moves in toward 0, whereas the values of g, although they keep reaching values greater than B as x moves in toward 0, never stay that way, but rather always come back down below B again. This leads us to the following definition.

Let f be a function and let a be a number. Suppose that for each number B there is a positive number δ such that $f(x) > B$ for all x in the domain of f satisfying $a < x < a + δ$. Then we say that *the right-hand limit of f at a is infinite*, and we write

$$\lim_{x \to a+} f(x) = \infty.$$

Again it must be remarked that there is no number ∞, and that the symbolism above is only an abbreviation for the longer sentence which precedes it. And again we shall agree to talk only of those x which are in the domain of f, without bothering to say so each time.

If for each number B there is a positive number δ such that $f(x) < B$ for all x satisfying $a < x < a + \delta$, then we write

$$\lim_{x \to a+} f(x) = -\infty.$$

Since the condition $f(x) < B$ is equivalent to the condition $-f(x) > -B$, we see that $\lim_{x \to a+} f(x) = -\infty$ if and only if $\lim_{x \to a+} (-f(x)) = \infty$.

The definition of $\lim_{x \to a-} f(x) = \infty$ (or $-\infty$) is had by replacing the condition $a < x < a + \delta$ by the condition $a - \delta < x < a$ in the above. If both $\lim_{x \to a+} f(x) = \infty$ and $\lim_{x \to a-} f(x) = \infty$, then we shall write simply $\lim_{x \to a} f(x) = \infty$.

The following theorem reduces the study of infinite limits to that of finite limits.

Theorem 13.1: *We have* $\lim_{x \to a+} f(x) = \infty$ *(or* $-\infty$*) if and only if* $\lim_{x \to a+} \dfrac{1}{f(x)} = 0$ *and* $f(x) > 0$ *(or* $f(x) < 0$*) for all x in some interval of the form* $(a, a + \delta_1)$.

Proof: Suppose first that $\lim_{x \to a+} \dfrac{1}{f(x)} = 0$ and that $f(x) > 0$ for all x in $(a, a + \delta_1)$. Given a number B, we must find a positive δ such that $f(x) > B$ whenever $a < x < a + \delta$. We may assume that B is positive, since if we can make $f(x)$ greater than any positive number, then we can certainly make it greater than any other number. Take $\epsilon = 1/B$ in the definition of $\lim_{x \to a+} \dfrac{1}{f(x)} = 0$. Then we know that there is a positive δ_2 such that

$$\left| \frac{1}{f(x)} \right| < \frac{1}{B}$$

whenever $a < x < a + \delta_2$. Hence, if we let δ be the smaller of δ_1 and δ_2, then we have

$$0 < \frac{1}{f(x)} < \frac{1}{B}$$

whenever $a < x < a + \delta$. This implies that $B < f(x)$ for such x, and so this proves that $\lim_{x \to a+} f(x) = \infty$.

Conversely, suppose that $\lim_{x \to a+} f(x) = \infty$. In the first place, we can take $B = 0$ in the definition of the infinite limit to see that $f(x) > 0$ for all x in some interval of the form $(a, a + \delta_1)$. To show that $\lim_{x \to a+} \dfrac{1}{f(x)} = 0$, we must show that, given a positive ϵ, there is a positive δ such that $\left|\dfrac{1}{f(x)}\right| < \epsilon$ whenever $a < x < a + \delta$. But this follows by taking $B = 1/\epsilon$ in the definition of $\lim\limits_{x\to a+} f(x) = \infty$, since the condition $1/\epsilon < f(x)$ is equivalent to $1/f(x) < \epsilon$.

The statement involving $-\infty$ follows by applying what we have already proved to the function $-f$. ∎

A similar theorem holds, of course, for left-hand limits. In this case the interval $(a, a + \delta_1)$ must be replaced by the interval $(a - \delta_1, a)$.

Example 1: We investigate

$$\lim_{x\to\pi/2} \frac{1 - x}{\cos x}.$$

First we have

$$\lim_{x\to\pi/2} \frac{\cos x}{1 - x} = 0.$$

Now $\dfrac{1 - x}{\cos x}$ is positive for x in the interval $\left(\dfrac{\pi}{2}, \dfrac{3\pi}{2}\right)$, and is negative in the interval $\left(1, \dfrac{\pi}{2}\right)$. Consequently, by theorem 13.1 we have

$$\lim_{x\to\frac{\pi}{2}+} \frac{1 - x}{\cos x} = \infty \quad \text{and} \quad \lim_{x\to\frac{\pi}{2}-} \frac{1 - x}{\cos x} = -\infty.$$

We shall now investigate the infinite limits of any rational function. Such a function is of the form $f = \dfrac{p}{q}$ where p and q are polynomials. In the first place, we may assume that p and q have no roots in common, for if a were a root of both of them, then by theorem 22.2 of chapter I, $(x - a)$ would be a factor of both of them and so we could cancel. Now since rational functions are continuous, for those numbers a at which $q(a) \neq 0$ we have simply

$$\lim_{x\to a} f(x) = f(a) = \frac{p(a)}{q(a)}.$$

Thus the only places where f can have infinite limits are at the roots of q. Let a be a root of q of multiplicity m, so that we have

$$f(x) = \frac{p(x)}{(x - a)^m g(x)}$$

where $g(a) \neq 0$. Then also $p(a) \neq 0$ since p and q have no roots in common. Therefore we have

$$\frac{1}{f(x)} = (x - a)^m \frac{g(x)}{p(x)},$$

and so $\lim\limits_{x\to a} \left(\dfrac{1}{f(x)}\right) = 0.$

Case 1: Suppose that m is even. Then $(x - a)^m > 0$ for all $x \neq a$. Also since $\dfrac{p}{g}$ is a continuous function whose value at a is not 0, we see that $\dfrac{p(x)}{g(x)}$ has the same sign as $\dfrac{p(a)}{g(a)}$ for x in some neighborhood of a (see lemma 5.1). Consequently, if $\dfrac{p(a)}{g(a)} > 0$, then $f(x) > 0$ in some neighborhood of a, and so by theorem 13.1 we have $\lim\limits_{x \to a} f(x) = \infty$. Likewise, if $\dfrac{p(a)}{g(a)} < 0$, then $f(x) < 0$ in some neighborhood of a, and so $\lim\limits_{x \to a} f(x) = -\infty$.

Case 2: Suppose that m is odd. For $x > a$ we have $(x - a)^m > 0$, and so just as in case 1 we have $\lim\limits_{x \to a+} f(x) = \infty$ if $\dfrac{p(a)}{g(a)} > 0$ and $\lim\limits_{x \to a+} f(x) = -\infty$ if $\dfrac{p(a)}{g(a)} < 0$. On the other hand, for $x < a$ we have $(x - a)^m < 0$ since it is an odd power of a negative number. Hence, in this case if $\dfrac{p(a)}{g(a)} > 0$, then $f(x)$ is negative in a neighborhood to the left of a, and so $\lim\limits_{x \to a-} f(x) = -\infty$. Likewise, if $\dfrac{p(a)}{g(a)} < 0$, then $f(x)$ is positive in a neighborhood to the left of a, and so $\lim\limits_{x \to a-} f(x) = \infty$.

Example 2: Let

$$f(x) = \frac{x^3 + 5x^2 - 4x}{(x - 2)(x^2 + 3x + 1)}.$$

If we evaluate the numerator $p(x)$ at $x = 2$, we obtain 20, and so 2 is not a root of the numerator. Also, if we evaluate $g(x) = x^2 + 3x + 1$ at $x = 2$ we obtain 11. Hence 2 is not a root of g, and so the multiplicity of the root 2 of the denominator is 1. Now we have $\dfrac{p(2)}{g(2)} = \dfrac{20}{11} > 0$, and so by case 2 above we have $\lim\limits_{x \to 2+} f(x) = \infty$ and $\lim\limits_{x \to 2-} f(x) = -\infty$.

Example 3: Let

$$f(x) = \frac{x^3 + 3x^2 + 4x + 2}{(x + 1)^3(x^4 - 2x^3 + x - 3)}.$$

Evaluating the numerator at -1 we obtain 0. Hence, we know that $(x + 1)$ is a factor of the numerator, and using the method described in § 22 of chapter I, we find

$$x^3 + 3x^2 + 4x + 2 = (x + 1)(x^2 + 2x + 2).$$

Hence, after cancellation we have

$$f(x) = \frac{x^2 + 2x + 2}{(x + 1)^2(x^4 - 2x^3 + x - 5)}.$$

Here if we evaluate the numerator $p(x)$ at -1 we obtain 1, and if we evaluate $g(x) = x^4 - 2x^3 + x - 5$ at -1 we obtain -3. Consequently -1 is a root of multiplicity 2 of the denominator, and so since $\frac{p(-1)}{g(-1)} = -\frac{1}{3}$, by case 1 above we have $\lim\limits_{x \to -1} f(x) = -\infty$.

Example 4: Let us find $\lim\limits_{x \to 0} f(x)$ when

$$f(x) = \frac{x^5 - 3x^4 - 2x^3}{5x^6 + x^5 + x^3}.$$

Here after cancellation of x^3 we have

$$f(x) = \frac{x^2 - 3x - 2}{5x^3 + x^2 + 1}$$

for $x \neq 0$. But now 0 is no longer a root of the denominator, and so we have by the simple quotient rule for limits,

$$\lim_{x \to 0} f(x) = \lim_{x \to 0} \frac{x^2 - 3x - 2}{5x^3 + x^2 + 1} = \frac{-2}{1} = -2.$$

EXERCISES

1. Investigate each of the functions tan, cot, sec, and csc for infinite limits.

2. Find the limit of f at the indicated points in each of the following cases:

(a) $f(x) = \dfrac{4x - 1}{x^3 - 3x + 2}$ at -2 and 1.

(b) $f(x) = \dfrac{5x^2 + x}{x^8 + 2x^3}$ at 0 and 1.

(c) $f(x) = \dfrac{2x^4 - 4x^3 - x^2 + 3x - 2}{(x - 2)^5 x}$ at 0 and 2.

(d) $f(x) = \dfrac{\tan x}{(x - 1)^3}$ at 1.

(e) $f(x) = \dfrac{(x - 1)^3}{\tan x}$ at 0.

3. Show that if m is positive and even, then $\lim\limits_{x \to a} \dfrac{1}{(x - a)^m} = \infty$. On the other hand, show that if m is positive and odd, then

$$\lim_{x \to a+} \frac{1}{(x - a)^m} = \infty \quad \text{and} \quad \lim_{x \to a-} \frac{1}{(x - a)^m} = -\infty.$$

4. (a) Assume that there is a number m and a neighborhood of a such that $g(x) \geq m$ for all x in that neighborhood. (In particular, this will be true

if g has a finite limit at a or if $\lim g(x) = \infty$.) Show that if $\lim_{x \to a} f(x) = \infty$, then also

$$\lim_{x \to a} (f(x) + g(x)) = \infty.$$

State and prove a similar theorem for $-\infty$.

(b) Use part (a) to show that

$$\lim_{x \to 0} \left(\sin \left(\frac{1}{x} \right) + \frac{1}{x^2} \right) = \infty.$$

5. (a) Assume that there is a positive number m and a neighborhood of a such that $g(x) \geq m$ for all x in that neighborhood. Show that if $\lim_{x \to a} f(x) = \infty$, then also

$$\lim_{x \to 0} f(x)g(x) = \infty.$$

(b) Use part (a) to show that

$$\lim_{x \to 0} \frac{\sin (1/x) - 2}{x^2} = -\infty.$$

14. LIMITS AT INFINITY

Consider the function f defined by

$$f(x) = \frac{3x}{x + 1}$$

for all $x \geq 0$. The values of f are all less than 3. If we divide numerator and denominator by x (for $x \neq 0$) we obtain

$$f(x) = \frac{3}{1 + 1/x}.$$

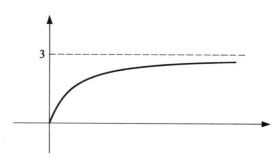

Fig. 14.1

As x gets large, the $1/x$ term in the denominator approaches 0, and so $f(x)$ approaches 3. The graph of f is sketched in figure 14.1.

The precise definition of what we mean for $f(x)$ to approach a number as x gets large is the following. Suppose that L is a number with the property that for each $\epsilon > 0$ there is a number b such that $|f(x) - L| < \epsilon$ whenever $x > b$. Then we call L the *limit of f at* ∞ and we write $\lim_{x \to \infty} f(x) = L$.

We shall also write $\lim_{x \to \infty} f(x) = \infty$ (or $-\infty$) if for each number B there is a b such that $f(x) > B$ (or $f(x) < B$) whenever $x > b$. For example, $\lim_{x \to \infty} (2x + 1) = \infty$, whereas $\lim_{x \to \infty} (1 - x) = -\infty$.

All the limit theorems proved in §§ 4 and 5 remain valid for limits at ∞. To prove them we could simply go through the old proofs, mechanically replacing each expression of the form "there exists a number $\delta > 0$ such that whenever $0 < |x - a| < \delta$" by the expression "there exists a number b such that whenever $x > b$". However, to save us the bother, there is a simple theorem which enables us to conclude any theorem about limits at ∞ once we know the truth of the theorem for ordinary limits.

Theorem 14.1:   *We have* $\lim_{x \to \infty} f(x) = L$ *if and only if* $\lim_{t \to 0+} f\left(\dfrac{1}{t}\right) = L$. *The same is true if L is replaced by ∞ or $-\infty$.*

Proof: Suppose first that $\lim_{t \to 0+} f\left(\dfrac{1}{t}\right) = L$. Given $\epsilon > 0$, we must show that there is a number b such that $|f(x) - L| < \epsilon$ whenever $x > b$. Now, we know there is a number $\delta > 0$ such that

$$\left| f\left(\frac{1}{t}\right) - L \right| < \epsilon \tag{1}$$

whenever $0 < t < \delta$. Suppose that $x > \dfrac{1}{\delta}$, or in other words, $0 < \dfrac{1}{x} < \delta$. Then we can replace t by $\dfrac{1}{x}$ in (1) to obtain $|f(x) - L| < \epsilon$ whenever $x > 1/\delta$. In other words, we can take $1/\delta$ as our b.

Conversely, suppose that $\lim_{x \to \infty} f(x) = L$. Given $\epsilon > 0$, we must show that there is a $\delta > 0$ such that $\left| f\left(\dfrac{1}{t}\right) - L \right| < \epsilon$ whenever $0 < t < \delta$. We know there is a number b such that

$$|f(x) - L| < \epsilon \tag{2}$$

whenever $x > b$, and we may as well assume that b is positive since once a number b satisfies the condition, then any number greater than it certainly satisfies the condition. Suppose that $0 < t < \dfrac{1}{b}$, or in other words, $\dfrac{1}{t} > b$. Then we can replace x by $\dfrac{1}{t}$ in (2) to obtain $\left| f\left(\dfrac{1}{t}\right) - L \right| < \epsilon$ whenever $0 < t < \dfrac{1}{b}$. In other words, we can take $\dfrac{1}{b}$ as our δ.

The proof of the theorem for the case where L is replaced by ∞ or $-\infty$ is entirely similar, and is left as an exercise. ∎

As an example of the use of theorem 14.1, we shall prove the product rule for limits at ∞. Suppose that $\lim\limits_{x\to\infty} f(x) = L$ and $\lim\limits_{x\to\infty} g(x) = M$. (Letters such as L and M are to denote numbers, and are never to stand for the symbol ∞.) Then, using theorem 14.1 together with the ordinary product rule for limits, we obtain

$$\lim_{x\to\infty} f(x)g(x) = \lim_{t\to 0+} f\left(\frac{1}{t}\right) g\left(\frac{1}{t}\right) = LM.$$

The definition of $\lim\limits_{x\to-\infty} f(x)$ is obtained by replacing the condition $x > b$ by the condition $x < b$ in the definition of $\lim\limits_{x\to\infty} f(x)$. One can make the obvious changes in the proof of theorem 14.1 to see that $\lim\limits_{x\to-\infty} f(x) = L$ if and only if

$$\lim_{t\to 0-} f\left(\frac{1}{t}\right) = L.$$

We shall now investigate $\lim\limits_{x\to\infty} f(x)$ and $\lim\limits_{x\to-\infty} f(x)$ for any rational function f. Suppose that f is given by

$$f(x) = \frac{a_m x^m + a_{m-1} x^{m-1} + \cdots + a_1 x + a_0}{b_n x^n + b_{n-1} x^{n-1} + \cdots + b_1 x + b_0}$$

where $a_m \neq 0$ and $b_n \neq 0$. Then

$$f\left(\frac{1}{t}\right) = t^{n-m} \frac{(a_m + a_{m-1}t + \cdots + a_1 t^{m-1} + a_0 t^m)}{(b_n + b_{n-1}t + \cdots + b_1 t^{n-1} + b_0 t^n)}.$$

Case 1: If $n > m$, then $\lim\limits_{t\to 0} f\left(\frac{1}{t}\right) = 0$. Consequently,

$$\lim_{x\to\infty} f(x) = 0 = \lim_{x\to-\infty} f(x).$$

Case 2: If $n = m$, then $\lim\limits_{t\to 0} f\left(\frac{1}{t}\right) = \frac{a_m}{b_n}$. Hence,

$$\lim_{x\to\infty} f(x) = \frac{a_m}{b_n} = \lim_{x\to-\infty} f(x).$$

Case 3: If $n < m$ and $m - n$ is even, then by case 1 of the previous section (with $a = 0$) we find

$$\lim_{t\to 0} f\left(\frac{1}{t}\right) = \infty \quad \text{if } \frac{a_m}{b_n} > 0$$

$$= -\infty \quad \text{if } \frac{a_m}{b_n} < 0.$$

Consequently,

$$\lim_{x\to\infty} f(x) = \infty = \lim_{x\to-\infty} f(x) \quad \text{if } \frac{a_m}{b_n} > 0$$

and

$$\lim_{x\to\infty} f(x) = -\infty = \lim_{x\to-\infty} f(x) \quad \text{if } \frac{a_m}{b_n} < 0.$$

Case 4: If $n < m$ and $m - n$ is odd, then by case 2 of the previous section we find

$$\lim_{t \to 0+} f\left(\frac{1}{t}\right) = \infty \quad \text{and} \quad \lim_{t \to 0-} f\left(\frac{1}{t}\right) = -\infty \quad \text{if } \frac{a_m}{b_n} > 0.$$

Consequently,

$$\lim_{x \to \infty} f(x) = \infty \quad \text{and} \quad \lim_{x \to -\infty} f(x) = -\infty \quad \text{if } \frac{a_m}{b_n} > 0.$$

Similarly, we find

$$\lim_{x \to \infty} f(x) = -\infty \quad \text{and} \quad \lim_{x \to -\infty} f(x) = \infty \quad \text{if } \frac{a_m}{b_n} < 0.$$

Example 1:   Let

$$f(x) = \frac{5x^3 + 3x^2 - 1}{7x^3 + 2}.$$

Then by case 2 we see that $\lim\limits_{x \to \infty} f(x) = \frac{5}{7} = \lim\limits_{x \to -\infty} f(x)$.

Example 2:   Let

$$f(x) = \frac{4x^2 - 3x + 2}{-7x^5 - 3x^2 + x}.$$

By case 1 we have $\lim\limits_{x \to \infty} f(x) = 0 = \lim\limits_{x \to -\infty} f(x)$.

Example 3:   Let

$$f(x) = \frac{-7x^5 - 3x^2 + x}{4x^2 - 3x + 2}.$$

Here $\dfrac{a_m}{b_n} = \dfrac{-7}{4}$, and so by case 4 we have $\lim\limits_{x \to \infty} f(x) = -\infty$ and $\lim\limits_{x \to -\infty} f(x) = \infty$.

EXERCISES

1. Using theorem 14.1 prove the sum and quotient rules for limits at ∞.
2. (a) If $\lim\limits_{x \to a} f(x) = b$ but $f(x) \neq b$ in some neighborhood of a, and if

   $$\lim_{u \to b} g(u) = L,$$

   show that $\lim\limits_{x \to a} g(f(x)) = L$.
   (b) Rework part (a) with L replaced by ∞.
   (c) Rework part (a) with b replaced by $-\infty$ and a replaced by ∞.
   (d) Rework part (a) with b replaced by ∞ and L replaced by $-\infty$.
   (e) How many theorems of the above type are there?
3. Find $\lim\limits_{x \to \infty} f(x)$ and $\lim\limits_{x \to -\infty} f(x)$ when $f(x)$ is given by each of the following expressions.

   (a) $3x + 1$ \hspace{3cm} (b) $2x^2 - 4x$

(c) $1 - x - x^3$

(d) $2x^2 - x^4$

(e) $\dfrac{x - 1}{x + 1}$

(f) $\dfrac{-3x^7 + 4x^3 - 8x}{-2x^4 + 1}$

(g) $\dfrac{2x^5 + 4x^3 - x^2}{-3x^3 + 2}$

(h) $\dfrac{2x^2 - x^3}{1 + x^4}$

(i) $\dfrac{4x^4 - 7x^2}{8x^4 + 5x^3}$

(j) $\dfrac{x^7}{2x^3 - 1}$

(k) $\dfrac{5x^9 - 2x^2 + 1}{1 + 2x + x^5}$

(l) 3

4. Find each of the following limits.

(a) $\lim\limits_{x \to \infty} \dfrac{\cos x}{x^2}$

(b) $\lim\limits_{x \to -\infty} \tan\left(\dfrac{5x^3 - 2x + 1}{x^4 + x^2}\right)$

(c) $\lim\limits_{x \to \infty} \sin\left(\dfrac{\pi x^3}{2x^3 - 1}\right)$

(d) $\lim\limits_{x \to -\infty} \tan^2\left(\dfrac{3\pi x^2 - 1}{2x^2 + 1}\right)$

(e) $\lim\limits_{x \to \infty} \dfrac{1}{x} \sin x$

5. Prove theorem 14.1 for the cases where L is replaced by ∞ and $-\infty$.

6. Show that $\lim\limits_{x \to -\infty} f(x) = L$ if and only if $\lim\limits_{x \to \infty} f(-x) = L$.

7. Prove that $\lim\limits_{x \to -\infty} f(x) = L$ if and only if $\lim\limits_{t \to 0-} f\left(\dfrac{1}{t}\right) = L$.

8. Show that $\lim\limits_{x \to \infty} x \sin \dfrac{1}{x} = 1$ and $\lim\limits_{x \to \infty} x^2 \sin \dfrac{1}{x} = \infty$, and hence justify the drawings in figures 12.4 and 12.5 for large values of x.

LEAST UPPER BOUNDS

III

1. FINAL AXIOM FOR THE NUMBERS

We have come quite far on the basis only of twelve axioms stated in chapter I. However, as was pointed out in § 19 of that chapter, such a basic fact as the existence of a number whose square is 2 cannot be established without introducing another axiom. Perhaps even more surprising is the fact that at this point we cannot prove that there is no number greater than all the integers.

Before stating the final axiom we make some definitions. Let S be a set of numbers, and let b be any number (which may or may not be in S). We say that b is a *lower bound* for S, or that S is *bounded below* by b, if $b \leq x$ for all $x \in S$. If, furthermore, b is greater than all other lower bounds of S, then b is called the *greatest lower bound* of S. Equivalently, we can say that b is the greatest lower bound of S if $b \leq x$ for all $x \in S$, and if for any positive number δ there is at least one member x of S satisfying $x < b + \delta$. Of course if S has a least member, then that member will be the greatest lower bound. However, a set may have a greatest lower bound without having a least member.

Example 1: Let S be the closed interval $[2, 5]$. Then 2 or any number less than 2 is a lower bound for S, but 2 is the greatest. Notice that in this case the greatest lower bound is a member of S.

Example 2: Let S be the open interval $(3, \infty)$. Then 3 is a lower bound for S, and consequently any number <3 is also a lower bound. Furthermore, if b is any number >3, then by lemma 14.4 of chapter I there is a number x such that $3 < x < b$. This shows that b cannot be a lower bound for S, and so 3 is the greatest lower bound. Observe that in this case the greatest lower bound is not a member of S. In other words, S has no least member.

Example 3: Let S be the set of all numbers. Then S has no lower bound, since if b is any number, then $b - 1$ is a member of S which is less than b.

Example 4: Let S be the set of all *positive* numbers x such that $x^2 > 2$. Then, for example, $3/2 \in S$ since $(3/2)^2 = 9/4 > 2$, whereas $7/5 \notin S$ since

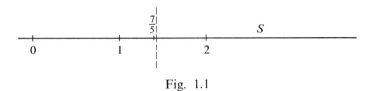

Fig. 1.1

$(7/5)^2 = 49/25 < 2$. A lower bound for S is 0. A greater one is $7/5$ (figure 1.1). Still a greater one is $141/100$. However, there is no way of showing the existence of a greatest lower bound. Of course, if we knew the existence of a number whose square is 2, then that number would be the greatest lower bound.

We now state the final axiom for the numbers.

Axiom XIII: Every nonempty set of positive numbers has a greatest lower bound.

Remark: If $\emptyset$ is the empty set and b is any number whatsoever, we can certainly say that $b \leq x$ for all x in $\emptyset$. In other words, every number is a lower bound for the empty set, and consequently there is no greatest lower bound. This is why we had to specify that the set be nonempty in axiom XIII.

Axiom XIII is stated only for sets of positive numbers. However, we can show immediately that it applies to any set of numbers, providing we assume that the set is bounded below to start with.

Theorem 1.1: *Let S be any nonempty set of numbers which has a lower bound. Then S has a greatest lower bound.*

Proof: Since S has a lower bound, there is a number b such that $b < x$ for all $x \in S$. Let S' be the set of all numbers of the form $x - b$ where $x \in S$. Then S' is a nonempty set of positive numbers, and so by axiom XIII, S' has a greatest lower bound. Now, the relation $m < x - b$ is equivalent to the relation $m + b < x$, and from this it follows easily (show it) that if m is the greatest lower bound of S', then $m + b$ is the greatest lower bound of S. ∎

We call a number B an *upper bound* for a set of numbers S if $x \leq B$ for all $x \in S$, in which case we say that S is *bounded above* by B. If, furthermore, B is less than all other upper bounds for S, then B is called the *least upper bound* of S. Now the relation $x \leq B$ is equivalent to the relation $-x \geq -B$. From this it follows that B is the least upper bound for S if and only if $-B$ is the greatest lower bound for the set S^* of numbers of the form $-x$ where $x \in S$. This enables us to give a quick proof of any theorem about least upper bounds once we know the truth of the corresponding theorem for greatest lower bounds. For example, corresponding to theorem 1.1 we have the following.

Theorem 1.2: *Let S be any nonempty set of numbers which has an upper bound. Then S has a least upper bound.*

Proof: If B is an upper bound for S, then $-B$ is a lower bound for S^*. Hence, by theorem 1.1, S^* has a greatest lower bound m, and so $-m$ is the least upper bound for S. ∎

We now prove that there is no number greater than all the integers.

Theorem 1.3: *Let B be any number.   Then there is an integer n such that $n > B$.*

Proof: Suppose that there is no such integer n.   Then B is an upper bound for the set of integers, and so by theorem 1.2 there is a least upper bound, say M. Now since $n + 1$ is an integer whenever n is an integer, we must have $n + 1 \leq M$ for all integers n.   Rewriting this, we see that $n \leq M - 1$ for all integers n.   In other words $M - 1$ is also an upper bound for the integers, contradicting the fact that M is the *least* upper bound.   This contradiction proves the theorem. ∎

Corollary 1.4: *If ϵ is any positive number, then there is a positive integer n such that $\dfrac{1}{n} < \epsilon$.*

Proof: If we take B to be $1/\epsilon$ in theorem 1.3, we obtain an integer n such that $n > 1/\epsilon$, and n must be positive since $1/\epsilon$ is positive.   Multiplying both sides of the inequality $n > 1/\epsilon$ by the positive number ϵ/n, we obtain $\epsilon > 1/n$, as required. ∎

Corollary 1.5: *If a is a positive number and b is any number, then there is an integer n such that $na > b$.*

Proof: By theorem 1.3 we can find an integer n such that $n > b/a$. Multiplying both sides by the positive number a gives $na > b$, as required. ∎

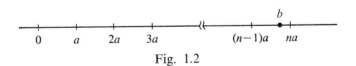

Fig. 1.2

Corollary 1.5 is sometimes called the *Archimedian property* of the numbers. Geometrically it says that if we keep laying off any length a, we can go as far as we wish (see figure 1.2).

In chapter I, lemma 14.4, we showed that between any two numbers there is another number.   We can now show that there is a *rational* number between any two numbers.

Theorem 1.6: *If $c < d$, then there is a rational number r such that $c < r < d$.*

Proof: Assume first that $0 \leq c$. By corollary 1.4, there is a positive integer n such that $1/n < d - c$. By corollary 1.5 there is a positive integer m such that $c < m/n$, and by theorem 14.6 of chapter I we may suppose that m is the least such positive integer. This means that $\dfrac{m-1}{n} \leq c$, and so combining this with the relation $1/n < d - c$ we obtain

$$c < \frac{m}{n} = \frac{m-1}{n} + \frac{1}{n} < c + (d - c) = d.$$

In other words, we can take m/n as the required rational number. This handles the case $0 \leq c$.

Now if $d \leq 0$, then $-d \geq 0$. Therefore, since the condition $c < r < d$ is equivalent to the condition $-d < -r < -c$, and since the negative of a rational number is also rational, this case follows from the first one. The only remaining possibility is where $c < 0 < d$, in which case we can take $r = 0$. ∎

In chapter II, § 1 we defined various special subsets of the numbers which we called intervals. These all had the property that they contain all the numbers between any two of their members. Conversely, we can now prove that any set of numbers with this latter property must be an interval.

Theorem 1.7: *Let S be a set of numbers with the property that if $s < x < t$ and s and t are members of S, then x is a member of S. If S has at least two members, then S is an interval.*

Proof: Suppose first that S is bounded both above and below. Let M and m be the least upper bound and the greatest lower bound respectively for S.

Since S has at least two members, $m \neq M$. Let x be any number satisfying $m < x < M$. Then, since m is the greatest lower bound of S, there must be at least one number $s \in S$ satisfying $m \leq s < x$. Similarly, there must be a number $t \in S$ satisfying $x < t \leq M$. But then the relations $s < x < t$ with $s \in S$ and $t \in S$ imply by hypothesis that $x \in S$. Hence, S contains all the numbers between m and M, and so S is one of the bounded intervals $[m, M]$, $(m, M]$, $[m, M)$, or (m, M) depending on which of the two numbers m and M it happens to contain.

Now suppose that S is bounded below but not above, and again let m be the greatest lower bound of S. Let x be any number satisfying $m < x$. Then again, we must have a number $s \in S$ such that $m \leq s < x$. Also, since S is not bounded above, there must be a number $t \in S$ such that $x < t$. Hence, again by hypothesis, we have $x \in S$, and so S contains all numbers greater than m. Therefore S must be one of the two infinite intervals $[m, \infty)$ or (m, ∞) depending on whether or not it contains m.

It is left to the reader to show that if S is bounded above but not below, then S is of the form $(-\infty, M]$ or $(-\infty, M)$, and that if S is bounded neither above nor below, then S is the set of all numbers. ∎

Let S be a set of numbers, and let c be some fixed number. Then we shall let cS denote the set of all numbers of the form cx such that $x \in S$.

Theorem 1.8: *If M is the least upper bound of S and $c > 0$, then cM is the least upper bound of cS. If m is the greatest lower bound of S and $c > 0$, then cm is the greatest lower bound of cS.*

Proof: Since $x \leq M$ for all x in S and $c > 0$, we have $cx \leq cM$ for all x in S. Therefore cM is an upper bound for cS. To show that it is the least upper bound, we must show that given $\epsilon > 0$ there is at least one x in S such that

$$cx > cM - \epsilon. \tag{1}$$

Now since M is the least upper bound of S, there is a number $x \in S$ such that

$$x > M - \frac{\epsilon}{c}. \tag{2}$$

Then (1) follows from multiplying (2) by the positive number c.

The proof for greatest lower bounds is left as an exercise. ∎

If a set of numbers S is bounded both above and below, then we shall say simply that S is *bounded*. In this case we have numbers b and B such that $b \leq x \leq B$, or in other words, $x \leq B$ and $-x \leq -b$ for all x in S. Therefore, if we let A denote the maximum of the numbers B and $-b$, then $|x| \leq A$ for all x in S. Conversely, if we are given a number A such that $|x| \leq A$ for all x in S, then S is bounded above by A and below by $-A$, and so S is bounded.

We remark that this section had nothing whatsoever to do with functions. It was concerned only with sets of numbers.

EXERCISES

1. Let m denote the greatest lower bound of the set S of positive numbers whose squares are greater than 2. Show that $m^2 = 2$. (Hint: If $m^2 > 2$, show that there is a positive ϵ such that $(m - \epsilon)^2 > 2$, contradicting the fact that m is a lower bound for S. If $m^2 < 2$, show that there is a positive ϵ such that $(m + \epsilon)^2 < 2$, contradicting the fact that m is the greatest lower bound for S.)

2. If $c < d$, show that there is an irrational number t such that $c < t < d$. (Hint: Apply theorem 1.6 to the inequality $c - \sqrt{2} < d - \sqrt{2}$.)

3. Let f be the function defined by

   $f(x) = 0$ for x rational,
   $f(x) = 1$ for x irrational.

   Show that f is discontinuous at all numbers x. (You must use theorem 1.6 and exercise 2.)

4. Prove theorem 1.8 for greatest lower bounds similarly to the way it was proved for least upper bounds. Then give another proof, replacing S by its set of negatives and using the result for least upper bounds.

5. In each of the following cases, state whether the set S is bounded, bounded above, or bounded below. Give the least upper and greatest lower bounds where possible, stating whether or not they are members of S.

(a) $S = (2, 5] \cup (-8, -3)$

(b) $S = (-\infty, -4]$

(c) $S = \left\{ -2, 7, \dfrac{-5}{2}, 6, 11, 0 \right\}$

(d) S is any finite set of numbers.

(e) S is any infinite set of positive integers.

(f) S is the set of all numbers x such that $x^2 > 2$. (This is not the same set as that of example 4.)

(g) S is the set of all numbers x such that $x^3 > 2$.

(h) S is the set of all numbers of the form $\dfrac{1}{n}$ where n is a positive integer. Justify your answer by quoting a theorem in the text.

6. A collection (finite or infinite) of open intervals is said to *cover* a set of numbers if each member of the set is a member of one of the open intervals. Show that if a collection of open intervals covers a closed interval $[a, b]$, then there are a finite number of the open intervals which also cover $[a, b]$. (Hint: Consider the set S of all numbers x in $[a, b]$ with the property that $[a, x]$ is covered by a finite number of the open intervals. Let c be the least upper bound of S. Use the fact that c contains members of S arbitrarily close to it and that c is in one of the open intervals to show that c is a member of S. Then use the fact that c is in one of the open intervals to show that if c were not b, then there would be members of S greater than c, contradicting the fact that c is an upper bound for S. This result is known as the *Heine-Borel theorem*.)

2. THE INTERMEDIATE VALUE THEOREM

Consider the function f defined on the interval $[1, 3]$ by the rules $f(x) = x - 1$ for $1 \le x \le 2$ and $f(x) = 2$ for $2 < x \le 3$. Its graph is shown in figure 2.1. Now although $f(1) = 0$ and $f(3) = 2$, it is not true that f takes on all the values between 0 and 2. (Consider, for example, $3/2$.) We are going to show that this phenomenon is not possible for a continuous function.

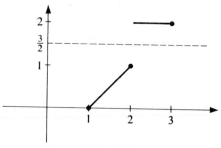

Fig. 2.1

Lemma 2.1:   *If f is continuous in the interval $[a, b]$ and if $f(a) < 0 < f(b)$, then there is a number $c \in [a, b]$ such that $f(c) = 0$.*

Proof: Consider the set S of numbers x in $[a, b]$ such that $f(x) \geq 0$. Then S is nonempty since, by hypothesis, b is a member. Also S is bounded below by a. Let c be the greatest lower bound of S. We shall show that $f(c) = 0$. (See figure 2.2.) If $f(c) > 0$, then since $f(a) < 0$ we cannot have

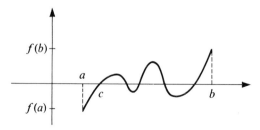

Fig. 2.2

$c = a$. Therefore, since f is continuous at c, it follows from lemma 5.1 of chapter II that there is a number $\delta > 0$ such that $f(x) > 0$ for all x satisfying $c - \delta < x < c$ (figure 2.3). But this would imply that there are members of S less than c, contradicting the fact that c is a lower bound for S. Hence we cannot have $f(c) > 0$.

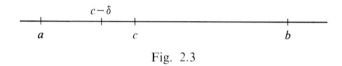

Fig. 2.3

Assume, on the other hand, that $f(c) < 0$. Then since $f(b) > 0$, we cannot have $c = b$. Therefore it follows again from lemma 5.1 of chapter II that there is a $\delta > 0$ such that $f(x) < 0$ for all x satisfying $c < x < c + \delta$ (figure 2.4). But this would mean that there are no members of S less than $c + \delta$, contradicting the fact that c is the greatest lower bound of S. Consequently we must have $f(c) = 0$. ∎

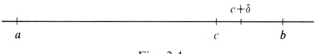

Fig. 2.4

Theorem 2.2 (The Intermediate Value Theorem): *If f is continuous in the interval $[a, b]$ and if t is between $f(a)$ and $f(b)$, then there is a number c in (a, b) such that $f(c) = t$.*

Proof: Suppose first that $f(a) < t < f(b)$. Then if we define $g(x) = f(x) - t$, we have $g(a) < 0 < g(b)$. Consequently, by lemma 2.1 there is a number c such that $g(c) = 0$, or in other words, such that $f(c) - t = 0$, which is what is required.

Now if $f(a) > t > f(b)$, or equivalently $-f(a) < -t < -f(b)$, then we can apply what we proved above to the function $-f$ to obtain a number c such that $-f(c) = -t$. In other words, $f(c) = t$, and so we have again proved our assertion. ∎

Example: Let $f(x) = x^2$, and take $a = 0$ and $b = 2$. Then $f(0) < 2 < f(2)$, and so since f is continuous, theorem 2.2 guarantees the existence of a number c such that $c^2 = 2$.

EXERCISES

1. Show that there is a number c such that $c^3 = 17$. More generally, show that if t is any positive number and n is any positive integer, then there is a number c such that $c^n = t$. In the case where n is odd, show that this is also true for negative numbers t.

2. Show that any polynomial of odd degree has a root, and explain why your proof would not work for a polynomial of even degree. Give an example of a polynomial of even degree which has a root, and an example of one which doesn't have a root.

3. Explain why theorem 2.2 guarantees the existence of a number x such that $\sin x = \frac{1}{4}$, but not of one such that $\sin x = 4$.

4. If t is any number, show that there are an infinite number of x's such that $\tan x = t$.

3. INVERSE FUNCTIONS

Recall that the inverse of a one to one correspondence f is the function g which assigns to each y in the image of f that number x such that $f(x) = y$ (see chapter I, § 5). Thus we have $g(f(x)) = x$ for all x in the domain of f and $f(g(y)) = y$ for all y in the image of f. Geometrically, if f is a one to one correspondence from one set of numbers to another, then the point (x, y) will be on the graph of f if and only if the point (y, x) lies on the graph of g. Now the point (y, x) is obtained from the point (x, y) by placing a mirror along the graph of the

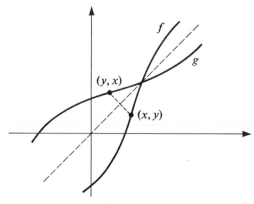

Fig. 3.1

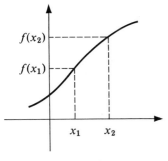

Fig. 3.2

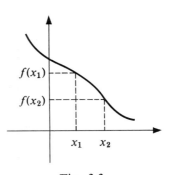

Fig. 3.3

identity function and taking the reflection. Hence, the relation which the graph of g bears to the graph of f is as shown in figure 3.1.

A special case of a 1–1 correspondence is what is known as an increasing function. We say that f is *increasing* if whenever x_1 and x_2 are in the domain of f and $x_1 < x_2$, we have $f(x_1) < f(x_2)$ (figure 3.2). Likewise, we say that f is *decreasing* if whenever $x_1 < x_2$ we have $f(x_1) > f(x_2)$ (figure 3.3). Since the last condition is equivalent to the condition $-f(x_1) < -f(x_2)$, we see that f is decreasing if and only if $-f$ is increasing.

Theorem 3.1: *Let f be an increasing (or decreasing) function whose domain is some interval. Then the inverse function g is also increasing (or decreasing) and is, furthermore, continuous. If also f is continuous, then the domain of g is an interval.*

Proof: Suppose that f is increasing. To show that g is increasing, let y_1 and y_2 be in the domain of g such that $y_1 < y_2$. If $g(y)_1 \geq g(y_2)$, then since f is increasing, we must have $f(g(y_1)) \geq f(g(y))$. But this last is the same as $y_1 \geq y_2$, which is a contradiction. Hence $g(y_1) < g(y_2)$, and so g is increasing.

To see that g is continuous, let c be in the domain of g, and let $g(c) = a$, or in other words, $f(a) = c$. We suppose first that a is not an endpoint of the domain of f. Given $\epsilon > 0$, we must show there is a $\delta > 0$ such that $|g(y) - g(c)| < \epsilon$ whenever $|y - c| < \delta$. Since a is not an endpoint of the domain of f, we may assume that ϵ is small enough so that $a + \epsilon$ and $a - \epsilon$ are both in the domain of f. Since f is increasing we can write $f(a + \epsilon) = c + \delta_1$ for some positive number δ_1, so that $g(c + \delta_1) = a + \epsilon$. Similarly $g(c - \delta_2) = a - \epsilon$ for some positive number δ_2 (figure 3.4). If we take δ to be the smaller of the two numbers δ_1 and δ_2, then, using the fact that g is increasing we see that $a - \epsilon < g(y) < a + \epsilon$ whenever $c - \delta < y < c + \delta$ and y is in the domain of g, which is what is required. The case where a is an endpoint of the domain of f is handled by restricting the above argument to one side of a (so that only one of the numbers δ_1 and δ_2 will be involved).

Finally, if f is continuous, then by the intermediate value theorem, theorem 2.2, it follows that the image of f contains any number between any

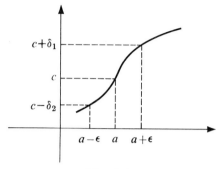

Fig. 3.4

two of its members. In other words, by theorem 1.7, the image of f is an interval. Since the domain of g is the same as the image of f, this shows that the domain of g is an interval.

The proof for f decreasing is left as an exercise. ∎

The following theorem shows how to compute the derivative of the inverse function in terms of the derivative of the original function.

Theorem 3.2: *Let f be an increasing (or decreasing) continuous function on some interval, and let a be a number such that f is differentiable at a and $f'(a) \neq 0$. If g is the inverse function and $g(c) = a$ (so that $c = f(a)$), then g is differentiable at c, and we have*

$$g'(c) = \frac{1}{f'(a)} .$$

Proof: By definition of derivative we have

$$g'(c) = \lim_{h \to 0} \frac{g(c + h) - g(c)}{h} ,$$

provided the limit exists. Define

$$k(h) = g(c + h) - g(c).$$

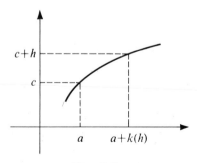

Fig. 3.5

Then since g is increasing (or decreasing) we have $k(h) \neq 0$ for $h \neq 0$, and since g is continuous we have $\lim_{h \to 0} k(h) = 0$. Observe that

$$a + k(h) = g(c) + k(h) = g(c + h),$$

so that $f(a + k(h)) = c + h$. (See figure 3.5.) This gives us

$$f(a + k(h)) - f(a) = (c + h) - c = h.$$

Consequently, we have

$$\frac{g(c + h) - g(c)}{h} = \frac{k(h)}{f(a + k(h)) - f(a)} = \frac{1}{(f(a + k(h)) - f(a))/k(h)},$$

and so, using the quotient rule for limits and lemma 10.1 of chapter II, this gives us $g'(c) = \dfrac{1}{f'(a)}$. ∎

We shall encounter important examples of inverse functions in the following two sections.

EXERCISES

1. Carry out the proof of theorem 3.1 for f a decreasing function.

2. Let f be a decreasing function, so that $-f$ is an increasing function. Let g be the inverse function of f, and let $\bar{g}$ be the inverse function of $-f$. How does the domain of $\bar{g}$ compare with the domain of g? How does the image of $\bar{g}$ compare with the image of g? Illustrate with a diagram. Show that $g(x) = \bar{g}(-x)$ for all x in the domain of g (that is, g is the composition of $\bar{g}$ with the function which takes negatives), and then show how theorem 3.1 for decreasing functions follows from the result for increasing functions.

3. If f is an increasing (or decreasing) odd function, show that its inverse function is odd. If f is even, can it have an inverse function?

4. RADICALS

Let f be the function defined by $f(x) = x^n$ for all numbers x, where n is an odd positive integer. If $n > 1$, then the graph of f is something like that in figure 4.1. If $n = 1$, then f is just the identity function, and so there is no bend in the graph. In any case f is an increasing function, and consequently there is an inverse function g. Since $\lim_{x \to \infty} f(x) = \infty$ and $\lim_{x \to -\infty} f(x) = -\infty$, it follows that the image of f, or in other words the domain of g, is all of the numbers. Likewise the image of g, being the domain of f, is all of the numbers. The graph of g is shown in figure 4.2.

If y is any number, we shall denote $g(y)$ in this case by $\sqrt[n]{y}$ and we shall call $\sqrt[n]{y}$ the nth *root* of y. Thus, when n is odd, $\sqrt[n]{y}$ denotes the unique number x such that $x^n = y$. Since $f'(x) = nx^{n-1}$, we have, using theorem 3.2,

$$g'(y) = \frac{1}{f'(g(y))} = \frac{1}{n(\sqrt[n]{y})^{n-1}} \tag{1}$$

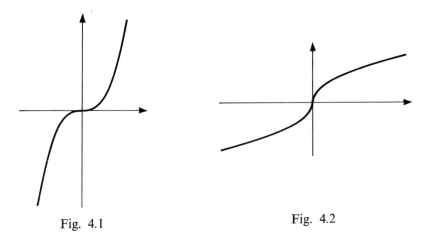

Fig. 4.1   Fig. 4.2

for all $y \neq 0$. At 0, g has no derivative. Nevertheless, theorem 3.1 guarantees that g is continuous at 0.

If we take n to be an even positive integer in the above, then the function f takes on equal values at different x's, and so there is no inverse function (figure 4.3). However, if we define $f(x) = x^n$ *for* $x \geq 0$ *only*, then f is an increasing function (figure 4.4). The graph of the inverse function g is therefore as given in figure 4.5.

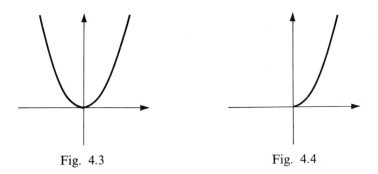

Fig. 4.3   Fig. 4.4

Again we shall denote $g(y)$ by $\sqrt[n]{y}$. Thus when n is even, $\sqrt[n]{y}$ denotes the unique *positive* number x such that $x^n = y$. The other number whose nth power is y is $-\sqrt[n]{y}$. Since the image of f is not all of the numbers, but only the nonnegative numbers, $\sqrt[n]{y}$ makes sense only for y nonnegative. The derivative of g is again given by the formula (1) for all $y > 0$.

In particular if $n = 2$, then we write $\sqrt{y}$ in place of $\sqrt[2]{y}$, and we call $\sqrt{y}$ the *square root* of y. Thus $\sqrt{y}$ always denotes a nonnegative number, and makes sense only for y nonnegative. The derivative formula (1) in the special case of $n = 2$ becomes

$$g'(y) = \frac{1}{2\sqrt{y}}$$

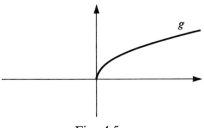

Fig. 4.5

for $y \neq 0$. Using the chain rule we can immediately differentiate any other function given in terms of square roots (or nth roots). For example, if $f(x) = \sqrt{x^2 + 3x}$ for $x \notin (-3, 0)$ (what is wrong with these x's?) then we have

$$f'(x) = \frac{1}{2\sqrt{x^2 + 3x}}(2x + 3).$$

Now that we have square roots at our disposal, we can investigate the roots of a quadratic polynomial. By definition, this is a polynomial of the form $ax^2 + bx + c$ where $a \neq 0$. Suppose first that there is a root r. Then we have

$$ar^2 + br + c = 0,$$

and so multiplying both sides by $4a$, we obtain

$$4a^2r^2 + 4abr + 4ac = 0.$$

After b^2 has been added to both sides, this last can be rewritten

$$(2ar + b)^2 = b^2 - 4ac. \tag{2}$$

Case 1: $b^2 - 4ac < 0$. Then, since the left side of (4) is a square, we see that there cannot be any roots.

Case 2: $b^2 - 4ac \geq 0$. Then from (2) we have either $2ar + b = \sqrt{b^2 - 4ac}$ or $2ar + b = -\sqrt{b^2 - 4ac}$. In other words, we see that the only numbers which can qualify as roots are

$$r_1 = \frac{-b + \sqrt{b^2 - 4ac}}{2a} \quad \text{and} \quad r_2 = \frac{-b - \sqrt{b^2 - 4ac}}{2a}. \tag{3}$$

On the other hand, it is straightforward to check that

$$a(x - r_1)(x - r_2) = ax^2 + bx + c,$$

and so we see that r_1 and r_2 are indeed roots of the polynomial. They are distinct if $b^2 - 4ac > 0$ and are the same if $b^2 - 4ac = 0$.

We are now going to derive a fact about square roots which is useful in many parts of mathematics. First let x and y be any two numbers. Since the square of any number is nonnegative, we have $0 \le (x - y)^2$. Expanding the right side and dividing by 2, we see that this can be written

$$xy \le \tfrac{1}{2}(x^2 + y^2). \tag{4}$$

Now consider any two sequences of n numbers $a_1, a_2, \ldots, a_n$ and $b_1, b_2, \ldots, b_n$. For any ordered pair of integers i and j between 1 and n, replace x by $a_i b_j$ and y by $a_j b_i$ in (4). This gives

$$a_i b_i a_j b_j \le \tfrac{1}{2}(a_i^2 b_j^2 + a_j^2 b_i^2). \tag{5}$$

Now add up the inequalities (5) for every ordered pair i, j. On the right side every term $a_i^2 b_j^2$ appears twice, each time with a coefficient of $1/2$. Thus we obtain

$$(a_1 b_1 a_1 b_1 + a_1 b_1 a_2 b_2 + a_2 b_2 a_1 b_1 + \cdots + a_n b_n a_n b_n)$$
$$\le (a_1^2 b_1^2 + a_1^2 b_2^2 + a_2^2 b_1^2 + \cdots + a_n^2 b_n^2).$$

But this is the same as

$$\left(\sum_{i=1}^{n} a_i b_i \right)^2 \le \left(\sum_{i=1}^{n} a_i^2 \right) \left(\sum_{i=1}^{n} b_i^2 \right).$$

Taking square roots on both sides preserves the inequality since the square root function is increasing. Therefore we have

$$\sum_{i=1}^{n} a_i b_i \le \sqrt{\sum_{i=1}^{n} a_i^2} \; \sqrt{\sum_{i=1}^{n} b_i^2}.$$

This is known as *Schwarz's inequality*. Multiplying by 2 and adding

$$\sum_{i=1}^{n} a_i^2 + \sum_{i=1}^{n} b_i^2$$

to both sides yields

$$\sum_{i=1}^{n} (a_i + b_i)^2 \le \left(\sqrt{\sum_{i=1}^{n} a_i^2} + \sqrt{\sum_{i=1}^{n} b_i^2} \right)^2.$$

Taking square roots of both sides then gives us

$$\sqrt{\sum_{i=1}^{n} (a_i + b_i)^2} \le \sqrt{\sum_{i=1}^{n} a_i^2} + \sqrt{\sum_{i=1}^{n} b_i^2}. \tag{6}$$

The inequality (6) is known as the "triangle inequality." To see why it is so called, consider any three sequences of n numbers $x_1, \ldots, x_n$, $y_1, \ldots, y_n$, and $z_1, \ldots z_n$. Put $a_i = x_i - y_i$, and $b_i = y_i - z_i$ in (6). Then (6) becomes

$$\sqrt{\sum_{i=1}^{n} (x_i - z_i)^2} \le \sqrt{\sum_{i=1}^{n} (x_i - y_i)^2} + \sqrt{\sum_{i=1}^{n} (y_i - z_i)^2}. \tag{7}$$

In particular suppose $n = 2$, and let P, Q, and R be the points in the plane with coordinates (x_1, x_2), (y_1, y_2), and (z_1, z_2) respectively. Then (7) expresses the geometrically obvious fact that the distance from P to R is less than or

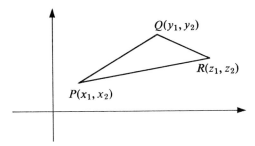

Fig. 4.6

equal to the distance from P to Q plus the distance from Q to R. (See figure 4.6. When would we have equality?)

Consider the inequality (6) in the special case where $n = 1$. This gives

$$\sqrt{(a_1 + b_1)^2} \leq \sqrt{a_1^2} + \sqrt{b_1^2},$$

or in other words,

$$|a_1 + b_1| \leq |a_1| + |b_1|.$$

This is just the "triangle inequality" of chapter I, theorem 12.3.

Finally, take $z_i = 0$ for all i in (7). Then we obtain

$$\sqrt{\sum_{i=1}^{n} x_i^2} - \sqrt{\sum_{i=1}^{n} y_i^2} \leq \sqrt{\sum_{i=1}^{n} (x_i - y_i)^2}.$$

Interchanging x_i and y_i does not change the right side since

$$(x_i - y_i)^2 = (y_i - x_i)^2.$$

Therefore we have

$$\left| \sqrt{\sum_{i=1}^{n} x_i^2} - \sqrt{\sum_{i=1}^{n} y_i^2} \right| \leq \sqrt{\sum_{i=1}^{n} (x_i - y_i)^2}, \tag{8}$$

valid for any numbers $x_1, \ldots, x_n$ and $y_1, \ldots, y_n$.

EXERCISES

1. (a) Show that $\sqrt[1]{x} = x$ for all numbers x. Does the function f defined for all x by $f(x) = x^0$ have an inverse function?

   (b) If n is even, show that $\sqrt[n]{(x^n)} = |x|$ for all numbers x.

   (c) If n is odd, show that $\sqrt[n]{-x} = -\sqrt[n]{x}$ for all numbers x.

   (d) If a and b are any numbers (nonnegative numbers in the case where n is even), show that

   $$\sqrt[n]{a}\sqrt[n]{b} = \sqrt[n]{ab}.$$

2. Using the relations

   $$\cos 2a = 2 \cos^2 a - 1$$
   $$\cos 3a = 4 \cos^3 a - 3 \cos a$$

which were derived in the exercises of chapter I, § 23, establish the following:

$$\sin \frac{\pi}{4} = \frac{1}{\sqrt{2}}, \quad \cos \frac{\pi}{4} = \frac{1}{\sqrt{2}}$$

$$\sin \frac{\pi}{3} = \frac{\sqrt{3}}{2}, \quad \cos \frac{\pi}{3} = \frac{1}{2}$$

$$\sin \frac{\pi}{6} = \frac{1}{2}, \quad \cos \frac{\pi}{6} = \frac{\sqrt{3}}{2}.$$

3. State the values of x for which the following expressions make sense, and find the derivative.

(a) $\sqrt{2 - x - x^2}$

(b) $\sqrt[3]{x^2 - 1}$

(c) $\dfrac{1 + \sqrt{x}}{1 - \sqrt{x}}$

(d) $\dfrac{\sqrt{x - 3}}{\sqrt{2 - x}}$

(e) $\sqrt[4]{1 - \tan x}$

(f) $\sin \sqrt{1 - x^2}$

(g) $\sqrt{x^2 - 2x + 2}$

(h) $(\sqrt{x})^2$

(i) $\sqrt{2 \cos x - 1}$

(j) $\sqrt[4]{9 - \sqrt{x}}$

(k) $\sqrt[5]{\tan x + \sec x}$

(l) $\sqrt{\sin^2 x + \cos^2 x}$

4. Show that if there is a nonnegative number t such that $b_i = ta_i$ for $i = 1, 2, \ldots, n$, then Schwarz's inequality is actually an equality. Conversely, by examining the steps used to derive the inequality, show that in the case where it is an equality and $a_j \neq 0$ for some j, we must have $b_i = ta_i$ for all i where $t = b_j/a_j$.

5. If $a_1, a_2, \ldots, a_n$ are nonnegative numbers, then their *arithmetic mean* is the number

$$A = \frac{a_1 + a_2 + \cdots + a_n}{n}$$

and their *geometric mean* is the number

$$G = \sqrt[n]{a_1 a_2 \cdots a_n}.$$

Show that $A \geq G$, with equality holding if and only if $a_1 = a_2 = \cdots = a_n$. (Hint: If $a_1 < A < a_n$, replace a_1 by A and a_n by $a_1 + a_n - A$. Show that this increases the geometric mean, whereas the arithmetic mean remains the same.)

5. INVERSE TRIGONOMETRIC FUNCTIONS

The function sin has equal values at different points, and so it has no inverse function. However, if we let f be the restriction of sin to the interval $\left[\dfrac{-\pi}{2}, \dfrac{\pi}{2} \right]$, then f is an increasing function whose graph is shown in figure 5.1. Therefore the inverse function, which we denote by arcsin, has a graph which looks like that in figure 5.2.

The domain of arcsin, being the image of f, is the interval $[-1, 1]$, and the image of arcsin, being the domain of f, is $[-\pi/2, \pi/2]$. Thus for

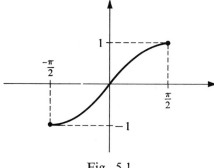

Fig. 5.1

$-1 \le y \le 1$, arcsin y denotes the unique number x *in the interval* $[-\pi/2, \pi/2]$ such that sin $x = y$. To find the derivative of arcsin at a number y, let $x =$ arcsin y, or in other words, sin $x = y$. For x in $[-\pi/2, \pi/2]$ we have cos $x \ge 0$, and consequently cos $x = \sqrt{1 - \sin^2 x}$ for such x. Therefore, using theorem 3.2 we obtain

$$\text{arcsin}'\, y = \frac{1}{\sin' x} = \frac{1}{\cos x} = \frac{1}{\sqrt{1 - \sin^2 x}} = \frac{1}{\sqrt{1 - y^2}} \tag{1}$$

for $y \ne 1$ or -1. At 1 or -1 arcsin does not have a derivative. Nevertheless, by theorem 3.1 it is continuous at those points.

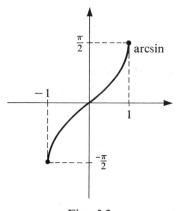

Fig. 5.2

Example 1: Let $f(x) = \arcsin \sqrt{x - 1}$. This makes sense only for $1 \le x \le 2$. Using formula (1) and the chain rule, we obtain

$$f'(x) = \frac{1}{\sqrt{1 - (x - 1)}} \cdot \frac{1}{2\sqrt{x - 1}} = \frac{1}{2\sqrt{(2 - x)(x - 1)}}$$

for $1 < x < 2$.

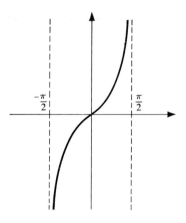

Fig. 5.3

Now let f be the restriction of tan to the open interval $(-\pi/2, \pi/2)$. Then f is an increasing function whose graph is shown in figure 5.3. If we denote the inverse function by arctan, then the graph of arctan is as given in figure 5.4.

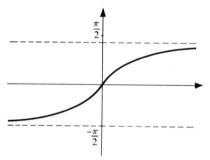

Fig. 5.4

The domain of arctan is the set of all numbers, and its image is $(-\pi/2, \pi/2)$. Thus arctan y denotes the unique number x in the interval $(-\pi/2, \pi/2)$ such that $\tan x = y$. Now $\tan'(x) = 1 + \tan^2 x$. Hence, the derivative of arctan is given by

$$\arctan'(y) = \frac{1}{\tan'(x)} = \frac{1}{1 + \tan^2 x} = \frac{1}{1 + y^2} \tag{2}$$

for all numbers y.

Example 2: Take $f(x) = \arctan \sqrt{3x^2 - 1}$. This makes sense for $|x| \geq 1/\sqrt{3}$. Formula (2) together with two applications of the chain rule gives us

$$f'(x) = \frac{1}{1 + (3x^2 - 1)} \cdot \frac{1}{2\sqrt{3x^2 - 1}} \cdot 6x$$

$$= \frac{1}{x\sqrt{3x^2 - 1}}$$

for $|x| > 1/\sqrt{3}$.

EXERCISES

1. Restrict cos to the interval $[0, \pi]$, and define a function arccos. Give its domain and image and draw its graph. Show that $\text{arccos}'(y) = \dfrac{-1}{\sqrt{1 - y^2}}$ for $-1 < y < 1$.

2. Restrict cot to $(0, \pi)$, and define a function arccot. Give its domain and image and draw its graph. Show that $\text{arccot}'(y) = \dfrac{-1}{1 + y^2}$.

3. Restrict sec to the interval $[0, \pi]$, excluding $\pi/2$, and define a function arcsec. Give its domain and image and draw its graph. Show that $\text{arcsec}'(y) = y\sqrt{1 - y^2}$.

4. Restrict csc to the interval $\left[\dfrac{-\pi}{2}, \dfrac{\pi}{2}\right]$, excluding 0, and define a function arccsc. Give its domain and image, draw its graph, and find its derivative.

5. Let $f(x) = \sin x$ for $3\pi/2 \le x \le 5\pi/2$. Let g be the inverse function of f. Show that $g = 2\pi + \arcsin$.

6. Find each of the following (§ 4, exercise 2 will be helpful).

   (a) arcsin 1   (b) arcsin $(\sqrt{3}/2)$ (c) arcsin $1/\sqrt{2}$

   (d) arcsin $(1/2)$ (e) arcsin 0   (f) arcsin $(-\sqrt{3}/2)$

   (g) arctan $\sqrt{3}$ (h) arctan 1   (i) arctan $(1/\sqrt{3})$

   (j) arctan 0   (k) arctan (-1)

7. (a) If $a = \arctan(1/2)$ and $b = \arctan(1/3)$, show that $a + b < \pi/2$. Then use the sum rule for tan,

   $$\tan(a + b) = \frac{\tan a + \tan b}{1 - \tan a \tan b},$$

   to show that $\pi/4 = \arctan(1/2) + \arctan(1/3)$.

   (b) If $a = \arctan(1/5)$, use the sum rule for tan twice to find tan 4a. Then use the rule once more to show that

   $$\pi/4 = 4 \arctan(1/5) - \arctan(1/239).$$

8. State the x's for which each of the following expressions makes sense, and find the derivative.

   (a) arcsin $(x + 2)$ (b) arctan $\sqrt{3x}$

   (c) arcsin $(x^2 + 1)$ (d) arcsin $(x^2 - x - 5)$

   (e) $\sqrt{1 - \arcsin x}$ (f) arctan $\left(\dfrac{x + 1}{x - 1}\right)$

9. Let $f(x) = \arcsin(\sin x)$ for all x. Draw the graph of f.

10. Find the second derivatives of arcsin and arctan.

6. UNIFORM CONTINUITY

The definition of continuity of a function f requires that for each number a in the domain of f and each positive number ϵ, there exist a positive number δ such that $|f(x) - f(a)| < \epsilon$ whenever $|x - a| < \delta$. The number δ will in general depend not only on ϵ, but also on a. This is illustrated by the following example.

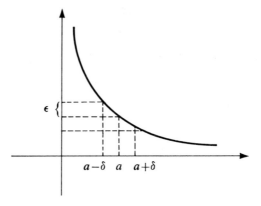

Fig. 6.1

Example 1:   Let f be the function whose domain is the set of all positive numbers, and which is defined by $f(x) = 1/x$ for all those numbers. Given any a in the domain of f and any positive ϵ, we can find a positive δ such that $|f(x) - f(a)| < \epsilon$ whenever $|x - a| < \delta$.   This is illustrated in figure 6.1, where we have located the biggest δ corresponding to the given ϵ.

We can actually calculate the biggest δ in this case by writing

$$\frac{1}{a - \delta} - \frac{1}{a} = \epsilon,$$

which gives

$$\delta = \frac{\epsilon a^2}{1 + \epsilon a}.$$ (1)

Now, using the *same* ϵ but taking a smaller a, we find that the biggest δ in this case is smaller than the previous one (figure 6.2). In fact we can see from the expression (1) that the biggest δ corresponding to a given ϵ approaches 0 as a approaches 0, and so there is no positive δ which works simultaneously (or *uniformly*, as we say) for all a's in the domain of f.

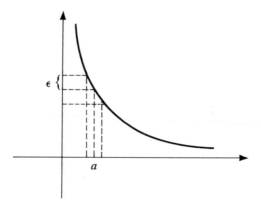

Fig. 6.2

Example 2: Let $f(x) = 1/x$ for all $x \geq 1/2$. This is not the same function as that of example 1 since its domain is different. Its graph is shown in figure 6.3.

For any a and any x in the domain of f we have

$$|f(x) - f(a)| = \left| \frac{1}{x} - \frac{1}{a} \right| = \left| \frac{x-a}{xa} \right|$$

$$\leq \frac{|x-a|}{(1/2)(1/2)} = 4|x-a|.$$

Thus we see that given $\epsilon > 0$, if we take $\delta = \epsilon/4$, then $|f(x) - f(a)| < \epsilon$ whenever $|x - a| < \delta$, and this is true for *all* a in the domain of f.

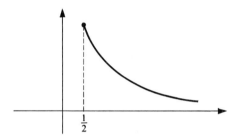

$\frac{1}{2}$

Fig. 6.3

These two examples lead us to the following definition. We say that a function f is *uniformly continuous* if, given any $\epsilon > 0$, there exists a $\delta > 0$ such that $|f(x_1) - f(x_2)| < \epsilon$ whenever x_1 and x_2 are in the domain of f and satisfy $|x_1 - x_2| < \delta$.

The definition immediately implies that a uniformly continuous function is continuous. On the other hand, example 1 shows that a function can be continuous without being uniformly continuous. Nevertheless, we have the following important theorem.

Theorem 6.1: *Let f be a continuous function whose domain is a finite closed interval $[a, b]$. Then f is uniformly continuous.*

Proof: For a *fixed* number $\epsilon > 0$, let S be the set of all those numbers s in $[a, b]$ which have the following property: there exists a positive δ such that whenever x_1 and x_2 are in $[a, s]$ and satisfy $|x_1 - x_2| < \delta$ we have $|f(x_1) - f(x_2)| < \epsilon$. If we can show that $b \in S$, and if our argument does not depend on which fixed $\epsilon > 0$ we work with, then the theorem will be proved.

Since S is not empty (a is certainly a member) and is bounded above (b is an upper bound), we know that S has a least upper bound, say c. Since f is continuous at c, we can find $\delta_1 > 0$ such that $|f(x) - f(c)| < \epsilon/2$ whenever x is simultaneously in $(c - \delta_1, c + \delta_1)$ and $[a, b]$. (In figure 6.4, $c - \delta_1$ is to the right of a, but it could equally well be to the left. Likewise $c + \delta_1$ could equally well be to the right of b. In fact, we are going to show that $c = b$, so that $c + \delta_1$ will have to be to the right of b.) Since c is the least upper bound of S, there is a member s of S such that $c - \delta_1/2 < s \leq c$.

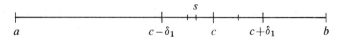

Fig. 6.4

Now in order for s to be a member of S, there must be a number $\delta_2 > 0$ such that $|f(x_1) - f(x_2)| < \epsilon$ whenever x_1 and x_2 are in $[a, s]$ and satisfy $|x_1 - x_2| < \delta_2$. Let δ be the smaller of the two numbers $\delta_1/2$ and δ_2. Let x_1 and x_2 be any two numbers which are simultaneously in $[a, c + \delta_1/2]$ and $[a, b]$ and which satisfy $|x_1 - x_2| < \delta$. If x_1 and x_2 are both $\leq s$, then we know from above that $|f(x_1) - f(x_2)| < \epsilon$. On the other hand, if they are not both $\leq s$, then, since they differ in absolute value by less than $\delta_1/2$, they must both be in $(c - \delta_1, c + \delta_1)$. (See figure 6.4.) Consequently we have in this case

$$|f(x_1) - f(x_2)| \leq |f(x_1) - f(c)| + |f(c) - f(x_2)|$$
$$< \epsilon/2 + \epsilon/2 = \epsilon.$$

Thus in any case we have $|f(x_1) - f(x_2)| < \epsilon$. From this we conclude not only that $c \in S$, but also if $c < b$ (as in figure 6.4), then there are members of S greater than c, contradicting the fact that c is an upper bound for S. Hence $c = b$, and so b is a member of S. ∎

EXERCISES

1. (a) If f is a uniformly continuous function and if $\overline{f}$ is the restriction of f to some subset of its domain, is $\overline{f}$ uniformly continuous?

    (b) Combine theorem 6.1 with your answer to part (a) (providing it is correct) to show that if f is the function defined by $f(x) = \dfrac{x^2 - 1}{x^2 + 1}$ for all x in the open interval $(1, 5)$, then f is uniformly continuous.

2. (a) Let $f(x) = \sin(1/x)$ for all x in the interval $(0, 1]$. Is f continuous? Is it uniformly continuous? Why does this function not contradict theorem 6.1?

    (b) Let f be the function whose domain is $[0, 1]$, such that $f(x) = \sin(1/x)$ for $x \neq 0$ and such that $f(0) = 0$. Is f uniformly continuous? Why does this not contradict theorem 6.1?

3. Let $f(x) = ax + b$ for all numbers x. Show that f is uniformly continuous.

4. Show that if c is any positive number and $f(x) = 1/x$ for all $x \geq c$, then f is uniformly continuous.

5. Let $f(x) = x^n$ for $x \in [0, 10]$, where n is an integer ≥ 2. Given $\epsilon > 0$, find a number δ such that $|f(x_1) - f(x_2)| < \epsilon$ whenever $|x_1 - x_2| < \delta$ and x_1, x_2 are in the domain of f. (Hint: Use lemma 22.1 of chapter I to find an expression for $|f(x_1) - f(x_2)|$.)

    Show, on the other hand, that if $f(x) = x^n$ for *all* x, then f is not uniformly continuous.

6. Show that $\sin$ is uniformly continuous. What guarantees that $\arcsin$ is uniformly continuous?

7. Prove that

$$\tan x_1 - \tan x_2 = \frac{\sin (x_1 - x_2)}{\cos x_1 \cos x_2},$$

and hence show that tan is not uniformly continuous. From looking at the graph, do you suppose that arctan is uniformly continuous?

7. BOUNDED FUNCTIONS

A function f is said to be *bounded* if its image is a bounded set of numbers. That is, f is bounded if there is a number B such that $|f(x)| \le B$ for all x in the domain of f. For example, sin is a bounded function since $|\sin x| \le 1$ for all x. On the other hand, if $f(x) = x^2$ for all x, then f is unbounded.

Theorem 7.1: *Let f be a continuous function whose domain is a finite closed interval $[a, b]$. Then f is bounded.*

Proof: By theorem 6.1, f is uniformly continuous, and so taking $\epsilon = 1$ in the definition of uniform continuity, we know there is a number $\delta > 0$ such that $|f(x_1) - f(x_2)| < 1$ whenever $|x_1 - x_2| < \delta$. By corollary 1.5 there is an integer n such that $n\delta > b - a$, or in other words, $(b - a)/n < \delta$. For each integer i such that $0 \le i \le n$, let us define

$$x_i = a + i(b - a)/n.$$

Thus the points $x_0, \ldots, x_n$ divide the interval $[a, b]$ into n equal parts (figure 7.1).

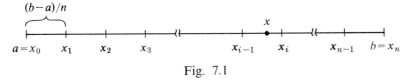

Fig. 7.1

Now if $x \in [a, b]$, let i be the first integer such that $x \le x_i$. Then we have $x_{i-1} < x \le x_i$. We write

$$f(x) = (f(x) - f(x_{i-1})) + (f(x_{i-1}) - f(x_{i-2})) + \cdots$$
$$+ (f(x_1) - f(x_0)) + f(x_0).$$

On the right side each term except the last is a difference of values of f taken at points which differ by less than δ. Hence, each of these terms has absolute value less than 1. Since the absolute value of a sum is less than or equal to the sum of the absolute values, this gives us

$$|f(x)| \le 1 + 1 + \cdots + 1 + 1 + |f(x_0)| = i + |f(x_0)|.$$

Since $i \le n$, we therefore have

$$|f(x)| \le n + |f(a)|$$

for all x in $[a, b]$. In other words, f is bounded by the number $n + |f(a)|$. ∎

If a function f is bounded, then the set of its values (that is, its image) will have a least upper bound and a greatest lower bound. However, it will not always be the case that the function attains these numbers; that is, it will not always be the case that the least upper bound or greatest lower bound is a value of the function.

Example 1: The function sin has 1 as its least upper bound and -1 as its greatest lower bound. In this case both the least upper bound and the greatest lower bound are values of the function, since $\sin \pi/2 = 1$ and $\sin 3\pi/2 = -1$.

Example 2: Let $f(x) = 1 - x^2$ for x in the open interval $(-1, 1)$. Then 1 is the least upper bound of f, and 0 is the greatest lower bound (figure 7.2). Now $f(0) = 1$, and so in this case the least upper bound is attained. However, there is no number x in the interval $(-1, 1)$ such that $f(x) = 0$, and so the greatest lower bound is not attained.

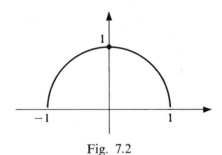

Fig. 7.2

Example 3: Let $f(x) = 1 - x^2$ for $-1 \leq x < 0$ and for $0 < x \leq 1$, and let $f(0) = 1/2$. Again 1 is the least upper bound of f and 0 is the greatest lower bound, and since $f(1) = 0$, we see that the greatest lower bound is attained. However, in this case the least upper bound is not attained (figure 7.3).

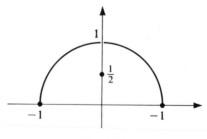

Fig. 7.3

Notice that in example 2 the domain of the function is not a closed interval, and in example 3, although the domain is a closed interval, the function is not continuous.

Theorem 7.2: *Let f be a continuous function whose domain is a finite closed interval* [a, b]. *Then there are numbers c and d in* [a, b] *such that* f(c) *is the least upper bound for f and* f(d) *is the greatest lower bound.*

Proof: By theorem 7.1, we know that f is bounded, and so let M be its least upper bound. Then we have $M - f(x) \geq 0$ for all x in [a, b]. We wish to show that for some x we have equality. Suppose to the contrary that $M - f(x) > 0$ for all x in [a, b]. Then we can define a function g by the rule

$$g(x) = \frac{1}{M - f(x)}$$

for all x in [a, b]. Moreover, by theorem 6.1 of chapter II, g is continuous, and so by theorem 7.1 g is bounded. Thus let B be a number such that $g(x) \leq B$, or in other words,

$$\frac{1}{M - f(x)} \leq B \tag{1}$$

for all x in [a, b]. Since $1/(M - f(x)) > 0$, (1) can be rewritten

$$\frac{1}{B} \leq M - f(x),$$

or equivalently,

$$f(x) \leq M - \frac{1}{B}$$

for all x in [a, b]. But this says that $M - 1/B$ is an upper bound for f, contradicting the fact that M is the least upper bound. This contradiction shows that there must be some number c in [a, b] such that $M = f(c)$, as required.

Now if we denote the greatest lower bound of f by m, then $-m$ is the least upper bound for the function $-f$. Hence, by what we have already proved, there is a d in [a, b] such that $-f(d) = -m$, or in other words, such that $f(d) = m$, as required. ∎

EXERCISES

1. (a) Consider $f(x) = 1/x$ for all $x \in (0, 1]$. Show that f is not bounded. Why does this not contradict theorem 7.1?
   (b) Consider $f(x) = 1/x$ for $x \in (0, 1]$, and define $f(0) = 1$. Then the domain of f is the closed interval [0, 1], but f is not bounded. Why does this not contradict theorem 7.1?

2. Consider the function defined for $0 \leq x \leq 1$ by the rules

   $$f(x) = \frac{1}{1 + x} \sin 1/x \quad \text{for } 0 < x \leq 1,$$
   $$f(0) = 0.$$

   Is either the least upper bound or the greatest lower bound attained?

3. In each of the following, state whether or not f is bounded, and give the least upper bound and/or greatest lower bound where possible. Also state when these numbers are attained.

(a) $f(x) = 2x + 1$ for $x \in (-\infty, -7)$
(b) $f(x) = -3x^2 + 4$ for $x \in [-1, 3)$
(c) $f = \arctan$
(d) $f(x) = \cos x$ for $x \in [-\pi/4, \pi/4]$
(e) $f(x) = \dfrac{1}{1 + x^2}$ for all x
(f) $f(x) = \dfrac{1}{1 - x^2}$ for all $x \neq 1$
(g) $f(x) = \sqrt{1 - x}$ for $-3 \leq x < 1$

4. Let f be a continuous function whose domain is a finite closed interval. Which theorems show that the image of f is a finite closed interval?

5. If f is continuous at x, show that there is a neighborhood of x such that the restriction of f to that neighborhood is bounded. Then use exercise 6 of § 1 to give another proof of the fact that a continuous function whose domain is a closed interval is bounded.

8. MAXIMA AND MINIMA

A number c where a function f attains its least upper bound is called a *maximum* for the function. In other words, c is a maximum for f if $f(x) \leq f(c)$ for all x in the domain of f. Likewise, we say that d is a *minimum* for f if $f(x) \geq f(d)$ for all x in the domain of f. A function may have more than one maximum or minimum. For example, the numbers $\dfrac{\pi}{2}, \dfrac{5\pi}{2}, \ldots$ are all maxima for sin, and the numbers $\dfrac{3\pi}{2}, \dfrac{7\pi}{2}, \ldots$ are all minima.

Notice that a function may have a least upper bound or a greatest lower bound without having a maximum or a minimum. The examples of the preceding section illustrate this. On the other hand, theorem 7.2 guarantees that a continuous function whose domain is a finite closed interval always has at least one maximum and at least one minimum.

Consider the graph (figure 8.1) of a function f defined on a finite closed interval $[a, b]$. The function has a minimum at the endpoint a, and has a maximum at x_2. However, it seems as though the points x_0, x_1, x_3, and b should also qualify as maxima and minima in some sense. For this reason we define a number c to be a *relative maximum* for f if it is a maximum for the

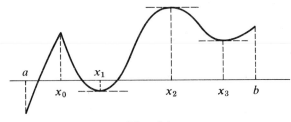

Fig. 8.1

restriction of f to some neighborhood of c. In other words, c is a relative maximum for f if there is a number $\delta > 0$ such that $f(x) \leq f(c)$ for all x in the domain of f satisfying $c - \delta < x < c + \delta$. Likewise, d is called a *relative minimum* for f if it is a minimum for the restriction of f to some neighborhood of d. In figure 8.1, the numbers a, x_1, and x_3 are relative minima, and the numbers x_0, x_2, and b are relative maxima.

A glance at figure 8.1 suggests that at a relative maximum or minimum which is not an endpoint of the domain of f, the tangent line to the graph must be horizontal, or in other words, the derivative must be 0. Of course this does not apply at an endpoint such as a (where the derivative is far from being zero), or at a point such as x_0, where there is no derivative. We shall now prove this criterion as a theorem.

Theorem 8.1:   *Let f be a function whose domain is an open interval. If c is a minimum (or maximum) for f, and if f has a derivative at c, then $f'(c) = 0$.*

Proof: Since the domain of f is an open interval and c is in that interval, it makes sense to talk about $f(c + h)$ for values of h either positive or negative (and sufficiently small). Now if c is a minimum for f, we must have

$$f(c + h) \geq f(c)$$

whenever the left side makes sense. Therefore the expression

$$\frac{f(c + h) - f(c)}{h}$$

is ≥ 0 if $h > 0$ and is ≤ 0 if $h < 0$. Consequently, we have

$$\lim_{h \to 0+} \frac{f(c + h) - f(c)}{h} \geq 0$$

and

$$\lim_{h \to 0-} \frac{f(c + h) - f(c)}{h} \leq 0$$

providing these limits exist. But since f has a derivative at c, the limits do exist, and furthermore must be equal. Therefore, since one is ≤ 0 and the other is ≥ 0, they must both be 0, or in other words, $f'(c) = 0$.

Now if c is a maximum for f, then it is a minimum for $-f$, and so, applying what we have already proved, we have $(-f)'(c) = 0$. But $(-f)'(c) = -f'(c)$, and so again we have $f'(c) = 0$.   ∎

Theorem 8.1 provides us with a method for finding the maximum and minimum values of a continuous function on a closed interval. For, according to the theorem, we need only look at the values of the function at the places where its derivative is zero, and compare these values with the values at the endpoints of the interval (and also with the values at the places where the derivative does not exist, if there are any).

Example 1: Let $f(x) = \dfrac{x^3}{3} - x + 1$ for $\dfrac{-3}{2} \le x \le 3$. Then we have

$$f'(x) = x^2 - 1 = (x - 1)(x + 1),$$

and so the derivative is zero when $x = 1$ and $x = -1$. Hence, the candidates for maxima and minima are 1, -1, and the endpoints $\dfrac{-3}{2}$ and 3. Now we have

$$f(1) = \frac{1}{3}, \; f(-1) = \frac{5}{3}, \; f\left(\frac{-3}{2}\right) = \frac{11}{8}, \; f(3) = 7.$$

Consequently, 3 is the maximum, and 1 is the minimum. The graph of f is sketched in figure 8.2.

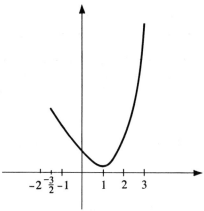

Fig. 8.2

Example 2: A cow has 90 feet of fence to make a rectangular pasture. She has the use of a cliff for one side. She decides to leave a 10 foot gap in the fence in case the grass should get greener on the other side. To make the largest possible pasture, she reasons as follows. "Let y denote the length of the side opposite the cliff, and let x denote the length of each of the other two sides. Then $2x + y = 90 + 10$, or in other words,

$$y = 100 - 2x.$$

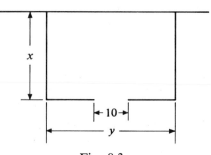

Fig. 8.3

Since neither x nor y can be negative, I must have $0 \le x \le 50$. The area of the pasture is given by

$$xy = x(100 - 2x) = 100x - 2x^2.$$

Thus if I let $A(x) = 100x - 2x^2$ for $x \in [0, 50]$, then the problem amounts to finding a maximum for the function A. Now I have

$$A'(x) = 100 - 4x,$$

and so $A'(x) = 0$ only when $x = 25$. Thus the maximum area is given by $A(25)$, or in other words, 1,250 square feet of pasture."

Example 3: A man wishes to make a bathtub. He has 40 square feet of bathtub material. The bathtub is to be in the shape of a box, with a square cross section, and rounded at the ends with half cylinders, as in figure 8.4. He wants us to find the dimensions of the bathtub which will hold the most water.

First let us find the total surface area in terms of x and y. There are three sides of area xy, plus (putting the ends together) a cylinder of height x and radius of the base $\dfrac{x}{2}$, open at one end. This must total 40. Thus we have

$$40 = 3xy + \pi \left(\frac{x}{2}\right)^2 + 2\pi \left(\frac{x}{2}\right) x.$$

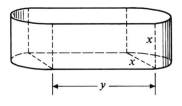

Fig. 8.4

This can be used to express y in terms of x, giving

$$y = \frac{160 - 5\pi x^2}{12x}. \tag{1}$$

On the other hand, the volume of the bathtub is given by the expression

$$x^2 y + \pi \left(\frac{x}{2}\right)^2 x,$$

which, using equation (1), becomes

$$x^2 \frac{(160 - 5\pi x^2)}{12x} + \pi \left(\frac{x}{2}\right)^2 x,$$

or in other words,

$$\frac{40}{3} x - \frac{\pi}{6} x^3.$$

If we denote this last expression by $V(x)$, then the problem amounts to finding a maximum for the function V. Now we have

$$V'(x) = \frac{40}{3} - \frac{\pi}{2}x^2,$$

and thus $V'(x) = 0$ only for $x = \sqrt{80/3\pi}$ and $x = -\sqrt{80/3\pi}$. Since x must be positive, the second possibility is immediately ruled out. On the other hand, we have

$$V(\sqrt{80/3\pi}) = \frac{40}{3}\sqrt{\frac{80}{3\pi}} - \frac{\pi}{6}\left(\sqrt{\frac{80}{3\pi}}\right)^3$$

$$= \frac{80}{9}\sqrt{\frac{80}{3\pi}}.$$

Since $V(x)$ is negative for large values of x, and since $V(0) = 0$, we see therefore that $x = \sqrt{80/3\pi}$ does in fact give the maximum volume.

However, the man calculates $\sqrt{80/3\pi}$ on his slide rule, and finding it to be almost 3 feet, decides that this is too high for a bathtub and tells us that the bathtub should be no more than 2 feet high. Since there is no x in the interval $[0, 2]$ such that $V'(x) = 0$, the maximum volume is given at the endpoint $x = 2$. The man then calculates $V(2)$ on his slide rule and obtains approximately 22 cubic feet, whereupon he informs us that the bathtub must contain at least 25 cubic feet of water. This example shows that there are problems which the calculus cannot solve.

Example 4: Consider $f(x) = x^3$ for all x. A look at the graph of figure 8.5 shows that f has no relative minimum or maximum. On the other hand, we have $f'(x) = 3x^2$, and so $f'(0) = 0$. Thus we see that a function may have its derivative zero at a point without that point being a relative maximum or minimum.

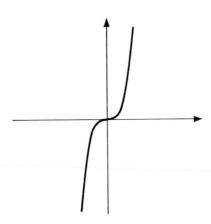

Fig. 8.5

Example 5:   From figure 8.1 it may seem that an endpoint of the domain of a function need always be a relative maximum or minimum. However, a counterexample is provided by taking

$$f(x) = x^2 \sin \frac{1}{x} \quad \text{for } x > 0$$

$$f(0) = 0.$$

Not only is 0 an endpoint here, but also we have $f'(0) = 0$ (chapter II, § 12, example 3). Nevertheless, the graph in figure 8.6 shows that 0 is neither a relative minimum nor a relative maximum.

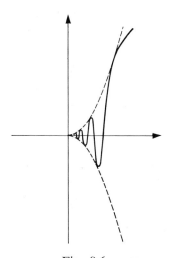

Fig. 8.6

EXERCISES

1. In each of the following, find the maximum and minimum for f.

(a) $f(x) = 3x + 4$ for $0 \le x \le 3$

(b) $f(x) = 2 - x^2$ for $-1 \le x \le 1$

(c) $f(x) = 2x^2 + 1$ for $0 \le x \le 5$

(d) $f(x) = \dfrac{x^3}{3} + \dfrac{x^2}{2}$ for $-3 \le x \le \frac{1}{4}$

(e) $f(x) = 3x^4 - 4x^3 - 12x^2 + 1$ for $-2 \le x \le 3$

(f) $f(x) = \dfrac{x^3}{3} - x^2 + x - 2$ for $-3 \le x \le 2$

2. Let f be defined by the rules

$$f(x) = 2x^3 - 3x^2 + 1 \quad \text{for } -2 \le x < 2;$$

$$f(x) = 7 - x \qquad\qquad \text{for } 2 \le x \le 3.$$

Find the maximum and minimum for f.

3. A toothpaste manufacturer wants to sell toothpaste in right circular cylindrical tin cans in 30 cubic inch units. Find the height and diameter of the can which uses the least amount of tin.

4. The cow of example 2 decides to use her 90 feet of fence to make two pastures, one circular and one square. There are to be no openings, and furthermore, she decides it would be dangerous to live at the base of a cliff. What is the maximum total pasture she can obtain? What is the minimum pasture she can obtain?

5. A man lives on a plain at the point (3, 4). There is a highway along the graph of $f(x) = x^3$. He wants to make the shortest lane possible between his house and the highway. Tell him how to go about it, without actually producing any figures for him.

6. Show that the biggest cylindrical piece of ice cream which can be put into a cone so that there is no ice cream showing above the top of the cone has altitude one third that of the cone.

7. A space capsule is in the form of a sphere of radius r. What is the volume of the largest astronaut which can be put inside the capsule. You may assume that an astronaut has the shape of a right circular cylinder.

8. Repeat exercise 7, only this time assume that astronauts are shaped like cones. (The volume of a cone is $1/3$ the area of its base times its height.)

9. A snail, who can travel at 3 feet per hour (running), is 10 miles from the nearest point P on a straight highway. She wishes to travel to a point Q 50 miles along the highway from P, and she can arrange to have a turtle pick her up anywhere along the highway. The turtle travels at 60 feet per hour. What point on the highway should the snail head for so as to arrive at Q in the shortest possible time?

10. The strength of a beam of rectangular cross section is proportional to its breadth times the cube of its depth. What are the dimensions of the strongest beam that can be cut from a log of radius r?

11. Find the largest rectangle which can be inscribed in a semicircle of radius r.

12. A piece of cardboard is a inches long and b inches wide. An open box is to be made from the cardboard by cutting squares out of the four corners and folding up the sides. What is the volume of the largest box which can be so made?

9. THE MEAN VALUE THEOREM

Consider the graph in figure 9.1 of a smooth function (that is, one which has a derivative everywhere) defined on a closed interval $[a, b]$. It seems reasonable to suppose that somewhere between a and b, the tangent to the graph is parallel to the straight line joining the endpoints of the graph. The slope of the latter is given by

$$\frac{f(b) - f(a)}{b - a},$$

and the slope of the tangent to the graph at the point $(c, f(c))$ is given by $f'(c)$. Thus, what we are asking for is a number c between a and b such that

$$f'(c) = \frac{f(b) - f(a)}{b - a}. \tag{1}$$

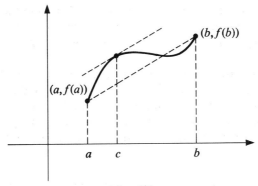

Fig. 9.1

(In figure 9.1 there are two such numbers.)

The fact that there is such a number c is known as the Mean Value Theorem. To prove it, we first handle the case where $f(a)$ and $f(b)$ are equal, so that the expression on the right side of equation (1) is 0. This case is known as Rolle's Theorem, after the French mathematician Michel Rolle (1652–1719). It is illustrated in figure 9.2.

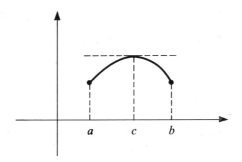

Fig. 9.2

Lemma 9.1 (Rolle's Theorem): *If f is a continuous function whose domain is a closed interval $[a, b]$ and $f(a) = f(b)$, and if f has a derivative everywhere in the open interval (a, b), then there is at least one c in (a, b) such that $f'(c) = 0$.*

Proof: Case 1: Suppose that $f(x) = f(a)$ for all x in $[a, b]$. Then f is a constant function, and so its derivative is everywhere zero. Hence, in this case we can take c to be any point we wish in (a, b).

Case 2:   Suppose that $f(x) > f(a)$ for some x in $[a, b]$. Since f is continuous, by theorem 7.2 there must be some point c in $[a, b]$ such that $f(c)$ is the maximum value of f. Now by assumption there are values of f greater than $f(a)$, and hence greater than $f(b)$ since $f(b) = f(a)$, and consequently we see that c is neither a not b. Therefore by hypothesis f has a derivative at c, and so by theorem 8.1, we must have $f'(c) = 0$.

Case 3:   If f is not constant, and if on the other hand there is no x such that $f(x) > f(a)$, then there must be some x such that $f(x) < f(a)$. This case then follows by applying case 2 to the function $-f$. ∎

We shall now prove a theorem which says more than the mean value theorem.   It is a theorem about two functions, and is due to the French mathematician Augustin-Louis Cauchy (1789–1857), who did much work toward putting the calculus on a rigorous foundation.   In particular, it was Cauchy who first developed and used the definition of limit which we use today.

Theorem 9.2: *Let f and g be functions which are continuous in $[a, b]$, and suppose that f and g have derivatives everywhere in the open interval (a, b). If for all x in (a, b) we have $g'(x) \neq 0$, then there is at least one c in (a, b) such that*

$$\frac{f(b) - f(a)}{g(b) - g(a)} = \frac{f'(c)}{g'(c)}. \tag{2}$$

Proof: Notice that $g(a) \neq g(b)$, for otherwise Rolle's theorem would say that g' is zero somewhere in (a, b), contradicting the hypothesis.   Therefore the left side of (2) makes sense.   We define a function F by the rule

$$F(x) = (f(x) - f(a)) - \frac{f(b) - f(a)}{g(b) - g(a)} (g(x) - g(a))$$

for all x in $[a, b]$.   The derivative of F is given by

$$F'(x) = f'(x) - \frac{f(b) - f(a)}{g(b) - g(a)} g'(x) \tag{3}$$

for all x in (a, b).   Now $F(a) = 0$ and $F(b) = 0$, and so Rolle's theorem gives us a number c in (a, b) such that $F'(c) = 0$.   But in view of (3), this is the desired result. ∎

Corollary 9.3 (The Mean Value Theorem):   *If f is continuous in $[a, b]$ and has a derivative in (a, b), then for at least one c in (a, b) we have*

$$f'(c) = \frac{f(b) - f(a)}{b - a}.$$

Proof: Take $g(x) = x$ for all x in $[a, b]$.   Then $g(b) - g(a) = b - a$, and $g'(x) = 1$ for all x in $[a, b]$.   Hence, the result follows from theorem 9.2. ∎

Example 1:   Consider $f(x) = x^3$ in the interval $[-1, 2]$.   Then we have

$$\frac{f(2) - f(-1)}{2 - (-1)} = \frac{2^3 - (-1)^3}{3} = 3.$$

Now $f'(x) = 3x^2$, and so by the mean value theorem, there should be a number c in $(-1, 2)$ such that $3c^2 = 3$, or in other words, such that $c^2 = 1$.   And of course there is one, namely $c = 1$. (Notice that $c = -1$ does not count, since it is not in the open interval $(-1, 2)$.)

Example 2: Consider the function arcsin. We have

$$\frac{\arcsin(1) - \arcsin(-1)}{1 - (-1)} = \frac{\pi/2 - (-\pi/2)}{2} = \frac{\pi}{2}.$$

Now arcsin has a derivative in the open interval $(-1, 1)$, but not at the endpoints -1 and 1. However, the mean value theorem applies here, since the theorem requires only that the function be continuous at the endpoints, and this is true of arcsin. Thus there is at least one number c in $(-1, 1)$ such that

$\arcsin'(c) = \dfrac{\pi}{2}$. (Actually there are two. See exercise 5.)

Example 3: Let $f(x) = |x|$ for $-1 \le x \le 1$. Then we have

$$f(-1) = f(1).$$

However, there is no c in $(-1, 1)$ such that $f'(c) = 0$. The reason this does not contradict Rolle's theorem is that f does not have a derivative at all points in $(-1, 1)$. See figure 9.3.

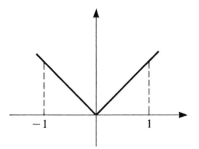

Fig. 9.3

The mean value theorem has several important corollaries. First, recall that the derivative of a constant function is always 0. One corollary of the mean value theorem is the converse of this statement. Namely:

Corollary 9.4: *If f is continuous in $[a, b]$, and if $f'(x) = 0$ for all x in (a, b), then $f(x) = f(a)$ for all x in $[a, b]$.*

Proof: Let x be any point such that $a < x \le b$. Applying the mean value theorem to f on the interval $[a, x]$, we see that there must be some number c in (a, x) such that

$$f'(c) = \frac{f(x) - f(a)}{x - a}.$$

But by hypothesis $f'(c)$ must be 0, and so we obtain $f(x) = f(a)$, as required. ∎

Corollary 9.5: *Let f and g be two continuous functions in [a, b], and suppose that f'(x) = g'(x) for all x in (a, b). Then there is a number C such that*

$$f(x) - g(x) = C$$

for all x in [a, b].

Proof: This follows by applying corollary 9.4 to the function $f - g$. The number C is just $f(a) - g(a)$. ∎

As another corollary of the mean value theorem, we obtain a criterion for determining if a function is increasing or decreasing.

Corollary 9.6: *Suppose that f is continuous in [a, b]. If f'(x) > 0 for all x in (a, b), then f is increasing in [a, b]. If f'(x) < 0 for all x in (a, b), then f is decreasing in [a, b].*

Proof: Suppose that x_1 and x_2 are points in [a, b] such that $x_1 < x_2$. Applying the mean value theorem to f on the interval $[x_1, x_2]$, we see that there is a number c in (x_1, x_2) such that

$$f(x_2) - f(x_1) = f'(c)(x_2 - x_1). \tag{4}$$

Hence, if $f'(x) > 0$ for all x in (a, b), then the right side of (4) is positive, and so $f(x_2) > f(x_1)$. This proves that f is increasing. Likewise, if $f'(x) < 0$ for all x in (a, b), then the right side of (4) is negative, and so f is decreasing. ∎

EXERCISES

1. A function f is said to be *nondecreasing* if $f(x_1) \leq f(x_2)$ whenever $x_1 < x_2$, and *nonincreasing* if $f(x_1) \geq f(x_2)$ whenever $x_1 < x_2$. Suppose that f is continuous in an interval [a, b]. Show that if $f'(x) \geq 0$ for all x in (a, b), then f is nondecreasing, and that if $f'(x) \leq 0$ for all x in (a, b), then f is nonincreasing.

2. (a) Show that if f is a differentiable function which is nondecreasing, then $f'(x) \geq 0$ for all x.
   (b) Show by an example that a differentiable function may be increasing without it being true that $f'(x) > 0$ for all x.

3. (a) Let f be a differentiable function whose domain is some interval (finite or infinite). Suppose that the derivative of f is bounded; that is, there is a number B such that $|f'(x)| \leq B$ for all x in the domain of f. Show that for any two points x_1 and x_2 in the domain of f, we have

   $$|f(x_1) - f(x_2)| \leq B|x_1 - x_2|.$$

   Hence, show that f is uniformly continuous.
   (b) Use part (a) to show that sin and cos are uniformly continuous. Do likewise with arctan.

4. Show that $x > \sin x$ for all $x > 0$. (Hint: Observe that when $x = 0$, they are equal. Then show that $x - \sin x$ is increasing.)

5. In example 2, find two numbers c such that $\arcsin' (c) = \dfrac{\pi}{2}$.

6. In each of the following, find a number c such that

$$f'(c) = \frac{f(b) - f(a)}{b - a}.$$

(a) $f(x) = 3x + 4$, $a = 1$, $b = 5$
(b) $f(x) = x^2 - 3$, $a = -3$, $b = 1$
(c) $f(x) = x^3 - 2x + 1$, $a = 0$, $b = 2$

(d) $f(x) = \arctan x$, $a = \dfrac{1}{\sqrt{3}}$, $b = \sqrt{3}$

(e) $f(x) = x^{12}$, $a = -23$, $b = 23$

7. Consider the function tan in the interval $[0, \pi]$. We have

$$\frac{\tan \pi - \tan 0}{\pi - 0} = \frac{0 - 0}{\pi} = 0.$$

However, there is no c such that $\tan' (c) = 0$. Why does this not contradict the mean value theorem?

10. THE INTERMEDIATE VALUE THEOREM FOR DERIVATIVES

The intermediate value theorem says that a function which is continuous in a closed interval must take on all values between those at the ends of the interval. We shall now prove a theorem which shows that the same is true of a function (continuous or not) which is the derivative of some function. This theorem is due to the French mathematician J. G. Darboux (1842–1917), whose name we shall encounter again in connection with the integral.

Theorem 10.1: *Suppose that f has a derivative everywhere in the closed interval $[a, b]$, and let t be a number between $f'(a)$ and $f'(b)$. Then there is at least one number c in $[a, b]$ such that $f'(c) = t$.*

Proof: Suppose first that $f'(a) < t < f'(b)$. Consider the function g defined by

$$g(x) = f(x) - tx$$

for all x in $[a, b]$. Then the derivative of g is given by

$$g'(x) = f'(x) - t \tag{1}$$

for all x in $[a, b]$, and so we have $g'(a) < 0$ and $g'(b) > 0$. Now since g is differentiable in $[a, b]$, it is certainly continuous, and so by theorem 7.2 there is a number c in $[a, b]$ such that $g(c)$ is the minimum value of g in $[a, b]$ (figure 10.1). Since $g'(a) < 0$, there must be values of g less than $g(a)$; and similarly, since $g'(b) > 0$, there must be values of g less than $g(b)$. Hence c can be neither a nor b, and so by theorem 8.1 we have $g'(c) = 0$. But in view of equation (1), this is the desired result.

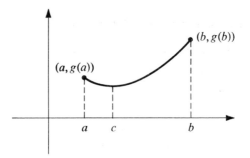

Fig. 10.1

The case where $f'(a) > t > f'(b)$ is handled by the usual process of replacing f by its negative. ∎

Remark: In the following chapter, we shall prove that every continuous function whose domain is a closed interval is the derivative of some function. This fact together with theorem 10.1 will give us another proof of the intermediate value theorem.

Corollary 10.2: *Let f be a function whose domain is some interval (not necessarily closed or finite) and suppose that $f'(x)$ exists and is never zero in that interval. Then f is either increasing or decreasing.*

Proof: Suppose that f' is negative at some point and positive at some other point. Then by theorem 10.1, f' must be zero somewhere in between, contradicting the hypothesis. Therefore f' must be either always negative or always positive, and so the result follows from corollary 9.6. ∎

EXERCISES

1. Let $f(x) = x$ for $x < 1$, and let $f(x) = 1 + x$ for $x \geq 1$. Can f be the derivative of some function?

2. Suppose that f has a jump discontinuity (chapter II, § 12). Prove that f cannot be the derivative of some function.

3. Let f be defined by $f(x) = x^2 \sin(1/x)$ for $x \neq 0$, and let $f(0) = 0$. (See chapter II, § 12, example 3.) Use theorem 10.1 to show that if t is any number between 0 and $4/\pi^2$, then there is a number c such that $f'(c) = t$.

4. Prove theorem 10.1 for the case where $f'(a) > t > f'(b)$, without resorting to the trick of replacing f by its negative.

11. GRAPH SKETCHING

We now have enough material at our disposal to enable us to sketch the graphs of most of the continuous functions which we encounter. We make a list of some of the rules which will help us.

1. The points $(x, f(x))$ where $f'(x) = 0$ will give us the places where the tangent to the graph is horizontal, or the *level* points, as we shall say. We also look for points where the derivative does not exist.

2. Near the points where the right-or left-hand limits of f are ∞ or $-\infty$, the graph of f will rise or descend almost vertically.

3. Between any two consecutive points a and b of the type mentioned in rules 1 and 2, the graph of f must be either increasing or decreasing by corollary 10.2. (This assumes, of course, that the entire interval (a, b) is in the domain of f.)

4. If the domain of f extends to arbitrarily large numbers, then we can investigate $\lim_{x \to \infty} f(x)$ to find out what happens to the graph for large values of x. Similarily, $\lim_{x \to -\infty} f(x)$ will tell us what happens to the graph for large negative values of x.

5. If there are any points which are obviously on the graph of f, then our picture will be improved by making sure the graph passes through them. For example, it is usually easy to compute $f(0)$, in which case we obtain immediately the point where the graph crosses the second axis. In some cases it is easy to see as well the x's for which $f(x) = 0$, which give us the points where the graph crosses the first axis.

Example 1:   We sketch the graph of the polynomial function f given by

$$f(x) = x^4 + \tfrac{4}{3}x^3 - 4x^2 + 5.$$

We have

$$f'(x) = 4x^3 + 4x^2 - 8x$$
$$= 4x(x - 1)(x + 2).$$

Hence the level points on the graph are at $x = 0, 1$, and -2. The values of f at these points are $f(0) = 5, f(1) = 10/3$, and $f(-2) = -17/3$. Since f is an even degree polynomial with positive leading coefficient, we have $\lim_{x \to \infty} f(x) = \infty$ and $\lim_{x \to -\infty} f(x) = \infty$. There are no points with infinite limits and in this case it is not easy to see the places where $f(x) = 0$. To help give us an idea of what the graph looks like to the left of -2 and to the right of 1, we compute $f(-3) = 14$ and $f(2) = 47/3$. Collecting our information we see that the graph of f is something like that in figure 11.1. The fact that the second crossing of the first axis is to the left of -1 and not to the right can be seen by computing $f(-1) = 2/3$. Thus we see that the polynomial has two roots, one between -3 and -2, and one between -2 and -1. These roots could be pinned down more precisely by computing further values of f between -1 and -3.

Example 2:   We sketch the graph of the rational function f given by

$$f(x) = \frac{6(x + 2)}{x^2 - x - 2}.$$

Here we have

$$f'(x) = \frac{-6x(x + 4)}{(x^2 - x - 2)^2},$$

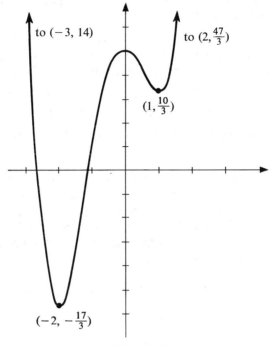

to (−3, 14)

to (2, $\frac{47}{3}$)

(1, $\frac{10}{3}$)

(−2, −$\frac{17}{3}$)

Fig. 11.1'

and so the level points are given by $x = 0$ and $x = -4$. The values of f at these points are $f(0) = -6$, and $f(-4) = -2/3$. The denominator of the expression for $f(x)$ can be factored as $(x - 2)(x + 1)$, and so $x = 2$ and $x = -1$ are points of infinite limits for f. Using the criterion developed in chapter II, § 13, we see that

$$\lim_{x \to 2+} f(x) = \infty \qquad \lim_{x \to 2-} f(x) = -\infty$$

$$\lim_{x \to (-1)+} f(x) = -\infty \qquad \lim_{x \to (-1)-} f(x) = \infty.$$

Also, from chapter II, § 14 we see that $\lim_{x \to \infty} f(x) = 0$ and $\lim_{x \to -\infty} f(x) = 0$. Finally, we have $f(0) = -6$, and the only x for which $f(x) = 0$ is $x = -2$. Thus the graph is as given in figure 11.2.

There are sometimes other tricks which help us in sketching graphs. For example, in the case of an even or an odd function, the graph for negative values of x can be obtained immediately once we have drawn it for positive values. We also have what are known as *periodic* functions. By definition, a function is periodic if there is a number t such that $f(x + t) = f(x)$ for all x in the domain of f. The least such number t is then called the *period* of the function. The functions sin and cos are periodic of period 2π. Also functions which are built up from sums, products, and quotients of sin and cos are often periodic. For example, tan is periodic of period π. If a function f has period t, then it suffices to draw its graph in any interval of length t, for example the interval $[-t/2, t/2]$. Outside that interval the function is just going to repeat itself.

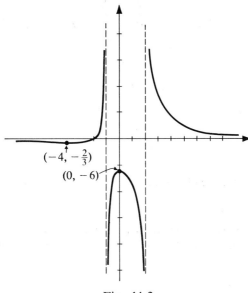

Fig. 11.2

Example 3: We sketch the graph of the function f given by

$$f(x) = \tan x - 8 \sin x.$$

We observe first that $f(x + 2\pi) = f(x)$ for all values of x where $f(x)$ makes sense, and so f is periodic of period 2π. Hence it suffices to consider f in the interval $[-\pi, \pi]$. Also we see that f is an odd function, and so it suffices to restrict f further to the interval $[0, \pi]$. Now we have

$$f'(x) = \frac{1 - 8 \cos^3 x}{\cos^2 x},$$

and so the level points are given by $1 - 8 \cos^3 x = 0$, or in other words, $\cos x = 1/2$. In the interval $[0, \pi]$, there is just one such x, namely $x = \pi/3$, and the value of f at $\pi/3$ is $-3\sqrt{3}$. At $x = \pi/2$ we have infinite limits for f given by

$$\lim_{x \to \frac{\pi}{2}+} f(x) = -\infty, \qquad \lim_{x \to \frac{\pi}{2}-} f(x) = \infty.$$

The points in the interval $[0, \pi]$ such that $f(x) = 0$ are $x = 0$, $x = \pi$, and the point x satisfying $\cos x = 1/8$ (which is a little less than $\pi/2$). Hence, the graph of f is roughly that shown in figure 11.3.

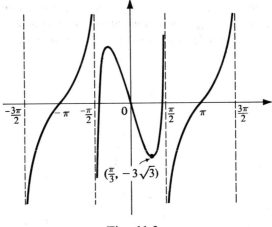

Fig. 11.3

Example 4: We sketch the graph of the function f given by

$$f(x) = \sqrt[3]{x^2 - 1}$$

for all numbers x. Observe first that f is an even function, and so it suffices to consider $x \geq 0$. Using equation (1) of §4, we see that the derivative of f is given by

$$f'(x) = \frac{2x}{3(\sqrt[3]{x^2 - 1})^2}$$

for $x \neq 1$. Near $x = 1$ the derivative becomes quite large. The only level point is given by $x = 0$, where the value of f is -1. Also we have $f(1) = 0$, $f(3) = 2$, and $\lim\limits_{x \to \infty} f(x) = \infty$. Hence the graph of f is as given in figure 11.4. The function has no derivative at $x = 1$ or -1, although it is continuous at those points.

We mention briefly one further aspect of graph sketching. The discussion will be rather intuitive, but it could be put on a rigorous basis. Suppose that a

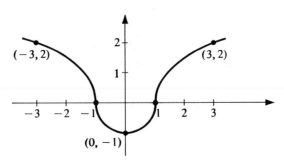

Fig. 11.4

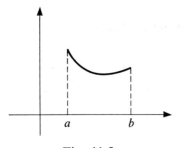

Fig. 11.5

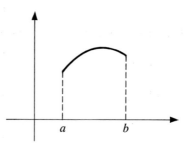

Fig. 11.6

function f has a second derivative throughout an interval (a, b), and that $f''(x) > 0$ for all x in that interval.   By corollary 9.6 this means that f' is increasing in the interval.   Now $f'(x)$ represents the slope of the tangent line to the graph of f.   Consequently the graph of f must be as in figure 11.5, and we say that f is *concave upward* in the interval (a, b).   Likewise, if $f''(x) < 0$ for all x in (a, b), then we say that f is *concave downward* in (a, b) (figure 11.6).

Now suppose that $a < c < b$, and that f is concave downward in one of the intervals (a, c) or (c, b) and concave upward in the other (figure 11.7).

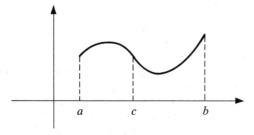

Fig. 11.7

The point c is then called a *point of inflection* for f.   It follows from the fact that a derivative cannot skip any values (theorem 10.1) that at a point of inflection c we must have $f''(c) = 0$.   However, just as the fact that $f'(c) = 0$ does not necessarily imply that c is a relative minimum or maximum for f (§ 8, example 4), the fact that $f''(c) = 0$ does not necessarily imply that c is a point of inflection for f.   (Consider $f(x) = x^4$ with $c = 0$.)

Let us locate the points of inflection for the function of example 1.   We have

$$f''(x) = 4(3x^2 + 2x - 2),$$

and so $f''(x) = 0$ for $x = \frac{1}{3}(\sqrt{7} - 1)$ and $x = -\frac{1}{3}(\sqrt{7} + 1)$.   Since these are the only possible points of inflection, this shows something we tacitly assumed in drawing the graph; namely, there is no turn to the right for $x > 1$ and no turn to the left for $x < -2$.   Likewise, in example 4, the fact that the graph makes no turn upwards for $x > 1$ or $x < -1$ could be verified by computing the second derivative and showing that it is never 0.

EXERCISES

1. Sketch the graph of f when $f(x)$ is given by each of the following expressions:

(a) $x^2 + 3x - 1$

(b) $\dfrac{x-1}{x+1}$

(c) $\dfrac{x^2}{x^4 - 1}$

(d) $\dfrac{x^2 + 2}{x^2 + x - 2}$

(e) $\sin^2 x$

(f) $(x - 2)\sqrt{x + 1}$

(g) $2x^3 + 3x^2$

(h) $\dfrac{x}{\sqrt{x - 9}}$

(i) $\dfrac{x^3}{x^2 - 2}$

(j) $\dfrac{x^5}{5} - \dfrac{x^4}{2} + \dfrac{x^3}{3} - 1$

(k) $2 \tan x - \sec x$

(l) $\dfrac{3}{x^2 - 4}$

(m) $3x + 4$

(n) $\dfrac{|x|}{x^2 + 1}$

(o) $\dfrac{x^4}{x^4 + 1}$

(p) $2 \sin 2x + \cos 4x$

(q) $(\sqrt[3]{x})^2$

(r) $\dfrac{x^2 - 1}{x - 2}$

(s) $\sqrt{1 + x^3}$

(t) $x^3 - 3x^2 + 3x - 2$

(u) $\sin^2 x + \sqrt{3} \sin x$

(v) $\dfrac{x(x - 1)}{x^2 - 4}$

(w) $\sqrt[3]{x}(x + 4)$

(x) $\dfrac{(x + 1)^2}{(x + 2)^2(x - 1)}$

(y) $(x + 2)^3(x - 1)^2$

(z) 5000

2. Find a function whose derivative is $x^2 + bx + c$. Then give an example of a third degree polynomial which has (a) two level points, (b) one level point, and (c) no level points.

3. (a) Suppose that $f'(x)$ is defined for all x and that $f(x) = 0$ for at least n distinct numbers x. Show that f has at least $n - 1$ distinct level points.

(b) Use part (a) to show that a polynomial of degree n can have no more than n distinct roots. (Hint: Show that its nth derivative does not have a root.)

(c) If $a_1, a_2, \ldots, a_n$ are distinct numbers, show that the function f defined by

$$f(x) = (x - a_1)(x - a_2) \cdots (x - a_n)$$

has precisely $n - 1$ level points.

12. AXIOMS FOR SIN AND COS

In this section we shall assume that we are given functions s and c such that

$$s'(x) = c(x), \quad c'(x) = -s(x) \tag{1}$$

for all real numbers x, and such that

$$s(0) = 0, \quad c(0) = 1. \tag{2}$$

Of course we know of one such pair of functions, namely sin and cos. However, our definitions of these functions and the proofs of some of their properties depended on pictures. In chapter VI we shall be able to show without pictures that there is a pair of functions s and c as above. (See also the exercise following §1 of chapter V.) It is therefore interesting to see how many of the properties of sin and cos are consequences of (1) and (2). It turns out that they all are, thanks to the mean value theorem and its corollaries.

First we prove the relation

$$s^2(x) + c^2(x) = 1. \tag{3}$$

Using (1) we see that the derivative of the left side is

$$2s(x)s'(x) + 2c(x)c'(x) = 2s(x)c(x) - 2c(x)s(x) = 0.$$

Thus the left side of (3) is constant, and from (2) it follows that the constant is 1. This proves (3). We then see from (3) that the values of s and c must all be between -1 and 1.

Next suppose that f and g are any functions satisfying

$$f'(x) = g(x), \quad g'(x) = -f(x) \tag{4}$$

for all x. Then there are constants a and b such that

$$s(x)f(x) + c(x)g(x) = a$$
$$c(x)f(x) - s(x)g(x) = b.$$

This follows since each of the left sides has derivative 0. Then, using (3) we can solve for $f(x)$ and $g(x)$ to obtain

$$f(x) = as(x) + bc(x)$$
$$g(x) = ac(x) - bs(x). \tag{5}$$

Putting $x = 0$ in (5), we find $a = g(0)$ and $b = f(0)$. In particular, if $f(0) = 0$ and $g(0) = 1$, then $f = s$ and $g = c$. In other words, there is at most one pair of functions satisfying both conditions (1) and (2).

Now we shall prove the sum rules

$$s(x + y) = s(x)c(y) + c(x)s(y)$$
$$c(x + y) = c(x)c(y) - s(x)s(y). \tag{6}$$

To do this we fix y and we define $f(x) = s(x + y)$ and $g(x) = c(x + y)$. Then f and g satisfy (4), and equations (5) in this case become (6).

Similarly, by taking $f(x) = c(-x)$ and $g(x) = s(-x)$, we find

$$c(-x) = c(x), \quad s(-x) = -s(x). \tag{7}$$

Suppose now that we have never heard of π. Then we can define $\pi/2$ as the least positive number t such that $c(t) = 0$. However, there is a catch here, since it is not obvious that there are any positive numbers x such that $c(x) = 0$. Of course, if there are any such numbers, then we can let t be their greatest lower bound, and since c is continuous (it is differentiable) it follows that $c(t) = 0$. Thus t will be the least positive number such that $c(t) = 0$.

To see that $c(x) = 0$ for some $x > 0$, it suffices to show that $c(x) = 1/\sqrt{2}$ for some $x > 0$, since from (3) and (6) it then follows that

$$c(2x) = c^2(x) - s^2(x) = \tfrac{1}{2} - \tfrac{1}{2} = 0.$$

Suppose that there is no positive number x such that $c(x) = 1/\sqrt{2}$. Since $c(0) = 1$, it follows from the intermediate value theorem that $c(x) > 1/\sqrt{2}$ for all positive x. Then from the mean value theorem we obtain

$$s(2) = s(2) - s(0) = c(z) \cdot 2 > \frac{2}{\sqrt{2}} = \sqrt{2}$$

for some z between 0 and 2. But this contradicts the fact that the values of s are all between -1 and 1.

Thus we have justified the definition of $\pi/2$ as the least positive number such that $c(\pi/2) = 0$. Since $c(0) = 1$, it follows from the intermediate value theorem that $c(x) > 0$ for all x in $[0, \pi/2)$, and consequently, since $s' = c$, we see that s is increasing in $[0, \pi/2]$. But $s(0) = 0$, and so $s(x) > 0$ for x in $(0, \pi/2]$. Thus, since $c' = -s$, we see that c is decreasing in $[0, \pi/2]$. Because $c(\pi/2) = 0$, we deduce from (3) that $s(\pi/2) = 1$. We summarize our information in the graphs of figure 12.1. The rest of the graphs can be obtained from the rules

$$s(x + \pi/2) = c(x) \quad \text{and} \quad c(x + \pi/2) = -s(x), \tag{8}$$

which are easy consequences of the sum rules (6).

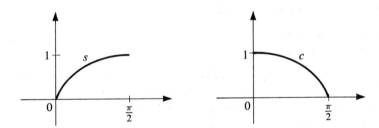

Fig. 12.1

EXERCISES

1. Verify the rules (8), and hence complete the graphs of s and c.
2. Let x and y be any numbers satisfying $x^2 + y^2 = 1$. Show that there is a unique number t in $[0, 2\pi)$ satisfying $x = c(t)$ and $y = s(t)$. (There are four cases, depending on the signs of x and y. Use your graphs of s and c and also the intermediate value theorem.)
3. Show that

$$\lim_{h \to 0} \frac{s(h)}{h} = 1.$$

$$\left(\text{Hint: Write } \frac{s(h)}{h} = \frac{s(h) - s(0)}{h}. \right)$$

INTEGRALS   IV

1. UPPER AND LOWER SUMS

Let f be a continuous function defined in a closed interval $[a, b]$, and suppose for the moment that $f(x) \geq 0$ for all x in $[a, b]$. The notion of the integral comes from the attempt to say what is meant by the "area" of the portion of the plane lying between the graph of f and the first axis. Take any finite set P of points in $[a, b]$ such that both a and b are members of P. Such a set is called a *partition* of $[a, b]$. We then name its points $x_0, x_1, \ldots, x_n$ in such a way that

$$a = x_0 < x_1 < x_2 < \cdots < x_{n-1} < x_n = b.$$

In particular, if $n = 1$, then P consists simply of the two endpoints a and b. In figure 1.1, $n = 6$.

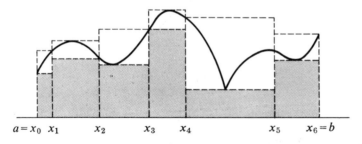

$$a = x_0 \quad x_1 \qquad x_2 \qquad x_3 \qquad x_4 \qquad\qquad x_5 \qquad x_6 = b$$

Fig. 1.1

Now, for each integer i such that $1 \leq i \leq n$, let M_i denote the maximum value of f in the interval $[x_{i-1}, x_i]$. Then the number $M_i(x_i - x_{i-1})$ gives the area of the tall rectangle above $[x_{i-1}, x_i]$ (figure 1.1). The sum of all such numbers

$$M_1(x_1 - x_0) + M_2(x_2 - x_1) + \cdots + M_n(x_n - x_{n-1}) \quad (1)$$

represents the combined area of all the tall rectangles. Thus (1) is a number which in general is somewhat larger than the "true" area under the graph of f, whatever that means.

In order to make things precise, and so as not to restrict ourselves to functions with positive values, let us now assume only that f is a function which is bounded in the interval $[a, b]$, where $a < b$. Of course if f is continuous, then by theorem 7.1 of chapter III, f will automatically be bounded. However, we are going to make our theory applicable to functions which are not necessarily continuous. Now, given a partition P of $[a, b]$, it may not make sense to talk about the maximum value of f in $[x_{i-1}, x_i]$, since f is not necessarily continuous (see chapter III, §7, example 3). However, since f is bounded, it does make sense to talk about the least upper bound of f in $[x_{i-1}, x_i]$, and this is what we shall take as M_i. The sum (1) is then called the *upper sum* of f relative to the partition P, and is denoted by $U(P, f)$. Thus, using our summation notation we can write

$$U(P, f) = \sum_{i=1}^{n} M_i(x_i - x_{i-1}).$$

Since we are not necessarily assuming that the values of f are positive, it may be that some of the numbers M_i are negative. This is illustrated in figure 1.2. Thus the contribution of the term $M_i(x_i - x_{i-1})$ to the upper sum in this case is not the shaded area in figure 1.2, but rather the negative of that area.

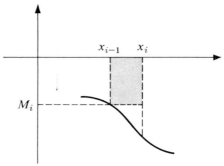

Fig. 1.2

Now let m_i denote the greatest lower bound of f in $[x_{i-1}, x_i]$. We define

$$L(P, f) = \sum_{i=1}^{n} m_i(x_i - x_{i-1})$$

and we call $L(P, f)$ the *lower sum* of f relative to the partition P. Thus, in figure 1.1 the lower sum is represented by the combined area of all the shorter rectangles. Statements about lower sums can be obtained from the corresponding statements about upper sums by the following device. If m is the greatest lower bound of a function f in some interval, then $-m$ is the least upper bound of the function $-f$ in the same interval. Hence

$$L(P, f) = \sum_{i=1}^{n} m_i(x_i - x_{i-1}) = -\sum_{i=1}^{n} -m_i(x_i - x_{i-1})$$
$$= -U(P, -f). \tag{2}$$

Since $m_i \leq M_i$ for each i, and since the numbers $x_i - x_{i-1}$ are all positive, we can write

$$\sum_{i=1}^{n} m_i(x_i - x_{i-1}) \leq \sum_{i=1}^{n} M_i(x_i - x_{i-1}),$$

or in other words,

$$L(P,f) \leq U(P,f) \qquad (3)$$

for any partition P.

Consider a partition P whose points are $x_0, x_1, \ldots, x_n$. Let x be a point in $[a, b]$ which is not in P. If we add x to P we obtain a new partition P'. Suppose that x falls in the interval $[x_{k-1}, x_k]$. Then from figure 1.3 it is intuitively clear that the upper sum $U(P',f)$ is less than or equal to the upper sum $U(P,f)$. The difference between the two is just the shaded area.

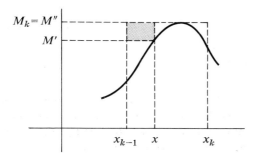

Fig. 1.3

More generally, we can prove the following.

Lemma 1.1:   *Let P' and P be partitions of $[a, b]$ such that P is a subset of P'. If f is any function which is bounded in $[a, b]$, then*

$$U(P',f) \leq U(P,f)$$

and

$$L(P',f) \geq L(P,f).$$

Proof: First consider the case where P' is obtained from P by the addition of a single point x. Let the points of P be $x_0, x_1, \ldots, x_n$, and let M_i be least upper bound of f in the interval $[x_{i-1}, x_i]$ for each i. Suppose that k is the first integer such that $x < x_k$, so that we have $x_{k-1} < x < x_k$. Now M_k, being an upper bound for f in the interval $[x_{k-1}, x_k]$, is certainly an upper bound for f in the smaller interval $[x_{k-1}, x]$. Consequently, if we let M' be the least upper bound of f in $[x_{k-1}, x]$, we have $M' \leq M_k$. Similarly, if M'' denotes the least upper bound of f in $[x, x_k]$, then $M'' \leq M_k$. Hence we can write

$$M'(x - x_{k-1}) + M''(x_k - x) \leq M_k(x - x_{k-1}) + M_k(x_k - x)$$
$$= M_k(x_k - x_{k-1}).$$

Consequently, using the definition of upper sum, we have

$$U(P', f) = \sum_{i=1}^{k-1} M_i(x_i - x_{i-1}) + M'(x - x_{k-1})$$
$$+ M''(x_k - x) + \sum_{i=k+1}^{n} M_i(x_i - x_{i-1})$$
$$\leq \sum_{i=1}^{k-1} M_i(x_i - x_{i-1}) + M_k(x_k - x_{k-1})$$
$$+ \sum_{i=k+1}^{n} M_i(x_i - x_{i-1})$$
$$= U(P, f).$$

The case where P' is obtained from P by the addition of more than one point now follows from what we have proved and induction on the number of points added.

For lower sums we have, using equation (2) and applying what we have proved to the function $-f$,

$$L(P', f) = -U(P', -f) \geq -U(P, -f) = L(P, f). \quad \blacksquare$$

The inequality (3) says that a lower sum is less than or equal to an upper sum provided we use the same partition P to compute both sums. We are now going to prove that any lower sum is less than or equal to any upper sum, even when we use different partitions to compute them.

Theorem 1.2: *Let P_1 and P_2 be any two partitions of $[a, b]$. Then*

$$L(P_1, f) \leq U(P_2, f).$$

Proof: Let $P = P_1 \cup P_2$. Then P is a partition of $[a, b]$ and P_1 and P_2 are both subsets of P. Consequently, using lemma 1.1 and the inequality (3) we obtain

$$L(P_1, f) \leq L(P, f) \leq U(P, f) \leq U(P_2, f),$$

as required. $\blacksquare$

EXERCISES

1. In figure 1.3 we have $M'' = M_k$ and $M' < M_k$. Draw a situation where $M'' < M_k$ and $M' = M_k$. Also draw a situation where $M'' = M_k$ and $M' = M_k$. Prove that both $M'' < M_k$ and $M' < M_k$ cannot hold.

2. Compute the lower and upper sums for each of the following, using the indicated partitions. It will help to sketch the graphs. Do not simplify your answers.

   (a) $f(x) = 2x$, $P = \{0, 1, \frac{3}{2}, 3, 5\}$.

   (b) $f(x) = 1 - x$, $P = \{-2, -\frac{4}{3}, 0, 1, 3, 9\}$.

   (c) $f(x) = x^2$, $P = \{-3, -2, -1, \frac{1}{2}, 2\}$.

   (d) $f(x) = 1 - 2x^3$, $P = \{\frac{1}{3}, \frac{1}{2}, 3\}$.

(e) $f(x) = x^2 - 4x + 1$, $P = \{0, 1, \frac{5}{2}, 4\}$.

(f) $f(x) = 2x^3 - 3x^2 - 1$, $P = \{-2, -1, \frac{1}{3}, 2, 4\}$.

(g) $f(x) = \sin x$, $P = \left\{-\pi, -\dfrac{\pi}{2}, \dfrac{\pi}{6}, \dfrac{2\pi}{3}, 2\pi\right\}$.

(h) $f(x) = \cos x$, $P = \left\{-\dfrac{\pi}{2}, \dfrac{3\pi}{2}\right\}$.

3. Let f be the function defined in the interval $[0, 3]$ by the rules

$$
\begin{aligned}
f(x) &= x^2 &&\text{for } 0 \le x < 1 \\
&= 1 - x &&\text{for } 1 \le x < 2 \\
&= x - 2 &&\text{for } 2 \le x \le 3.
\end{aligned}
$$

Draw the graph of f and compute its lower and upper sums relative to the partition $\{0, \frac{1}{2}, \frac{4}{3}, \frac{5}{2}, 3\}$.

4. Let $f(x) = \dfrac{1}{x}$ for $x \ne 0$ and let $f(0) = 0$. If P is a partition of the interval $[-1, 1]$, does $U(P, f)$ make sense? If P is a partition of the interval $[1, 4]$, does $U(P, f)$ make sense?

5. Let P be the partition of the interval $[a, b]$ into n equal parts (that is,

$$
x_i = a + i\frac{(b - a)}{n} \quad \text{for } 0 \le i \le n).
$$

If $f(x) = x$, show that

$$
U(P, f) = \frac{b^2 - a^2}{2} + \frac{(b - a)^2}{2n}
$$

and

$$
L(P, f) = \frac{b^2 - a^2}{2} - \frac{(b - a)^2}{2n}.
$$

$\left(\text{Hint: Use the formula } 1 + 2 + 3 + \cdots + n = \dfrac{n(n + 1)}{2}.\right)$

6. Write out a proof of the relation

$$
L(P', f) \ge L(P, f)
$$

of lemma 1.1 without appealing to the result for upper sums.

2. UPPER AND LOWER INTEGRALS

For a given bounded function f defined in an interval $[a, b]$, consider the set of upper sums corresponding to all possible partitions P of $[a, b]$. By Theorem 1.2 this set of numbers is bounded below by any lower sum. Hence, if we denote its greatest lower bound by $\overline{\int_a^b} f$, then we have

$$
L(P, f) \le \overline{\int_a^b} f
$$

for any partition P of $[a, b]$. Thus $\int_a^{\bar{b}} f$ is an upper bound for the set of all lower sums, and so if we denote the least upper bound of this set by $\int_{\underline{a}}^b f$, then we have

$$\int_{\underline{a}}^b f \le \int_a^{\bar{b}} f. \tag{1}$$

The numbers $\int_{\underline{a}}^b f$ and $\int_a^{\bar{b}} f$ depend only on the function f and the interval $[a, b]$, and are called the *lower integral* and *upper integral* respectively for f in $[a, b]$.

We say that f is *integrable* on $[a, b]$ if

$$\int_{\underline{a}}^b f = \int_a^{\bar{b}} f.$$

In this case the upper or lower integral is denoted simply by

$$\int_a^b f.$$

and is called the *integral* of f from a to b. The following lemma gives us a criterion for determining when a function is integrable.

Lemma 2.1: *A bounded function f is integrable on $[a, b]$ if and only if for each $\epsilon > 0$, there is at least one partition P of $[a, b]$, such that*
$$U(P, f) - L(P, f) < \epsilon. \tag{2}$$

Proof: Suppose first that for every $\epsilon > 0$ there is a partition P such that (2) holds. Then from the inequalities

$$L(P, f) \le \int_{\underline{a}}^b f \le \int_a^{\bar{b}} f \le U(P, f)$$

we deduce that

$$0 \le \int_a^{\bar{b}} f - \int_{\underline{a}}^b f < \epsilon.$$

Since this holds for every $\epsilon > 0$, we must have

$$\int_{\underline{a}}^b f = \int_a^{\bar{b}} f,$$

and so f is integrable.

Conversely, suppose that f is integrable, and let ϵ be any positive number. Since $\int_a^{\bar{b}} f$ is the greatest lower bound of all upper sums, there must be at least one partition P_1 such that

$$U(P_1, f) < \int_a^{\bar{b}} f + \epsilon/2. \tag{3}$$

Likewise, since $\int_{\underline{a}}^b f$ is the least upper bound of all lower sums, there is a partition P_2 such that

$$\int_{\underline{a}}^b f - \epsilon/2 < L(P_2, f). \tag{4}$$

If we let $P = P_1 \cup P_2$, then using (3) and lemma 1.1 we obtain

$$U(P, f) < \int_a^{\bar{b}} f + \epsilon/2. \tag{5}$$

Similarly, from (4) and lemma 1.1 we have

$$\int_{\underline{a}}^b f - \epsilon/2 < L(P, f). \tag{6}$$

The inequality (2) then follows by adding (5) and (6). ∎

In figure 1.1 the difference between the upper and lower sums is given by the combined area of the white rectangles. It may seem that by taking enough points in the partition and by spacing the points closely enough together, we could always make the lower sum come as close as we like to the upper sum. To see that this is not the case, consider the following example.

Example 1: Let f be the function defined in the interval $[0, 1]$ by the rules

$$f(x) = 0 \quad \text{if } x \text{ is rational}$$
$$= 1 \quad \text{if } x \text{ is irrational.}$$

Recalling that between any two numbers there is both a rational number (chapter II, theorem 1.6) and an irrational number (chapter II, § 1, exercise 3), it follows that relative to any partition P of $[0, 1]$ we have $M_i = 1$ and $m_i = 0$ for each i. Consequently, we have

$$U(P, f) = \sum_{i=1}^n M_i(x_i - x_{i-1})$$

$$= \sum_{i=1}^n (x_i - x_{i-1}) = 1.$$

Thus all upper sums are equal to 1, and so $\int_0^{\bar{1}} f = 1$. On the other hand,

$$L(P, f) = \sum_{i=1}^n m_i(x_i - x_{i-1}) = 0.$$

In other words, all lower sums are 0, and so $\int_{\underline{0}}^1 f = 0$. Therefore, in this case the lower and upper integrals are not the same, and so f is not integrable. The intuitive reasoning given prior to the example breaks down due to the fact that f is so badly discontinuous. You will appreciate the need for precise definitions and theorems if you keep in mind that most functions, far from being like the smooth rational and trigonometric functions which we usually deal with in our examples, are as discontinuous as the function f of this example.

By definition, the lower integral of f in $[a, b]$ is the least upper bound of the numbers of the form $L(P, f)$. In view of equation (2) of § 1, this means that the lower integral is the least upper bound of the numbers $-U(P, -f)$. But the latter is the negative of the greatest lower bound of the numbers $U(P, -f)$. In other words,

$$\underline{\int_a^b} f = - \overline{\int_a^b} (-f) \tag{7}$$

for any function f bounded in $[a, b]$.

Lemma 2.2: *If f is integrable on $[a, b]$, then so is $-f$, and we have*

$$\int_a^b (-f) = - \int_a^b f. \tag{8}$$

Proof: In (7) replace f by $-f$, and multiply both sides by -1. This gives us

$$-\underline{\int_a^b} (-f) = \overline{\int_a^b} f. \tag{9}$$

Now since f is integrable, the left side of (7) is the same as the right side of (9). Hence the right side of (7) is the same as the left side of (9), showing that $-f$ is integrable. Equation (8) then follows from either (7) or (9). ∎

We shall not consider the problem of computing integrals until § 5. However, there is one type of function whose integral follows almost immediately from the definition.

Lemma 2.3: *For any constant function c in an interval $[a, b]$, we have*

$$\int_a^b c = c(b - a).$$

Proof: Let P be the partition of $[a, b]$ consisting of only the endpoints a and b. Then we have

$$L(P, c) = c(b - a) = U(P, c). \tag{10}$$

But since we must have also

$$L(P, c) \leq \int_{\underline{a}}^{b} c \leq \int_{a}^{\overline{b}} c \leq U(P, c),$$

equations (10) show that both the lower and upper integral must be $c(b - a)$, as required. ∎

A function f is said to be *nondecreasing* if whenever x_1 and x_2 are in the domain of f and $x_1 < x_2$, we have $f(x_1) \leq f(x_2)$; see figure 2.1. In particular, any constant function is nondecreasing. On the other hand, we say that f is *nonincreasing* if $f(x_1) \geq f(x_2)$ whenever $x_1 < x_2$; see figure 2.2.

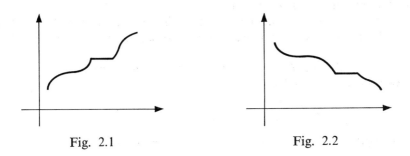

Fig. 2.1   Fig. 2.2

We shall now prove that any function which is nondecreasing throughout an interval is integrable on that interval. First it will be convenient to make one more definition. Given a partition P whose points are $x_0, x_1, \ldots, x_n$, the maximum of the numbers

$$x_1 - x_0, x_2 - x_1, \ldots, x_n - x_{n-1}$$

is called the *mesh* of the partition, and is denoted by $|P|$. For example, in figure 2.3 $|P| = x_5 - x_4$.

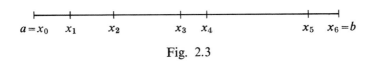

Fig. 2.3

Theorem 2.4: *If f is a bounded function which is nondecreasing (or nonincreasing) in $[a, b]$, then f is integrable on $[a, b]$.*

Proof: If f is constant in $[a, b]$, then it is integrable by lemma 2.3. Thus, suppose that f is not constant, so that since f is nondecreasing we must have $f(b) > f(a)$. We shall apply the criterion of lemma 2.1. Given $\epsilon > 0$, let P be any partition whose mesh is less than $\epsilon/(f(b) - f(a))$. Now if the points of P are $x_0, x_1, \ldots, x_n$, then since f is nondecreasing we must have

$M_i = f(x_i)$ and $m_i = f(x_{i-1})$

for each i. Consequently,

$$
\begin{aligned}
U(P, f) - L(P, f) &= \sum_{i=1}^{n} M_i(x_i - x_{i-1}) - \sum_{i=1}^{n} m_i(x_i - x_{i-1}) \\
&= \sum_{i=1}^{n} (f(x_i) - f(x_{i-1}))(x_i - x_{i-1}) \\
&< \sum_{i=1}^{n} (f(x_i) - f(x_{i-1})) \frac{\epsilon}{f(b) - f(a)} \\
&= (f(b) - f(a)) \frac{\epsilon}{f(b) - f(a)} = \epsilon.
\end{aligned}
$$

Therefore by lemma 2.1, f is integrable.

In the case where f is nonincreasing, $-f$ is nondecreasing, and so applying lemma 2.2 and what we have already proved, we see again that f is integrable. ∎

Example 2: Let f be the function defined in the interval $[0, 1]$ as follows. For each integer $n \geq 0$, let

$$
f(x) = \frac{1}{2^n} \quad \text{for} \quad \frac{1}{2^{n+1}} < x \leq \frac{1}{2^n}.
$$

Also let $f(0) = 0$. Then the graph of f is as given in figure 2.4. Observe that f is discontinuous at $\frac{1}{2^n}$ for each $n > 0$. Nevertheless, since f is nondecreasing in $[0, 1]$, it follows from theorem 2.4 that f is integrable. Thus we see that a function may be discontinuous at an infinite number of points in an interval, and still be integrable in that interval.

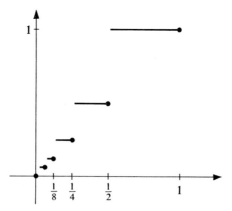

Fig. 2.4

EXERCISES

1. If $f(x) = x$ for all x in $[a, b]$, use exercise 5 of §1 to show that f is integrable, and that

$$
\int_a^b f = \frac{b^2 - a^2}{2}.
$$

2. Let f be the function defined in the interval $[0, 1]$ by the rules

$f(x) = 0$ for x rational

$\quad\ \ = x$ for x irrational.

Show that $\int_0^{\overline{1}} f = \frac{1}{2}$, whereas $\underline{\int_0^1} f = 0$.

3. Let f be the function defined in the interval $[0, 2]$ by the rules

$f(x) = 1$ for $0 \leq x \leq 1$

$\quad\ \ = 2$ for $1 < x \leq 2$.

If $\epsilon > 0$, find points x_1 and x_2 in $[0, 2]$ such that, relative to the partition $P = \{0, x_1, x_2, 2\}$, we have

$$U(P, f) - L(P, f) < \epsilon.$$

4. Let $f(x) = [x]$ (the greatest integer $\leq x$) for $0 \leq x \leq 9/2$. Given $\epsilon > 0$, find a partition $P = \{0, x_1, x_2, \ldots, x_8, 9/2\}$ such that

$$U(P, f) - L(P, f) < \epsilon.$$

5. Without using the result for nondecreasing functions, write out a proof that a bounded function which is nonincreasing in an interval is integrable on that interval.

6. Let f be the function defined in the interval $[0, 1]$ by the rules

$f(x) = 0$ for x irrational,

$$= \frac{1}{q} \text{ for } x = \frac{p}{q},$$

where it is assumed that p and q are nonnegative integers with no common factor. Show that f is continuous at all irrational numbers and is discontinuous at all rational numbers. Show also that f is integrable on $[0, 1]$ and the integral is 0.

3. PROPERTIES OF THE INTEGRAL

Theorem 3.1:   *If f is integrable on $[a, b]$ and c is any number, then cf is integrable on $[a, b]$, and*

$$\int_a^b cf = c \int_a^b f \tag{1}$$

Proof: Suppose first that $c > 0$. If P is a partition of $[a, b]$ and M_i is the least upper bound of f in $[x_{i-1}, x_i]$, then it follows from theorem 1.8 of chapter III that cM_i is the least upper bound of cf in $[x_{i-1}, x_i]$. Consequently,

$$U(P, cf) = \sum_{i=1}^{n} cM_i(x_i - x_{i-1})$$

$$= c \sum_{i=1}^{n} M_i(x_i - x_{i-1})$$

$$= cU(P, f).$$

Then, again using theorem 1.8 of chapter III, we obtain

$$\int_a^{\bar{b}} cf = c \int_a^{\bar{b}} f. \tag{2}$$

Using equation 7 of § 2, we obtain from (2)

$$\int_{\underline{a}}^b cf = c \int_{\underline{a}}^b f. \tag{3}$$

Now since f is integrable, the right side of (2) is the same as the right side of (3). Consequently the left sides are equal, and so cf is integrable. Equation (1) then follows from either (2) or (3).

If $c = 0$, then both sides of (1) are clearly 0. If $c < 0$, then we apply what we have already proved to the constant $-c$, which is positive, and the function $-f$, which is integrable according to lemma 2.2. We obtain

$$\int_a^b cf = \int_a^b (-c)(-f) = (-c) \int_a^b (-f)$$

$$= (-c) \left(-\int_a^b f \right) = c \int_a^b f.$$

Thus our assertion is proved in all cases. ∎

Lemma 3.2: *If f and g are bounded functions defined in $[a, b]$ and P is any partition of $[a, b]$, then*

$$U(P, f + g) \le U(P, f) + U(P, g).$$

Proof: Suppose that the points of P are $x_0, \ldots, x_n$, and let M_i', M_i'', and M_i denote the least upper bounds of f, g, and $f + g$ respectively in $[x_{i-1}, x_i]$. Then we have

$$f(x) + g(x) \le M_i' + M_i''$$

for all x in $[x_{i-1}, x_i]$, so that $M_i' + M_i''$ is an upper bound for $f + g$ in $[x_{i-1}, x_i]$. Consequently $M_i \le M_i' + M_i''$, and so we can write

$$U(P, f + g) = \sum_{i=1}^n M_i(x_i - x_{i-1})$$

$$\le \sum_{i=1}^n (M_i' + M_i'')(x_i - x_{i-1})$$

$$= \sum_{i=1}^n M_i'(x_i - x_{i-1}) + \sum_{i=1}^n M_i''(x_i - x_{i-1})$$

$$= U(P, f) + U(P, g),$$

as required. ∎

Theorem 3.3: *For any two bounded functions f and g defined in [a, b] we have*

$$\int_{\underline{a}}^b f + \int_{\underline{a}}^b g \le \int_{\underline{a}}^b (f+g) \le \int_a^{\overline{b}} (f+g) \le \int_a^{\overline{b}} f + \int_a^{\overline{b}} g. \quad (4)$$

Consequently if f and g are both integrable, then so is f + g, and we have

$$\int_{\underline{a}}^b (f+g) = \int_{\underline{a}}^b f + \int_{\underline{a}}^b g. \quad (5)$$

Proof: The second statement clearly follows from the first. Also if we can prove the right-hand inequality in (4), then the left-hand inequality will follow using equation (7) of § 2. We shall prove the right-hand inequality in (4) by showing that

$$\int_a^{\overline{b}} (f+g) < \int_a^{\overline{b}} f + \int_a^{\overline{b}} g + \epsilon \quad (6)$$

for every $\epsilon > 0$. Now, given $\epsilon > 0$, we can find partitions P_1 and P_2 of $[a, b]$ such that

$$U(P_1, f) < \int_a^{\overline{b}} f + \epsilon/2 \quad (7)$$

and

$$U(P_2, g) < \int_a^{\overline{b}} g + \epsilon/2. \quad (8)$$

Let $P = P_1 \cup P_2$. Then, adding (7) and (8) and using lemma 1.1, we obtain

$$U(P, f) + U(P, g) < \int_a^{\overline{b}} f + \int_a^{\overline{b}} g + \epsilon \quad (9)$$

The inequality (6) now follows by combining (9) with lemma 3.2 and using the fact that the upper integral is less than or equal to any upper sum. ∎

Suppose that f and g are bounded functions such that $f(x) \le g(x)$ for all x in $[a, b]$. Relative to a partition P of $[a, b]$, let M_i and M_i' denote the least upper bounds of f and g respectively in $[x_{i-1}, x_i]$. Then M_i' is certainly an upper bound for f in $[x_{i-1}, x_i]$, and so we have $M_i \le M_i'$. Consequently, we can write

$$\int_a^{\overline{b}} f \le U(P, f) = \sum_{i=1}^n M_i(x_i - x_{i-1})$$

$$\le \sum_{i=1}^n M_i'(x_i - x_{i-1}) = U(P, g).$$

Thus $\int_a^{\overline{b}} f$ is a lower bound for all upper sums of g, and so we obtain

$$\int_a^{\overline{b}} f \le \int_a^{\overline{b}} g.$$

This yields:

Lemma 3.4: *If $f(x) \leq g(x)$ for all x in $[a, b]$ and if f and g are integrable on $[a, b]$, then*

$$\int_a^b f \leq \int_a^b g. \quad \blacksquare$$

Now consider any function f defined in $[a, b]$, and define a new function f^+ in $[a, b]$ by the rules

$$f^+(x) = f(x) \quad \text{if } f(x) \geq 0$$
$$\qquad\quad = 0 \qquad \text{if } f(x) < 0.$$

The graph of f^+ is indicated by the dotted line in figure 3.1.

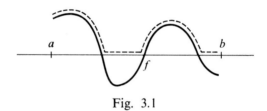

Fig. 3.1

Lemma 3.5: *If f is integrable on $[a, b]$, then so is f^+.*

Proof: By lemma 2.1 it suffices to show that given $\epsilon > 0$ there is a partition P of $[a, b]$ such that

$$U(P, f^+) - L(P, f^+) < \epsilon.$$

Since f is integrable, we know by lemma 2.1 that there is a partition P such that

$$U(P, f) - L(P, f) < \epsilon. \tag{10}$$

Suppose that the points of P are $x_0, x_1, \ldots, x_n$, and for each i let M_i and m_i be the least upper bound and greatest lower bound respectively of f in $[x_{i-1}, x_i]$. Also let M_i^+ and m_i^+ be the least upper bound and greatest lower bound for f^+ in $[x_{i-1}, x_i]$. Then since $f(x) \leq f^+(x)$ for all x, we must have

$$m_i \leq m_i^+. \tag{11}$$

Now if $M_i > 0$, then $M_i^+ = M_i$, and so it follows from (11) that

$$M_i^+ - m_i^+ \leq M_i - m_i. \tag{12}$$

On the other hand, if $M_i \leq 0$, then both M_i^+ and m_i^+ must be 0, and so (12) is true in any case. Consequently, using (10) and (12) we can write

$$U(P, f^+) - L(P, f^+) = \sum_{i=1}^n (M_i^+ - m_i^+)(x_i - x_{i-1})$$

$$\leq \sum_{i=1}^{n} (M_i - m_i)(x_i - x_{i-1}) < \epsilon,$$

which is what is required. ∎

If f is any function, then we let $|f|$ denote the function whose value at x is $|f(x)|$ for every x in the domain of f.

Theorem 3.6: *If f is integrable on $[a, b]$, then so is $|f|$, and we have*

$$\left| \int_a^b f \right| \leq \int_a^b |f|.$$
(13)

Proof: First, by treating separately the cases $f(x) \geq 0$ and $f(x) < 0$, one easily verifies the relation

$$|f| = f^+ + (-f)^+.$$
(14)

Now, since f is integrable, so is $-f$. Consequently, by lemma 3.5, so are f^+ and $(-f)^+$. Therefore, by theorem 3.3 and equation (14), $|f|$ is integrable. Furthermore, for all x in $[a, b]$ we have

$$f(x) \leq |f(x)| \quad \text{and} \quad -f(x) \leq |f(x)|.$$

Therefore lemma 3.4 yields

$$\int_a^b f \leq \int_a^b |f| \quad \text{and} \quad -\int_a^b f \leq \int_a^b |f|.$$

But since $|\int_a^b f|$ is one of the two numbers $\int_a^b f$ and $-\int_a^b f$, this proves (13). ∎

EXERCISES

1. If $c > 0$, prove that

$$\int_{\underline{a}}^b cf = c \int_{\underline{a}}^b f$$

similarly to the way that the corresponding equality for upper integrals was proved.

2. If $c < 0$, prove that

$$\int_{\underline{a}}^b cf = c \int_a^{\overline{b}} f$$

and

$$\int_a^{\overline{b}} cf = c \int_{\underline{a}}^b f.$$

(Hint: Write $cf = (-c)(-f)$, and use the results already proved for positive constants.)

3. If cf is integrable and $c \neq 0$, prove that f is integrable. Is this true if $c = 0$?

4. Let f be the function defined in the interval $[0, 1]$ by

$$f(x) = 0 \quad \text{for } x \text{ rational}$$
$$= 1 \quad \text{for } x \text{ irrational.}$$

Also let $g = -f$. Show that

$$\overline{\int_0^1} (f + g) = 0,$$

whereas

$$\overline{\int_0^1} f + \overline{\int_0^1} g = 1.$$

5. If $f(x) \leq g(x)$ for all x in $[a, b]$, prove that

$$\int_a^b f \leq \int_a^b g.$$

6. Let f be the function whose graph is in figure 3.2. Sketch the graphs of f^+, $-f$, $(-f)^+$, and $f^+ + (-f)^+$.

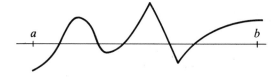

Fig. 3.2

7. Prove the inequality

$$\underline{\int_a^b} f + \underline{\int_a^b} g \leq \underline{\int_a^b} (f + g)$$

similarly to the way the corresponding inequality for upper integrals was proved.

4. THE FUNDAMENTAL THEOREM OF THE CALCULUS

Suppose that $a < c < b$, and that P is a partition of $[a, b]$ containing c as one of its points. Denote the points of P by $x_0, x_1, \ldots, x_n$, and assume that $c = x_k$. Then the points $x_0, \ldots, x_k$ form a partition P_1 of $[a, c]$, and the points $x_k, x_{k+1}, \ldots, x_n$ form a partition P_2 of $[c, b]$; see figure 4.1. Furthermore, if f is any bounded function defined in $[a, b]$, then letting M_i be the least upper bound of f in $[x_{i-1}, x_i]$, we have

$$U(P, f) = \sum_{i=1}^n M_i(x_i - x_{i-1})$$

$$= \sum_{i=1}^k M_i(x_i - x_{i-1}) + \sum_{i=k+1}^n M_i(x_i - x_{i-1})$$

$$= U(P_1, f) + U(P_2, f). \tag{1}$$

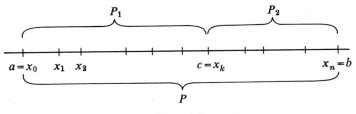

Fig. 4.1

Lemma 4.1: *If $a < c < b$ and f is any bounded function defined in* $[a, b]$, *then*

$$\int_a^{\overline{b}} f = \int_a^{\overline{c}} f + \int_c^{\overline{b}} f \tag{2}$$

and

$$\int_{\underline{a}}^b f = \int_{\underline{a}}^c f + \int_{\underline{c}}^b f. \tag{3}$$

Proof: Let P_1 and P_2 be any partitions of the intervals $[a, c]$ and $[c, b]$ respectively, and let $P = P_1 \cup P_2$. Then P is a partition of $[a, b]$, and using (1) we obtain

$$\int_a^{\overline{b}} f \leq U(P, f) = U(P_1, f) + U(P_2, f).$$

But this can be rewritten

$$\int_a^{\overline{b}} f - U(P_2, f) \leq U(P_1, f), \tag{4}$$

so that for a fixed partition P_2 of $[c, b]$, the left side of (4) is a lower bound for all upper sums of f on $[a, c]$. Consequently,

$$\int_a^{\overline{b}} f - U(P_2, f) \leq \int_a^{\overline{c}} f,$$

or in other words,

$$\int_a^{\overline{b}} f - \int_a^{\overline{c}} f \leq U(P_2, f). \tag{5}$$

Now (5) holds for all partitions P_2 of $[c, b]$, and consequently the left side of (5) is a lower bound for all upper sums of f on $[c, b]$. Therefore

$$\int_a^{\overline{b}} f - \int_a^{\overline{c}} f \leq \int_c^{\overline{b}} f,$$

or in other words,

$$\int_a^{\overline{b}} f \leq \int_a^{\overline{c}} f + \int_c^{\overline{b}} f. \tag{6}$$

Now start with any partition P of the big interval $[a, b]$, and let P' be the partition obtained from P by adding c. (Of course if c is already in P, then this last step would not be necessary.) Let P_1 and P_2 be the sets of points of P' which are in $[a, c]$ and $[c, b]$ respectively. Then using (1) and lemma 1.1 we obtain

$$U(P, f) \geq U(P', f) = U(P_1, f) + U(P_2, f) \geq \int_a^{\overline{c}} f + \int_c^{\overline{b}} f. \tag{7}$$

Thus the right side of (7) is a lower bound for all upper sums of f on $[a, b]$, and consequently,

$$\int_a^{\overline{b}} f \geq \int_a^{\overline{c}} f + \int_c^{\overline{b}} f. \tag{8}$$

Combining (6) and (8), we obtain (2). Equation (3) then follows by using equation (7) of § 2. ∎

Theorem 4.2: *If $a < c < b$, then f is integrable on $[a, b]$ if and only if it is integrable on both $[a, c]$ and $[c, b]$, in which case we have*

$$\int_a^b f = \int_a^c f + \int_c^b f. \tag{9}$$

Proof: If f is integrable on both $[a, c]$ and $[c, b]$, then the right sides of equations (2) and (3) are equal. Therefore the same is true of the left sides, showing that f is integrable on $[a, b]$.

Conversely, suppose that f is integrable on $[a, b]$. Then the left sides of (2) and (3) are equal, and so subtracting (3) from (2) we obtain

$$0 = \left(\int_a^{\overline{c}} f - \int_{\underline{a}}^c f \right) + \left(\int_c^{\overline{b}} f - \int_{\underline{c}}^b f \right). \tag{10}$$

But since each of the terms in parentheses in (10) is nonnegative, they must both be 0, and consequently f is integrable on both $[a, c]$ and $[c, b]$. Equation (9) then follows from either (2) or (3). ∎

If $a < b$, then we have a meaning for the symbol $\int_a^b f$, but not for the symbols $\int_a^a f$ and $\int_b^a f$. We would like to define the latter symbols in such a way that equation (9) will hold no matter what the relative positions of a, b, and c are. In the first place, if (9) is to hold in the case where $a = b = c$, then it must be true that

$$\int_a^a f = \int_a^a f + \int_a^a f,$$

and so we must define $\int_a^a f = 0$. Now if $a < b$ and f is integrable on $[a, b]$, then it must be true that

$$\int_a^a f = \int_a^b f + \int_b^a f. \tag{11}$$

But since we have defined the left side of (11) to be 0, this means that we must define

$$\int_b^a f = -\int_a^b f. \tag{12}$$

Now we must check that the definition (12) is actually such that (9) holds in all cases. Suppose, for example, that $c < a < b$, and that f is integrable on $[c, b]$. Then by theorem 4.2,

$$\int_c^b f = \int_c^a f + \int_a^b f,$$

which can be rewritten

$$-\int_c^a f + \int_c^b f = \int_a^b f.$$

But in view of our definition (12), this is equivalent to

$$\int_a^c f + \int_c^b f = \int_a^b f,$$

as required. The other cases are left as exercises.

It must be remarked that the inequality

$$\left| \int_a^b f \right| \le \int_a^b |f|,$$

proved in theorem 3.6, holds only in the case where $a < b$, since if $a > b$, the right side will in general be negative. In order to cover all cases we must write

$$\left| \int_a^b f \right| \le \left| \int_a^b |f| \right|. \tag{13}$$

The following theorem gives the connection between the differential calculus and the integral calculus.

Theorem 4.3 (The Fundamental Theorem of the Calculus):   *Let f be integrable on some interval containing a point a, and let F be the function defined by*

$$F(x) = \int_a^x f$$

for all x in that interval. Then F is continuous. Furthermore, at any point x where f is continuous, F has a derivative given by

$$F'(x) = f(x).$$

Proof: Let B be any number such that $|f(x)| < B$ for all x in the interval. To show that F is continuous, let x' and x'' be any two points of the interval. Then, using (9), (13), and lemmas 2.3 and 3.4, we obtain

$$|F(x') - F(x'')| = \left| \int_a^{x'} f - \int_a^{x''} f \right| = \left| \int_{x''}^{x'} f \right|$$

$$\leq \left| \int_{x''}^{x'} |f| \right| \leq \left| \int_{x''}^{x'} B \right| = B|x' - x''|.$$

Hence, given $\epsilon > 0$, we need only take $|x' - x''| < \epsilon/B$ to insure that $|F(x') - F(x'')| < \epsilon$. This proves continuity of F.

Now let c be any point where f is continuous. To prove that $F'(c) = f(c)$, by definition of derivative we must show that given $\epsilon > 0$, there exists $\delta > 0$ such that

$$\left| \frac{F(c + h) - F(c)}{h} - f(c) \right| < \epsilon$$

whenever $|h| < \delta$. Since f is continuous at c, we know that there does exist $\delta > 0$ such that

$$|f(x) - f(c)| < \epsilon$$

whenever $|x - c| < \delta$. Then, treating the number $f(c)$ as a constant function on the closed interval between c and $c + h$, we can write for $|h| < \delta$,

$$\left| \frac{F(c + h) - F(c)}{h} - f(c) \right| = \left| \frac{1}{h} \left(\int_a^{c+h} f - \int_a^c f \right) - \frac{1}{h} \int_c^{c+h} f(c) \right|$$

$$= \frac{1}{|h|} \left| \int_c^{c+h} f - \int_c^{c+h} f(c) \right|$$

$$= \frac{1}{|h|} \left| \int_c^{c+h} (f - f(c)) \right|$$

$$\leq \frac{1}{|h|} \left| \int_c^{c+h} |f - f(c)| \right| \leq \frac{1}{|h|} \left| \int_c^{c+h} \epsilon \right|$$

$$= \frac{1}{|h|} |\epsilon h| = \epsilon.$$

This is what is required. ∎

EXERCISES

1. Prove equation (3) similarly to the way equation (2) was proved.

2. If f is integrable on some interval and F is defined by

$$F(x) = \int_a^x f$$

for all x in the interval, what is $F(a)$? Show that if $f(x) \geq 0$ for all x in the interval, then F is nondecreasing, whereas if $f(x) \leq 0$ for all x in the interval, then F is nonincreasing.

3. Let F be defined by

$$F(x) = \int_0^x 2$$

for all numbers x. Draw the graph of F. What is its derivative?

4. Let $f(x) = x$ for all x, and define

$$F(x) = \int_0^x f$$

for all x. Use exercise 1 of § 2 to show that $F(x) = \dfrac{x^2 - 1}{2}$. Then show independently of theorem 4.3 that $F' = f$.

5. Use theorem 4.2 and induction on n to show that if $a_0 < a_1 < a_2 < \cdots < a_n$, then f is integrable on $[a_0, a_n]$ if and only if it is integrable on each of the intervals $[a_{i-1}, a_i]$, in which case we have

$$\int_{a_0}^{a_n} f = \int_{a_0}^{a_1} f + \int_{a_1}^{a_2} f + \cdots + \int_{a_{n-1}}^{a_n} f.$$

5. COMPUTATION OF THE INTEGRAL

In this section we shall establish integrability for a certain class of functions, and we shall find a method for computing their integrals.

Lemma 5.1: *If f is continuous in $[a, b]$ and ϵ is any positive number, there is a partition P of $[a, b]$ such that*

$$U(P, f) - L(P, f) < \epsilon.$$

Proof: Since f is continuous in $[a, b]$, it is uniformly continuous by theorem 6.1 of chapter III. Thus there is a $\delta > 0$ such that

$$|f(x') - f(x'')| < \frac{\epsilon}{b - a} \tag{1}$$

whenever $|x' - x''| < \delta$. Let P be any partition of $[a, b]$ such that $|P| < \delta$, and let the points of P be $x_0, x_1, \ldots, x_n$. In each interval $[x_{i-1}, x_i]$, we know by theorem 7.2 of chapter III that the least upper bound M_i and the greatest lower bound m_i are actually values of f. Consequently, since $|x_i - x_{i-1}| < \delta$, we see from (1) that

$$|M_i - m_i| < \frac{\epsilon}{b - a}$$

for each i. Therefore we can write

$$U(P, f) - L(P, f) = \sum_{i=1}^{n} (M_i - m_i)(x_i - x_{i-1})$$

$$< \sum_{i=1}^{n} \frac{\epsilon}{b - a} (x_i - x_{i-1}) = \frac{\epsilon}{b - a} (b - a) = \epsilon,$$

which is what is required. ∎

In view of lemma 2.1, the above lemma shows us that a continuous function in a closed interval is integrable on that interval. However, we can do slightly better than this. Namely:

Theorem 5.2: *Let f be a function which is bounded in some interval* $[a, b]$, *and suppose that f is continuous in the open interval* (a, b) *(but not necessarily at the endpoints a and b). Then f is integrable on* $[a, b]$.

Proof: By lemma 2.1 it suffices to show that given $\epsilon > 0$, there is a partition P of $[a, b]$ such that

$$|U(P, f) - L(P, f)| < \epsilon.$$

Let B be any number such that $|f(x)| < B$ for all x in $[a, b]$, and define

$$c = a + \frac{\epsilon}{8B}, \quad d = b - \frac{\epsilon}{8B}.$$

We assume that ϵ is small enough so that $c < d$ (see figure 5.1). Since f is continuous in $[c, d]$, by lemma 5.1 there is a partition P_1 of $[c, d]$ such that

$$U(P_1, f) - L(P_1, f) < \frac{\epsilon}{2}.$$

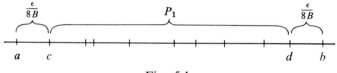

Fig. 5.1

Now if we denote the least upper bound and greatest lower bound for f in $[a, c]$ by M' and m' respectively, then we have $M' \leq B$ and $-m' \leq B$. Similarly, if M'' and m'' denote the least upper bound and greatest lower bound for f in $[d, b]$, then $M'' \leq B$ and $-m'' \leq B$. Consequently, if P denotes the partition of $[a, b]$ obtained by adding a and b to P_1, we can write

$$U(P,f) - L(P,f) = (M'(c - a) + U(P_1, f) + M''(b - d))$$
$$- (m'(c - a) + L(P_1, f) + m''(b - d))$$
$$\leq U(P_1, f) - L(P_1, f) + 4B\frac{\epsilon}{8B}$$
$$< \frac{\epsilon}{2} + \frac{\epsilon}{2} = \epsilon. \quad \blacksquare$$

Theorem 5.3: *Let f be bounded in some interval [a, b], and suppose that f is continuous in the open interval (a, b). Let G be a function which is continuous in the closed interval [a, b], and which is such that G'(x) = f(x) for all x in (a, b). Then*

$$\int_a^b f = G(b) - G(a).$$

Proof: By theorem 5.2, f is integrable on $[a, b]$, and so we can define

$$F(x) = \int_a^x f \tag{2}$$

for all x in $[a, b]$. Furthermore, by theorem 4.3, we know that F is continuous in $[a, b]$ and $F'(x) = f(x)$ for all x in (a, b). But then since F and G are continuous in a closed interval and have the same derivative in the open interval, by corollary 9.5 of chapter III they must differ by a constant, say

$$F(x) - G(x) = c \tag{3}$$

for all x in $[a, b]$. In particular (3) must hold for $x = a$, and so since $F(a) = 0$, it follows that $c = -G(a)$. Equation (3) then becomes

$$F(x) = G(x) - G(a),$$

and in particular putting $x = b$, this yields

$$\int_a^b f = F(b) = G(b) - G(a). \quad \blacksquare$$

A function G such that $G' = f$ is called an *antiderivative* for f. Thus, theorem 5.3 shows us how to compute the integral of a continuous function once we have found an antiderivative for the function. If G is any antiderivative for f, then since the derivative of a constant c is 0, it follows that $G + c$ is also an antiderivative for f. Thus if f has one antiderivative, then it has an infinite number of them. On the other hand, corollary 9.5 of chapter III shows that any two antiderivatives for a function in an interval must differ by a constant. The process of finding antiderivatives is largely a matter of guess work, although we shall later develop some methods which will help us in our guessing.

Before doing some examples, we introduce two notational conveniences. The first is to write

$$\int_a^b f(x)\,dx$$

in place of $\int_a^b f$. Thus, for example, if $f(x) = x^3 - 3x$ for all x in [2, 5], then $\int_2^5 f$ can also be denoted by

$$\int_2^5 (x^3 - 3x)\,dx. \tag{4}$$

Of course the symbol x plays no role in the value of the integral, and we could equally well denote (4) by

$$\int_2^5 (t^3 - 3t)\,dt$$

or

$$\int_2^5 (y^3 - 3y)\,dy.$$

The symbol dx is simply a device used to avoid ambiguity as to what the values of our function are. For example, the expression

$$\int_1^4 ux^2\,dx$$

stands for the integral of the function whose value at x is ux^2 where u is a constant, whereas

$$\int_1^4 ux^2\,du$$

stands for the integral of the function whose value at u is ux^2 where x is a constant.

The other notational convenience which we shall adopt is to write

$$[G(x)]_a^b$$

in place of $G(b) - G(a)$. For example,

$$[x^2 + 1]_{-1}^3 = (3^2 + 1) - ((-1)^2 + 1) = 8.$$

Example 1: Evaluate the integral

$$\int_1^3 x^3\,dx.$$

An antiderivative for x^3 is $\dfrac{x^4}{4}$. Therefore, by theorem 5.3 we have

$$\int_1^3 x^3\,dx = \left[\frac{x^4}{4}\right]_1^3 = \frac{81}{4} - \frac{1}{4} = 20.$$

More generally, we can compute integrals for any function of the form $f(x) = x^n$ where n is an integer not equal to -1, since clearly an antiderivative for f is given by

$$G(x) = \frac{x^{n+1}}{n+1}.$$ (5)

In particular, this enables us to integrate any polynomial function.

Example 2:   Evaluate the integral

$$\int_{-1}^{2} (x^2 - 3x + 2)\, dx.$$

An antiderivative for $x^2 - 3x + 2$ is $\dfrac{x^3}{3} - 3\dfrac{x^2}{2} + 2x$. Consequently, we have

$$\int_{-1}^{2} (x^2 - 3x + 2)\, dx = \left[\frac{x^3}{3} - 3\frac{x^2}{2} + 2x \right]_{-1}^{2} = \frac{9}{2}.$$

Example 3:   Evaluate the integral

$$\int_{0}^{\pi} \sin t\, dt.$$

An antiderivative for sin is $-\cos$. Thus we have

$$\int_{0}^{\pi} \sin t\, dt = [-\cos t]_0^{\pi} = (-\cos \pi) - (-\cos 0) = 2.$$

Example 4:   Evaluate

$$\int_{0}^{1/2} \frac{dx}{\sqrt{1 - x^2}}.$$

We have written $\dfrac{dx}{\sqrt{1 - x^2}}$ under the integral sign as an abbreviation for $\dfrac{1}{\sqrt{1 - x^2}}\, dx$. This is a standard practice in dealing with quotients. From chapter III, § 5 we see that arcsin is an antiderivative in this case. Therefore

$$\int_{0}^{1/2} \frac{dx}{\sqrt{1 - x^2}} = [\arcsin x]_0^{1/2} = \frac{\pi}{6}.$$

Example 5:   If $f(x) = \dfrac{1}{x^2}$ for all $x \neq 0$, then the symbol

$$\int_{-1}^{3} f$$

has no meaning, since f is not defined everywhere between -1 and 3. Furthermore, even if we defined f at 0, say $f(0) = 1$, the expression would still have no meaning since f is not bounded in the interval $[-1, 3]$. However, the expression

$$\int_1^3 \frac{dx}{x^2}$$

makes sense, and in fact

$$\int_1^3 \frac{dx}{x^2} = \left[\frac{-1}{x}\right]_1^3 = \left(\frac{-1}{3}\right) - (-1) = \frac{2}{3}.$$

Example 6: Consider the function f defined in the interval $[0, 4]$ as follows:

$$\begin{aligned} f(x) &= 1 + x && \text{for } 0 \le x \le \pi/2 \\ &= \sin x && \text{for } \pi/2 < x \le \pi \\ &= 2 + (x - \pi)^2 && \text{for } \pi < x \le 4. \end{aligned}$$

The graph of f is shown in figure 5.2. There are two points of discontinuity. By theorem 5.2, f is integrable on each of the intervals $[0, \pi/2]$, $[\pi/2, \pi]$, and $[\pi, 4]$, and we can write

$$\int_0^4 f = \int_0^{\pi/2} f + \int_{\pi/2}^{\pi} f + \int_{\pi}^4 f.$$

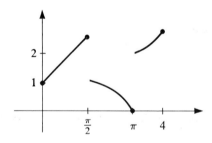

Fig. 5.2

Each of the three terms on the right can now be evaluated using theorem 5.3. Thus:

$$\int_0^{\pi/2} f = \left[x + \frac{x^2}{2}\right]_0^{\pi/2} = \pi/2 + \pi^2/8$$

$$\int_{\pi/2}^{\pi} f = [-\cos x]_{\pi/2}^{\pi} = 1$$

$$\int_{\pi}^4 f = [2x + (x - \pi)^3/3]_{\pi}^4 = 8 + \frac{(4 - \pi)^3}{3} - 2\pi.$$

Example 7: Evaluation of the integral

$$\int_1^5 \frac{1}{x}\, dx$$

would involve finding an antiderivative for x^{-1}. Now formula (5) gives an antiderivative for x^n for any integer n other than -1. However, it does not apply for $n = -1$, and in fact it is not possible to give an antiderivative for x^{-1} in terms of the functions we have encountered so far. Nevertheless, it would be a grave error to assume that the function has no antiderivative just because we can't find one in terms of the few functions which are within our experience. In fact, one of the antiderivatives of x^{-1} will give rise to the whole subject matter for §§ 1 and 2 of the following chapter.

EXERCISES

1. For each of the following functions, describe the intervals for which the integral $\int_a^b f$ makes sense.

   (a) $f(x) = x^{-5}$

   (b) $f(x) = \tan x$

   (c) $f(x) = (x^2 + 1)^{-4}$

   (d) $f(x) = \dfrac{1}{(x-1)(x+2)}$

2. Evaluate each of the following.

   (a) $\displaystyle\int_{-1}^3 (x^2 - 5x + 1)\, dx$

   (b) $\displaystyle\int_0^{10} (x^9 + x)\, dx$

   (c) $\displaystyle\int_0^{\pi/4} \cos x\, dx$

   (d) $\displaystyle\int_{-1}^1 \frac{dx}{1 + x^2}$

   (e) $\displaystyle\int_1^3 \frac{dx}{x^3}$

   (f) $\displaystyle\int_0^2 x(x^2 + 1)^3\, dx$

   (g) $\displaystyle\int_1^4 \frac{dx}{\sqrt{x}}$

   (h) $\displaystyle\int_{-\pi/4}^{\pi/4} \sec^2 x\, dx$

3. Find $\int_{-1}^2 |x|\, dx$.

4. Define $f(x) = \dfrac{x}{|x|}$ for $x \neq 0$, and define $f(0) = 0$. Find $\int_{-2}^1 f$.

5. Define
$$\begin{aligned} f(x) &= x^2 && \text{for } -2 \le x < 0, \\ &= \sqrt{x} + 1 && \text{for } 0 \le x < 1, \\ &= \frac{x}{\sqrt{1 + x^2}} && \text{for } 1 \le x \le 2. \end{aligned}$$

   Find $\int_{-2}^2 f$.

6. (a) Suppose that $f(x) = 0$ for all but a finite number of x in $[a, b]$. Show how it follows from theorems 4.2 and 5.2 that f is integrable on $[a, b]$ and $\int_a^b f = 0$.

(b) Suppose f is integrable on $[a, b]$, and let g be a function such that $g(x) = f(x)$ for all but a finite number of x in $[a, b]$. Show how it follows from part (a) and theorem 3.3 that g is integrable on $[a, b]$, and that

$$\int_a^b g(x)\, dx = \int_a^b f(x)\, dx.$$

7. Suppose that f is continuous in $[a, b]$, and let m and M be the greatest lower bound and least upper bound for f in $[a, b]$. Suppose also that $m \neq M$ (so that f is not constant). Prove that

$$m(b - a) < \int_a^b f < M(b - a).$$

8. Explain why it follows from theorem 10.1 of chapter III that if f is a function with a jump discontinuity somewhere in an interval $[a, b]$, then f can have no antiderivative on the interval. On the other hand, give an example of a function which has a discontinuity (necessarily due to oscillation) in an interval, but nevertheless has an antiderivative on that interval. (Hint: See § 12, example 3 of chapter II.)

6. DARBOUX'S THEOREM

In lemma 1.1 we showed that if we add some points to a partition P to obtain a new partition P', then

$$0 \leq U(P, f) - U(P', f).$$

In the following lemma, we show that the above difference cannot be "too big." Precisely:

Lemma 6.1: *Let B be a number such that $|f(x)| \leq B$ for all x in $[a, b]$, and let P be a partition of $[a, b]$. If P' is a partition obtained from P by the addition of N new points, then*

$$U(P, f) - U(P', f) \leq 2NB|P|. \tag{1}$$

Proof: Consider first the case where P' is obtained from P by the addition of one new point x, and suppose x falls in the kth interval $[x_{k-1}, x_k]$ determined by P. As in lemma 1.1, we let M', M'', and M_k be the least upper bound of f in the intervals $[x_{k-1}, x]$, $[x, x_k]$, and $[x_{k-1}, x_k]$ respectively. Then

$$U(P, f) - U(P', f) = M_k(x_k - x_{k-1}) - M'(x - x_{k-1}) - M''(x_k - x)$$
$$\leq B(x_k - x_{k-1}) + B(x - x_{k-1}) + B(x_k - x)$$
$$= 2B(x_k - x_{k-1}) \leq 2B|P|. \tag{2}$$

Now suppose that P' is obtained from P by adding N points. Then, using the fact that the addition of a point cannot increase the mesh of a partition, the inequality (1) follows by an easy induction on N using what we have already proved. ∎

By definition, the upper integral is the greatest lower bound of all the upper sums. Thus, given any positive ϵ, there must be at least one partition P satisfying

$$U(P, f) - \int_a^{\overline{b}} f < \epsilon.$$

The theorem we are now going to prove shows that in fact we can say a lot more than merely that there exists *one* partition satisfying the above inequality.

Theorem 6.2 (Darboux's Theorem): *If f is any function which is bounded in $[a, b]$, then for any positive number ϵ there exists a positive number δ such that for* all *partitions P satisfying $|P| < \delta$, we have*

$$U(P, f) - \int_a^{\overline{b}} f < \epsilon$$

and

$$\int_{\underline{a}}^b f - L(P, f) < \epsilon.$$

Proof: Given $\epsilon > 0$, we know that there is a partition P_0 satisfying

$$U(P_0, f) - \int_a^{\overline{b}} f < \epsilon/2.$$

Suppose that P_0 has N points, and let $\delta = \epsilon/4NB$, where B is any positive number such that $|f(x)| \leq B$ for all x in $[a, b]$. Let P be any partition such that $|P| < \delta$, and let P' be the partition obtained from P by adding the points of P_0. Using lemmas 1.1 and 6.1, we can then write

$$U(P, f) - \int_a^{\overline{b}} f = U(P, f) - U(P', f) + U(P', f) - \int_a^{\overline{b}} f$$

$$\leq 2NB|P| + U(P_0, f) - \int_a^{\overline{b}} f$$

$$< 2NB \frac{\epsilon}{4NB} + \frac{\epsilon}{2} = \epsilon,$$

as required. Now applying what we have already proved to the function $-f$, we know there exists a number $\delta > 0$ such that

$$U(P, -f) - \int_a^{\overline{b}} (-f) < \epsilon \tag{3}$$

whenever $|P| < \delta$. But (3) is equivalent to

$$\int_{\underline{a}}^b f - L(P, f) < \epsilon.$$

That the two numbers δ found above can be taken to be equal follows by using the smaller of the two. ∎

7. RIEMANN SUMS

Let P be the partition

$$a = x_0 < x_1 < \cdots < x_{n-1} < x_n = b,$$

and let f be a function defined in $[a, b]$. For each i, choose a number $x_i' \in [x_{i-1}, x_i]$ (figure 7.1). If M_i and m_i denote the least upper and greatest lower bounds for f in $[x_{i-1}, x_i]$, then

$$m_i \leq f(x_i') \leq M_i.$$

Consequently,

$$L(P, f) \leq \sum_{i=1}^{n} f(x_i')(x_i - x_{i-1}) \leq U(P, f). \tag{1}$$

The expression in the middle of (1) is called a *Riemann sum for f relative to the partition P*. It is named after the German mathematician Georg Friedrich Bernhard Riemann (1826–1866) who first put the theory of the integral on a rigorous basis. For each partition P there are as many Riemann sums as there are ways of picking points x_i' out of the intervals $[x_{i-1}, x_i]$ (which means quite a few).

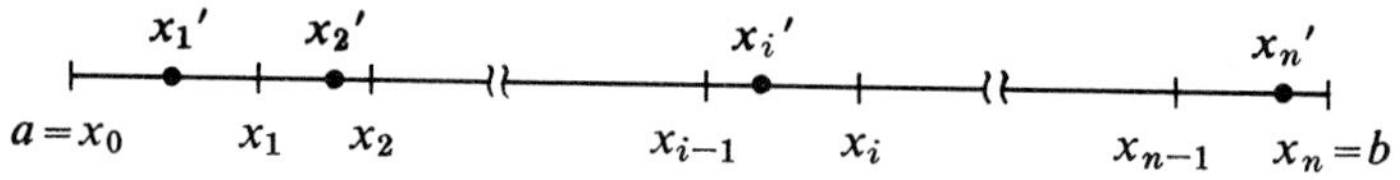

Fig. 7.1

Theorem 7.1: *Let f be integrable on $[a, b]$. Then for any positive number ϵ there exists a positive δ such that*

$$\left| R - \int_a^b f \right| < \epsilon \tag{2}$$

whenever R is a Riemann sum for f relative to a partition of mesh less than δ.

Proof: Replace ϵ by $\epsilon/2$ in theorem 6.2, and add the two inequalities of that theorem. The upper and lower integrals cancel since f is integrable. Thus we see that there exists a positive number δ such that

$$U(P, f) - L(P, f) < \epsilon \tag{3}$$

whenever $|P| < \delta$. Now if R is a Riemann sum for f relative to P, then from (1) we see that R is between $L(P, f)$ and $U(P, f)$. But since $\int_a^b f$ is also between these two numbers, the required inequality (2) follows from (3). ∎

As a converse of theorem 7.1 we have

Theorem 7.2: *Let f be any function which is bounded in $[a, b]$. Suppose that there is a number I with the property that for each positive ϵ there is a positive δ such that*

$$|R - I| < \epsilon$$

whenever R is a Riemann sum relative to a partition of mesh less than δ. Then f is integrable on $[a, b]$, and, furthermore,

$$\int_a^b f = I.$$

Proof: We shall show that

$$\left| \int_a^{\overline{b}} f - I \right| < \epsilon$$

for every positive number ϵ. This will prove that $I = \int_a^{\overline{b}} f$. A similar argument will show also that $I = \int_{\underline{a}}^b f$, and so this will prove the theorem.

Given $\epsilon > 0$, by hypothesis there is a number $\delta_1 > 0$ such that $|R - I| < \epsilon/3$ whenever R is a Riemann sum relative to a partition of mesh less than δ_1. Let P_1 be such a partition. Also let P_2 be a partition such that

$$U(P_2, f) - \int_a^{\overline{b}} f < \epsilon/3. \tag{4}$$

Let P be the union of P_1 and P_2. Then $|P| \le |P_1| < \delta$, and so $|R - I| < \epsilon/3$ whenever R is a Riemann sum relative to P. Also from (4) and lemma 1.1 we see

$$U(P, f) - \int_a^{\overline{b}} f < \epsilon/3. \tag{5}$$

Suppose that the points of P are

$$a = x_0 < x_1 < \cdots < x_{n-1} < x_n = b.$$

For each i choose a point x_i' in $[x_{i-1}, x_i]$ such that

$$M_i - f(x_i') < \epsilon/3(b - a),$$

where M_i is the least upper bound of f in $[x_{i-1}, x_i]$. Then

$$\left| \int_a^{\bar b} f - I \right| \le \left| \int_a^{\bar b} f - \sum_{i=1}^n M_i(x_i - x_{i-1}) \right|$$

$$+ \left| \sum_{i=1}^n (M_i - f(x_i'))(x_i - x_{i-1}) \right|$$

$$+ \left| \sum_{i=1}^n f(x_i')(x_i - x_{i-1}) - I \right|$$

$$< \frac{\epsilon}{3} + \sum_{i=1}^n \frac{\epsilon}{3(b-a)} (x_i - x_{i-1}) + \frac{\epsilon}{3}$$

$$= \frac{\epsilon}{3} + \frac{\epsilon}{3(b-a)} (b-a) + \frac{\epsilon}{3} = \epsilon,$$

as required. ∎

Riemann originally defined a bounded function f to be integrable on $[a, b]$ if there exists a number I satisfying the condition of theorem 7.2, in which case he called I the integral. The definition of the integral in terms of upper and lower sums is due to Darboux. Theorems 7.1 and 7.2 therefore establish the equivalence of the Riemann and Darboux definitions of the integral. There is another definition of the integral which is due to the French mathematician Henri Lebesgue (1875–1941). It turns out that any function which has a Riemann integral also has a Lebesgue integral, and the two integrals are equal. However, there are functions which have a Lebesgue integral which do not have a Riemann integral. Such is the case with the function f such that $f(x) = 1$ for x irrational in $[0, 1]$ and $f(x) = 0$ for x rational in that interval. In example 1 of § 2 we saw that this function is not integrable in the Darboux-Riemann sense. However, it turns out that its Lebesgue integral is 1. Nevertheless, there are bounded functions which do not even have a Lebesgue integral. The Lebesgue integral lends itself more readily than the Riemann integral to the generalizations which are necessary in treating functions whose domains, instead of being finite intervals, are arbitrary sets of points on the line, or in the plane, or in three or more dimensions. However, the reasoning involved in the Lebesgue theory is somewhat more sophisticated than that involved in the Darboux-Riemann theory. A proper understanding of the latter should come first.

Using theorem 7.1, we can give another proof of theorem 5.3. In fact, we can improve slightly on theorem 5.3, since that theorem required the function f to be continuous, whereas the theorem we are about to prove requires only that f be integrable.

Theorem 7.3: *Suppose that f is integrable on $[a, b]$, and let G be a continuous function in $[a, b]$ such that $G'(x) = f(x)$ for all x in (a, b). Then*

$$\int_a^b f = G(b) - G(a).$$

Proof: We prove the theorem by showing that

$$\left| G(b) - G(a) - \int_a^b f \right| < \epsilon \tag{6}$$

for every positive number ϵ. For fixed ϵ, it follows from theorem 7.1 that there is a partition P such that

$$\left| R - \int_a^b f \right| < \epsilon \tag{7}$$

whenever R is a Riemann sum for f relative to P. Now in each interval (x_{i-1}, x_i) determined by P we can find, by the mean value theorem (corollary 9.3 of chapter III), a number x_i' such that

$$G(x_i) - G(x_{i-1}) = G'(x_i')(x_i - x_{i-1}).$$

That is, using the fact that $G' = f$ in (a, b),

$$G(x_1) - G(x_0) = f(x_1')(x_1 - x_0)$$
$$G(x_2) - G(x_1) = f(x_2')(x_2 - x_1)$$
$$\vdots$$
$$G(x_n) - G(x_{n-1}) = f(x_n')(x_n - x_{n-1}).$$

Adding these equalities, we find that most of the terms on the left side cancel each other, and we are left with

$$G(x_n) - G(x_0) = \sum_{i=1}^{n} f(x_i')(x_i - x_{i-1}). \tag{8}$$

Now the right side is just a Riemann sum relative to P, and furthermore, $x_0 = a$ and $x_n = b$. Therefore the desired inequality (6) follows from (7) and (8). ∎

EXERCISES

1. Let f be bounded in $[a, b]$, and let I be a number. Suppose that for some fixed positive number ϵ there is a partition P such that

   $$|I - R| < \epsilon$$

   whenever R is a Riemann sum for f relative to P. Show that any partition obtained by adding one point (and hence any finite number of points) to P has the same property as P relative to the same positive ϵ.

2. Use exercise 1 to show that all we really needed to assume in theorem 7.2 was that for each positive ϵ there is at least *one* partition P with the given property.

8. PRODUCTS

In this section we shall show that if f and g are integrable on some interval, then fg is also integrable on that interval. We first prove a lemma concerning the least upper bound and greatest lower bound of the square of a function.

Lemma 8.1: *Suppose $f(x) \geq 0$ for all x in some set of numbers S, and let M and m denote respectively the least upper bound and greatest lower bound for f in S. Then M^2 and m^2 are the least upper bound and greatest lower bound for f^2 in S.*

Proof: For all x in S, $f(x) \leq M$. Since $f(x) \geq 0$, this means that $f^2(x) \leq M^2$. Hence M^2 is an upper bound for f^2. To prove that it is the *least* upper bound, we must show that given $\epsilon > 0$, there is an x_0 in S such that $M^2 - f^2(x_0) < \epsilon$. Since M is the least upper bound for f, we know there is an x_0 such that

$$M - f(x_0) < \frac{\epsilon}{2M + 1}.$$

Then

$$M^2 - f^2(x_0) = (M - f(x_0))(M + f(x_0))$$
$$\leq \frac{\epsilon}{2M + 1} 2M < \epsilon,$$

as required.

Similarly, we find that m^2 is a lower bound for f^2. To show that it is the greatest lower bound, we must show that given $\epsilon > 0$, there is an x_0 in S such that $f^2(x_0) - m^2 < \epsilon$. Since m is the greatest lower bound for f, there is an x_0 such that

$$f(x_0) - m < \frac{\epsilon}{2M + 1};$$

then

$$f^2(x_0) - m^2 = (f(x_0) - m)(f(x_0) + m)$$
$$\leq \frac{\epsilon}{2M + 1} 2M < \epsilon,$$

as required. ∎

Theorem 8.2:   *If f is integrable on $[a, b]$, then so is f^2.*

Proof: Since f is integrable, we know by theorem 3.6 that $|f|$ is also integrable. Therefore, since $f^2 = |f|^2$, we may as well start again and assume that $f(x) \geq 0$ for all x in $[a, b]$. This puts us in a position to apply lemma 8.1. To show that f^2 is integrable, by lemma 2.1 it suffices to show that, given $\epsilon < 0$, there exists a partition P of $[a, b]$ such that

$$U(P, f^2) - L(P, f^2) < \epsilon.$$

Let B be any positive upper bound for f in $[a, b]$. Since f is integrable, by lemma 2.1 there is a partition P such that

$$U(P, f) - L(P, f) < \frac{\epsilon}{2B}.$$

Now if M_i and m_i denote the least upper and greatest lower bounds for f on $[x_{i-1}, x_i]$, then by lemma 8.1 M_i^2 and m_i^2 are the least upper and greatest lower bounds for f^2 in this interval. Hence,

$$U(P, f^2) - L(P, f^2) = \sum_{i=1}^{n} (M_i^2 - m_i^2)(x_i - x_{i-1})$$

$$= \sum_{i=1}^{n} (M_i + m_i)(M_i - m_i)(x_i - x_{i-1})$$

$$\leq \sum_{i=1}^{n} (B + B)(M_i - m_i)(x_i - x_{i-1})$$

$$= 2B(U(P, f) - L(P, f))$$

$$< 2B \frac{\epsilon}{2B} = \epsilon,$$

is required. ∎

Corollary 8.3: *If f and g are integrable on [a, b], then so is fg.*

Proof: By theorem 3.3, $f + g$ is integrable on $[a, b]$. Now we can write

$$fg = \tfrac{1}{2}(f + g)^2 - \tfrac{1}{2}f^2 - \tfrac{1}{2}g^2.$$

Since each term on the right is a constant times the square of an integrable function, it follows that fg is also integrable. ∎

Remark: The formula

$$\int_a^b fg = \int_a^b f \int_a^b g$$

is not true in general. (See exercise 1.)

Theorem 8.4: *Let f be continuous in [a, b], and let g be a function integrable on [a, b] such that $g(x) \geq 0$ for all x in [a, b]. Then there is at least one number c in [a, b] such that*

$$\int_a^b fg = f(c) \int_a^b g. \tag{1}$$

Proof: Let M and m be the least upper and greatest lower bounds for f in $[a, b]$. Then

$$m \leq f(x) \leq M$$

for all x in $[a, b]$, and so since $g(x) \geq 0$,

$$mg(x) \leq f(x)g(x) \leq Mg(x)$$

for all x in $[a, b]$. Now by corollary 8.3, fg is integrable. Therefore, by theorem 3.1 and lemma 3.4 we obtain

$$m \int_a^b g \leq \int_a^b fg \leq M \int_a^b g. \tag{2}$$

If $\int_a^b g = 0$, then it follows from (2) that $\int_a^b fg = 0$, and so equation (1) is true for any c in $[a, b]$. Otherwise $\int_a^b g > 0$, and so (2) can be rewritten

$$m \le \frac{\int_a^b fg}{\int_a^b g} \le M. \tag{3}$$

Now by the intermediate value theorem (theorem 2.2 of chapter III) we know that f takes on all values between m and M, and furthermore, by theorem 7.2 of chapter III we know that f takes on m and M as well. Consequently, from (3) we see that there is a number c in $[a, b]$ such that $f(c)$ is the middle term in (3). This is the desired result. $\blacksquare$

If we take g to be the constant function 1 in theorem 8.4, we obtain:

Corollary 8.5 (The Mean Value Theorem for Integrals): *If f is continuous in $[a, b]$, then there is a number c in $[a, b]$ such that*

$$\int_a^b f = f(c)(b - a). \quad \blacksquare$$

Corollary 8.5 is illustrated in figure 8.1, where the area under the graph of f is equal to the area of the rectangle.

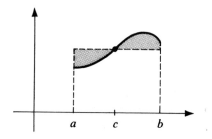

Fig. 8.1

EXERCISES

1. Let $f(x) = g(x) = x$ for all x in $[0, 1]$. Show that

$$\int_0^1 fg \ne \int_0^1 f \int_0^1 g$$

2. Use exercise 7 of § 5 to show that the number c of corollary 8.5 can actually be found in the open interval (a, b).

3. Give an example of an integrable function on an interval $[a, b]$ for which there is no c in $[a, b]$ satisfying

$$\int_a^b f = f(c)(b - a).$$

4. For each of the following integrals, find the numbers c satisfying the conditions of corollary 8.5.

$$\int_{-2\pi}^{2\pi} \sin x \, dx, \qquad \int_1^4 8 \, dx, \qquad \int_0^2 (x^2 + 1) \, dx.$$

5. Generalize lemma 8.1 by showing that if M and m are the least upper and greatest lower bounds of f on a set S and if g is increasing and continuous in the interval $[m, M]$, then $g(M)$ and $g(m)$ are the least upper and greatest lower bounds for $g \circ f$ on S.

9. DUHAMEL'S PRINCIPLE

Recall that if the points of a partition P of $[a, b]$ are

$$a = x_0 < x_1 < x_2 < \cdots < x_{n-1} < x_n = b, \tag{1}$$

then a Riemann sum for a function f relative to P is defined as any sum of the form

$$\sum_{i=1}^n f(x_i')(x_i - x_{i-1}) \tag{2}$$

where x_i' is in $[x_{i-1}, x_i]$ for each i. Theorem 7.2 showed that if there is a number I such that for each positive ϵ the Riemann sums can be made to be within ϵ of I simply by taking the mesh of P small enough, then f is integrable on $[a, b]$ and I is the integral. In some cases we encounter sums which look something like (2), but nevertheless are not Riemann sums for any function. For example, let f and g be any pair of functions defined in $[a, b]$, and relative to the above partition P, consider a sum of the form

$$\sum_{i=1}^n f(x_i')g(x_i'')(x_i - x_{i-1}) \tag{3}$$

where for each i, both x_i' and x_i'' are in $[x_{i-1}, x_i]$. If for each i we had $x_i' = x_i''$, then (3) would simply be a Riemann sum for the function fg. However, in practice we sometimes meet with sums of the form (3) where the points x_i' and x_i'' are not necessarily the same. We are interested in seeing what relation the sums (3) bear to the integral

$$\int_a^b fg.$$

Similarly, we may consider sums of the form

$$\sum_{i=1}^n \sqrt{f^2(x_i') + g^2(x_i'')} \, (x_i - x_{i-1}) \tag{4}$$

where both x_i' and x_i'' are in $[x_{i-1}, x_i]$. Again we observe that in the special case where $x_i' = x_i''$, (4) is just a Riemann sum for the function $\sqrt{f^2 + g^2}$. Thus we may hope to find a relation between the general sum (4) and the integral

$$\int_a^b \sqrt{f^2 + g^2}.$$

In order to put the problem in a general enough setting to handle all cases at once, let us assume that instead of being given a function on the interval $[a, b]$, we are given only a collection of numbers $\varphi(c, d)$ for each ordered pair of numbers c and d satisfying $a \leq c < d \leq b$. If P is the partition whose points are $x_0 < x_1 < \cdots < x_n$, consider a sum of the form

$$\sum_{i=1}^{n} y_i(x_i - x_{i-1}) \tag{5}$$

where for each i, the number y_i is to come from the collection $\varphi(x_{i-1}, x_i)$. Such a sum (5) will be called a *Duhamel sum* for φ relative to P.

For example, if f is a function defined in $[a, b]$ and $\varphi(c, d)$ is the collection of all values which f takes on in $[c, d]$, then a Duhamel sum (5) is just a Riemann sum for f relative to P. If f and g are a pair of functions defined in $[a, b]$ and $\varphi(c, d)$ is the collection of all numbers of the form $f(x')g(x'')$ where x' and x'' are in $[c, d]$, then the Duhamel sums relative to P are the sums (3) which we considered above. Likewise, if $\varphi(c, d)$ is the collection of numbers of the form

$$\sqrt{f^2(x') + g^2(x'')}$$

where x' and x'' are in $[c, d]$, then the Duhamel sums are the sums (4).

Given φ, suppose that there is a number L with the property that for every positive ϵ, there is a positive δ such that

$$\left| \sum_{i=1}^{n} y_i(x_i - x_{i-1}) - L \right| < \epsilon$$

whenever the sum is a Duhamel sum for φ relative to a partition P of mesh less than δ. Then we shall write

$$\lim_{|P| \to 0} \sum_{i=1}^{n} y_i(x_i - x_{i-1}) = L.$$

Theorem 9.1: *Given φ, suppose there is a function F which is integrable on $[a, b]$ and which has the following property: for each $\epsilon > 0$ there is a $\delta > 0$ such that whenever $d - c < \delta$ and $y \in \varphi(c, d)$, there is at least one number x in $[c, d]$ satisfying $|y - F(x)| < \epsilon$. Then*

$$\lim_{|P| \to 0} \sum_{i=1}^{n} y_i(x_i - x_{i-1}) = \int_{a}^{b} F.$$

Proof: Given $\epsilon > 0$, since F is integrable, there is a $\delta_1 > 0$ such that

$$\left| R - \int_{a}^{b} F \right| < \frac{\epsilon}{2} \tag{6}$$

whenever R is a Riemann sum for F relative to a partition of mesh less than δ_1 (theorem 7.1). Also, by hypothesis there is a $\delta_2 > 0$ such that whenever $d - c < \delta_2$ and $y \in \varphi(c, d)$, there is at least one number x in $[c, d]$ satisfying

$$|y - F(x)| < \frac{\epsilon}{2(b - a)}.$$

Let δ be the smaller of δ_1 and δ_2. Then if

$$\sum_{i=1}^{n} y_i(x_i - x_{i-1})$$

is a Duhamel sum relative to a partition P of mesh less than δ, we have

$$\left| \sum_{i=1}^{n} y_i(x_i - x_{i-1}) - \int_{a}^{b} F \right|$$

$$\leq \left| \sum_{i=1}^{n} y_i(x_i - x_{i-1}) - \sum_{i=1}^{n} F(x_i')(x_i - x_{i-1}) \right|$$

$$+ \left| \sum_{i=1}^{n} F(x_i')(x_i - x_{i-1}) - \int_{a}^{b} F \right| \quad (7)$$

where x_i' is in $[x_{i-1}, x_i]$ and satisfies

$$|y_i - F(x_i')| < \frac{\epsilon}{2(b-a)} \cdot$$

Now the second term on the right of (7) is less than $\epsilon/2$, by (6). Also the first term is less than or equal to

$$\sum_{i=1}^{n} |y_i - F(x_i')|(x_i - x_{i-1}) < \sum_{i=1}^{n} \frac{\epsilon}{2(b-a)}(x_i - x_{i-1}) = \frac{\epsilon}{2} \cdot$$

Consequently (7) is less than ϵ, as required. ∎

Example 1: Let f be integrable on $[a, b]$, and let g be continuous in $[a, b]$. Take $\varphi(c, d)$ to be all the numbers of the form $f(x')g(x'')$ where x' and x'' are in $[c, d]$. Letting $F = fg$, we show that the conditions of the theorem are satisfied. Notice that F is integrable, being the product of two integrable functions. Let M be a positive upper bound for $|f|$ in $[a, b]$. Given $\epsilon > 0$, by uniform continuity of g we can find $\delta > 0$ such that $|g(x') - g(x'')| < \epsilon/M$ whenever $|x' - x''| < \delta$. Therefore, if $y = f(x')g(x'')$ where x' and x'' are in an interval $[c, d]$ of length less than δ, then taking $x = x'$ we find

$$|y - F(x)| = |f(x')g(x'') - f(x')g(x')|$$
$$= |f(x')| \, |g(x'') - g(x')|$$
$$< M \frac{\epsilon}{M} = \epsilon.$$

Thus from theorem 9.1 we conclude

$$\lim_{|P| \to 0} \sum_{i=1}^{n} f(x_i')g(x_i'')(x_i - x_{i-1}) = \int_{a}^{b} fg.$$

Example 2: Let f and g be continuous in $[a, b]$, and let $\varphi(c, d)$ be the collection of numbers of the form $\sqrt{f^2(x') + g^2(x'')}$ where x' and x'' are in $[c, d]$. If $F = \sqrt{f^2 + g^2}$, then F is continuous (being the composition of two continuous functions) and hence integrable. Now given $\epsilon > 0$, by uniform continuity of f and g we can find $\delta > 0$ such that $|f(x') - f(x'')| < \epsilon/\sqrt{2}$ and $|g(x') - g(x'')| < \epsilon/\sqrt{2}$ whenever $|x' - x''| < \delta$. Let $y = \sqrt{f^2(x') + g^2(x'')}$

where x' and x'' are in an interval $[c, d]$ of length less than δ. Then taking x to be any point whatever in $[c, d]$, we find, using the inequality (8) of chapter III, § 4,

$$
\begin{aligned}
|y - F(x)| &= |\sqrt{f^2(x') + g^2(x'')} - \sqrt{f^2(x) + g^2(x)}| \\
&\leq \sqrt{(f(x') - f(x))^2 + (g(x'') - g(x))^2} \\
&< \sqrt{(\epsilon/\sqrt{2})^2 + (\epsilon/\sqrt{2})^2} = \epsilon.
\end{aligned}
$$

Therefore from theorem 9.1 we conclude

$$
\lim_{|P| \to 0} \sqrt{f^2(x') + g_2(x'')} \, (x_i - x_{i-1}) = \int_a^b \sqrt{f^2 + g^2}.
$$

We shall encounter applications of the two examples of this section in the following chapter.

EXERCISES

1. Let f, g, and h be three functions which are continuous in $[a, b]$. Show that

$$
\lim_{|P| \to 0} \sum_{i=1}^{n} f(x_i')g(x_i'')h(x_i''')(x_i - x_{i-1}) = \int_a^b fgh
$$

where x_i', x_i'', and x_i''' come from $[x_{i-1}, x_i]$. Generalize this result to n functions.

2. Let f, g, and h be continuous in $[a, b]$. Show that

$$
\lim_{|P| \to 0} \sum_{i=1}^{n} \sqrt{f^2(x_i') + g^2(x_i'') + h^2(x_i''')} \, (x_i - x_{i-1}) = \int_a^b \sqrt{f^2 + g^2 + h^2}
$$

where x_i', x_i'', and x_i''' come from $[x_{i-1}, x_i]$. Generalize this result to n functions.

3. State and prove a theorem for sums of functions corresponding to exercise 1.

CALCULATION and USES of the INTEGRAL

V

1. LOG AND EXP

Let a be a positive number. We have said what we mean by a^n for integers n, but we have not said what we mean by a^x for arbitrary numbers x. For rational x, say $x = m/n$ where m and n are integers, we could define a^x as the nth root of a^m, the definition being motivated by our desire to have the laws of exponents remain valid (see theorem 16.1 of chapter I). For irrational x we could then define a^x so as to make the function f defined by $f(x) = a^x$ a continuous function on the set of all numbers x. If $a > 1$ we would find that f is an increasing function, and for $0 < a < 1$ we would find that f is decreasing. In either case we could define the function $\log_a$ as the inverse of f. Notice that $\log_a (1) = 0$ since $a^0 = 1$. It would then be possible to show the existence of a special number e such that the derivative of the function $\log_e$ is given by

$$\log_e' (x) = \frac{1}{x} \cdot$$

Thus $\log_e x$ would be an antiderivative for $\dfrac{1}{x}$, and so we would have

$$\int_1^x \frac{1}{t} dt = \log_e x - \log_e 1$$
$$= \log_e x$$

for all $x > 0$.

The above sketch is the most natural approach to the subject of exponents and logarithms, and it is the one taken in many textbooks. However, the justification of all the steps involved is tedious, and in fact is usually omitted. On the other hand if, instead of starting with exponents, we start with $\log_e$, then the whole subject becomes very elegant, and provides excellent illustrations for some of our theorems of earlier chapters. This is just one of many situations in mathematics where the most obvious approach does not turn out to be the simplest.

Thus, motivated by the above, let us *define*

$$\log x = \int_1^x \frac{1}{t} dt.$$

This makes sense for any $x > 0$, since $\dfrac{1}{t}$ is continuous in the interval between 1 and x for all $t > 0$. Geometrically log x can thus be thought of as the area under the graph of $1/t$ for $x \geq 1$ (figure 1.1), and the negative of that area for $0 < x < 1$ (figure 1.2).

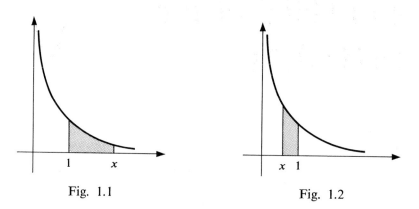

Fig. 1.1   Fig. 1.2

By the fundamental theorem of the calculus (chapter IV, theorem 4.3), we obtain

$$\log'(x) = \frac{1}{x}$$

for all $x > 0$. By corollary 9.6 of chapter III, this means that log is increasing. Therefore, since $\log 1 = 0$, we see that $\log x > 0$ for $x > 1$ and $\log x < 0$ for $0 < x < 1$.

Notice that we have *not* defined $\log x$ for $x \leq 0$, nor do we intend to. However, we *can* define $f(x) = \log |x|$ for all nonzero x, in which case it follows from the chain rule that $f'(x) = 1/x$ for all $x \neq 0$. This is because the derivative of the absolute value function is 1 for x positive and is -1 for x negative.

We now prove the equation

$$\log ux = \log u + \log x \tag{1}$$

for any positive numbers u and x. For fixed u, define $f(x) = \log ux$. Differentiating f by the chain rule, we find

$$f'(x) = \frac{1}{ux} \cdot u = \frac{1}{x} \cdot$$

Thus f and log have the same derivative on the interval $(0, \infty)$, and so by corollary 9.5 of chapter III, they must differ by a constant, say

$$\log(ux) - \log x = c. \tag{2}$$

Setting $x = 1$, we see that $c = \log u$. Thus equation (1) follows from equation (2).

Taking $x = u$ in (1), we find $\log x^2 = 2 \log x$. By induction we see more generally that

$$\log x^n = n \log x$$

for any positive integer n. Therefore, since $\log 2 > 0$, by taking n large enough we can make $\log 2^n$ greater than any prescribed number. Similarly, since $\log \tfrac{1}{2} < 0$ we can make $\log \left(\dfrac{1}{2^n} \right)$ less than any prescribed number. Consequently log, being a continuous increasing function defined on the set of positive numbers and taking on as large positive and negative numbers as we wish, must have as its image the set of all numbers. Its graph is drawn in figure 1.3.

Let exp denote the inverse function of log. Then exp is an increasing function whose domain is the set of all numbers and whose image is the set of all positive numbers. Its graph is drawn in figure 1.4. By definition of inverse function, the statements $y = \log x$ and $\exp y = x$ mean the same thing. The derivative of exp is obtained as follows, using theorem 3.2 of chapter III:

$$\exp'(x) = \frac{1}{\log'(\exp x)} = \frac{1}{1/\exp x} = \exp x.$$

In other words, exp has the remarkable property that it is its own derivative.

We define $e = \exp 1$, or equivalently, $\log e = 1$. Since

$$\frac{1}{2} \le \frac{1}{t} \le 1$$

for $1 \le t \le 2$, we find

$$\int_1^2 \frac{1}{2}\, dt \le \int_1^2 \frac{1}{t}\, dt \le \int_1^2 1\, dt,$$

or in other words,

$$\tfrac{1}{2} < \log 2 < 1.$$

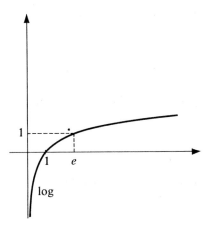

Fig. 1.3

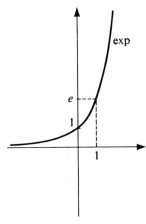

Fig. 1.4

From the left inequality we find $1 < \log 4$, and so $\log 2 < 1 < \log 4$. Thus we see that e must be a number between 2 and 4. In chapter VI we shall find a method for computing e as accurately as we wish.

Equation (1), written in terms of exp, becomes

$$\exp (x + y) = \exp x \cdot \exp y \tag{3}$$

for all numbers x and y. To see this, let $u = \exp x$ and $v = \exp y$, or equivalently, $\log u = x$ and $\log v = y$. Then

$$\exp (x + y) = \exp (\log u + \log v) = \exp (\log (uv))$$
$$= uv = \exp x \cdot \exp y.$$

EXERCISE

In the same spirit that log and exp were developed in this section, one can give a nongeometric treatment of the trigonometric functions. Recall the formula

$$\arctan' (x) = \frac{1}{1 + x^2}, \tag{4}$$

which yields

$$\arctan x = \int_0^x \frac{dt}{1 + t^2} \tag{5}$$

for all x. Now suppose that we had never heard of the trigonometric functions, and let us *define* arctan by (5).

(a) Show that arctan is an increasing odd function whose derivative is given by (4).

(b) Show that arctan is bounded, and hence define $\pi/2$ as its least upper bound. (Hint: Write

$$\int_0^x \frac{dt}{1 + t^2} < \int_0^1 \frac{dt}{1 + t^2} + \int_1^x \frac{dt}{t^2}$$

for $x > 1$.)

(c) Define tan as the inverse of arctan. Show that tan is an odd, increasing, unbounded function whose domain is $(-\pi/2, \pi/2)$ and whose derivative is $1 + \tan^2$.

(d) Define

$$\sin x = \frac{\tan x}{\sqrt{1 + \tan^2 x}}, \quad \cos x = \frac{1}{\sqrt{1 + \tan^2 x}}$$

for $-\pi/2 < x < \pi/2$. Prove that $\sin' = \cos$ and $\cos' = -\sin$ in

$$(-\pi/2, \pi/2).$$

(e) Show that if we define

$$\sin \pi/2 = 1, \quad \sin (-\pi/2) = -1, \quad \cos \pi/2 = 0, \quad \cos (-\pi/2) = 0,$$

then sin and cos are continuous in $[-\pi/2, \pi/2]$. From this deduce that $S' = \cos$ and $C' = -\sin$ in $[-\pi/2, \pi/2]$ where

$$S(x) = \int_0^x \cos t \, dt, \quad C(x) = 1 - \int_0^x \sin t \, dt$$

for $-\pi/2 \le x \le \pi/2$.

(f) From parts (d) and (e) conclude that $\sin = S$ and $\cos = C$ in

$[-\pi/2, \pi/2]$,

and hence that $\sin' = \cos$ and $\cos' = -\sin$ in $[-\pi/2, \pi/2]$.

(g) Show that the definitions

$$\sin (x + n\pi) = (-1)^n \sin x, \quad \cos (x + n\pi) = (-1)^n \cos x$$

for integers n and numbers x satisfying $-\pi/2 \le x \le \pi/2$ extend the domain of sin and cos in such a way that $\sin' x = \cos x$ and

$\cos' x = -\sin x$ for all x.

2. GENERAL EXPONENTS

If $a > 0$ and x is any number, we define

$a^x = \exp (x \log a)$.

In particular, taking $a = e$, we find

$e^x = \exp (x \log e) = \exp (x \cdot 1) = \exp x$.

Using only the elementary properties of exp and log developed in § 1, it is easy to verify the three laws of exponents

$$a^x a^y = a^{x+y} \tag{1}$$
$$(a^x)^y = a^{xy} \tag{2}$$
$$a^x b^x = (ab)^x. \tag{3}$$

For example, to prove rule (3) we can write

$$a^x b^x = \exp (x \log a) \exp (x \log b) = \exp (x \log a + x \log b)$$
$$= \exp (x (\log a + \log b)) = \exp (x \log (ab)) = (ab)^x.$$

Notice that

$a^1 = \exp (1 \cdot \log a) = \exp (\log a) = a.$

Using rule (1), we then see that

$a^x a = a^{x+1}$.

Thus, in the case where n is a positive integer, the definition of a^n given in this section agrees with the definition given in chapter I, § 16. Also $a^0 = \exp 0 = 1$, and so from (1) we see that $a^x a^{-x} = 1$. In other words,

$$a^{-x} = \frac{1}{a^x} .$$

For fixed $a > 0$, consider the function f defined for all x by

$f(x) = a^x = \exp (x \log a)$.

If $a > 1$, then $\log a > 0$, and so $x \log a$ increases from $-\infty$ to ∞ as x increases from $-\infty$ to ∞. Consequently, $\exp (a \log x)$ increases from 0 to ∞ as x increases from $-\infty$ to ∞, and so the graph of a^x is as in figure 2.1. On the other hand, if $0 < a < 1$, then $\log a < 0$, and so $x \log a$ decreases from ∞ to $-\infty$ as x increases from $-\infty$ to ∞. Consequently, $\exp(a \log x)$ decreases from ∞ to 0 as x increases from $-\infty$ to ∞, and so the graph of a^x in this case is as in figure 2.2. In either case f has an inverse function, which we denote by $\log_a$, whose domain is the set of positive numbers and whose image is the set of all numbers. The function $\log_a$ is increasing or decreasing, depending on whether $a > 1$ or $0 < a < 1$. One can easily sketch the graph using figures 2.1 and 2.2.

Notice that if $a = 1$, then $1^x = \exp(x \log 1) = \exp 0 = 1$. In other words f is the constant function 1, and so in this case there is no inverse function.

In the special case where $a = e$, we have $f(x) = e^x = \exp x$, and so the inverse function $\log_e$ is just the function which we have been previously calling log. It is sometimes referred to as the *natural logarithm function*.

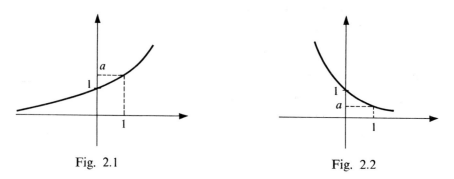

Fig. 2.1   Fig. 2.2

Let u and v be positive numbers. Let $x = \log_a u$ and $y = \log_a v$, or in other words, $a^x = u$ and $a^y = v$, where a is any positive number not equal to 1. Then

$$\log_a (uv) = \log_a (a^x a^y) = \log_a (a^{x+y})$$
$$= x + y = \log_a u + \log_a v.$$

Similarly, for any positive number u and any y, we have, writing $x = \log_a u$,

$$\log_a (u^y) = \log_a ((a^x)^y) = \log_a (a^{xy})$$
$$= xy = y \log_a u. \tag{4}$$

In particular, if $u \neq 1$, let $w = u^y$, or equivalently, $y = \log_u w$. Then (4) becomes

$$\log_a w = \log_a u \cdot \log_u w, \tag{5}$$

and when $a = e$, (5) can be written

$$\log_u w = \frac{\log w}{\log u}. \tag{6}$$

Thus the derivative of $\log_u$ is given by

$$\log_u' (x) = \frac{1}{\log u} \log' (x) = \frac{1}{x \log u}.$$

From (6) it follows that once a table of natural logarithms has been compiled, a table of logarithms to the base u is had by simply dividing the entries in the natural logarithm table by the constant $\log u$. We shall see how to compute natural logarithms in chapter VI.

For fixed positive a, let

$$f(x) = a^x = \exp(x \log a)$$

for all x. Then the derivative of f is given by the chain rule as follows:

$$f'(x) = \exp'(x \log a) \cdot \log a = \exp(x \log a) \cdot \log a = a^x \log a.$$

On the other hand, consider the function g defined by

$$g(x) = x^a = \exp(a \log x)$$

for all $x > 0$. Here a can be any number. The derivative of g is given by

$$g'(x) = \exp(a \log x) \cdot \frac{a}{x} = x^a \cdot \frac{a}{x} = ax^{a-1}.$$

This agrees with the formula proved in chapter II, corollary 9.4 for the special case where a was a positive integer.

To conclude this section we consider the limit

$$\lim_{h \to 0} (1 + h)^{1/h}.$$

It is not obvious what the limit should be, since as h approaches 0, we are taking very large powers of numbers which are close to 1. But using the definition of exponent as well as the definition of derivative and theorem 6.2 of chapter II, we find

$$\lim_{h \to 0} (1 + h)^{1/h} = \lim_{h \to 0} \exp\left(\frac{1}{h} \log(1 + h)\right)$$

$$= \lim_{h \to 0} \exp\left(\frac{\log(1 + h) - \log 1}{h}\right)$$

$$= \exp\left(\lim_{h \to 0} \frac{\log(1 + h) - \log 1}{h}\right)$$

$$= \exp(\log'(1)) = \exp\left(\frac{1}{1}\right) = e.$$

This would have been our *definition* of e if we had followed the approach to exponents sketched at the beginning of § 1.

EXERCISES

1. Verify the laws of exponents (1) and (2).
2. If $a > 0$ and $a \neq 1$, find an antiderivative for a^x. (Hint: Write down the derivative of a^x.)
3. If $a \neq -1$, find an antiderivative for x^a.

4. Find derivatives for each of the following expressions:

(a) xe^x (b) $x \log x$

(c) $e^{5 \sin x}$ (d) x^x

(e) $\log_{10} (e^{\sqrt{x}})$ (f) $\tan (\log 3x)$

(g) $\log |\sec x + \tan x|$

5. Sketch the graphs of the following:

$$xe^x, \quad xe^{1/x}, \quad \frac{e^{2x} - 1}{e^{2x} + 1}, \quad x \log x, \quad \frac{\log x}{\sqrt{x}}.$$

6. For all x define

$$\sinh x = \frac{e^x - e^{-x}}{2}, \quad \cosh x = \frac{e^x + e^{-x}}{2}.$$

Draw the graphs of sinh and cosh. Prove the following:

$\sinh' x = \cosh x$

$\cosh' x = \sinh x$

$\cosh^2 x - \sinh^2 x = 1$

$\sinh (x + y) = \sinh x \cosh y + \cosh x \sinh y$

$\cosh (x + y) = \cosh x \cosh y + \sinh x \sinh y$

7. Evaluate the following:

$$\int_0^1 e^x \, dx \qquad\qquad \int_2^9 (x - 1)^{4/3} \, dx$$

$$\int_1^4 x^\pi \, dx \qquad\qquad \int_0^1 e^x \cos (e^x) \, dx$$

$$\int_{-1}^1 xe^{-x^2} \, dx$$

8. Suppose that $f'(x) = f(x)$ for all x. Show that $f(x) = c \exp x$ for some constant c. (Hint: Differentiate the quotient $f(x)/\exp x$.) What if $f'(x) = af(x)$ for some constant a?

3. ANTIDIFFERENTIATION

Our method for computing an integral $\int_a^b f$ is to find an antiderivative for f in the interval $[a, b]$ and subtract the value of the antiderivative at a from the value at b. Since the last step is mechanical once the antiderivative has been found, we shall henceforth focus our attention on finding antiderivatives. A notational problem arises from the fact that we cannot talk about "the" anti-derivative of a function, since if a function has one antiderivative, then it has an infinite number of them. However, since any two antiderivatives defined in an interval must differ by a constant, this problem is not too serious. The value of an antiderivative for a function f at a number x will be denoted by

$$\int f(x) \, dx.$$

Thus for example,

$$\int x^2 \, dx = \frac{x^3}{3}.$$

However, we could equally well write

$$\int x^2 \, dx = \frac{x^3}{3} + 5.$$

In looking for an antiderivative, we don't have to worry too much about mathematical precision, since a rigorous proof that the function which we come up with actually is an antiderivative lies in simply differentiating it. Almost all antiderivatives are found by one or more of the following methods.

(1) If F and G are antiderivatives for f and g, then by the sum rule for derivatives,

$$(F + G)' = F' + G' = f + g.$$

In other words, an antiderivative for $f + g$ is $F + G$. Using the above notation, this rule becomes

$$\int (f(x) + g(x)) \, dx = \int f(x) \, dx + \int g(x) \, dx.$$

For example,

$$\int (x^4 + \cos x) \, dx = \int x^4 \, dx + \int \cos x \, dx = \frac{x^5}{5} + \sin x.$$

(2) Similarly, if c is a constant, then

$$\int cf(x) \, dx = c \int f(x) \, dx.$$

For example,

$$\int 5x^2 \, dx = 5 \int x^2 \, dx = 5 \frac{x^3}{3}.$$

(3) From the product rule for derivatives we obtain

$$\int f(x)g'(x) \, dx = f(x)g(x) - \int f'(x)g(x) \, dx.$$

One verifies this by showing that the derivative of the right side is $f(x)g'(x)$. This rule is known as *antidifferentiation by parts*. For example, consider

$$\int x \sin x \, dx.$$

Letting $f(x) = x$ and $g(x) = -\cos x$, we see that

$$\int x \sin x \, dx = -x \cos x - \int 1 \, (-\cos x) \, dx$$

$$= -x \cos x + \sin x.$$

We could also let $f(x) = \sin x$ and $g(x) = \dfrac{x^2}{2}$. This yields

$$\int x \sin x \, dx = \frac{x^2}{2} \sin x - \int \frac{x^2}{2} \cos x \, dx.$$

However, this does not simplify the problem, since the antiderivative on the right is harder to find than the one we started with. One can generally use a little foresight in deciding what should play the role of $f(x)$.

Sometimes it is necessary to apply the rule more than once. For example,

$$\int e^x \cos x \, dx = e^x \sin x - \int e^x \sin x \, dx$$

$$= e^x \sin x - (e^x (-\cos x) - \int e^x (-\cos x) \, dx)$$

$$= e^x (\sin x + \cos x) - \int e^x \cos x \, dx.$$

On the right side we have the expression we started with, but with a minus sign. Thus we can take it to the left side and divide by 2, to obtain

$$\int e^x \cos x \, dx = \frac{e^x (\sin x + \cos x)}{2}.$$

In a similar way one can find an antiderivative for any expression of the form $e^{ax} \cos bx$ (see exercise 3).

(4) Given a function f, suppose that we can find functions g and v such that

$$f(x) = g(v(x))v'(x).$$

If we can find an antiderivative for g, then an antiderivative for f is given by the formula

$$\int f(x) \, dx = \int g(t) \, dt,$$

where it is understood that after the right side has been calculated, t is to be replaced by $v(x)$. To see this, let G be such that $G'(t) = g(t)$. Then using the chain rule, we find

$$(G \circ v)'(x) = G'(v(x)) \cdot v'(x) = g(v(x))v'(x) = f(x).$$

We shall refer to this as the *first method of substitution*. As an example, consider

$$\int x e^{x^2} \, dx.$$

Here we would like to take $g(t) = e^t$ and $v(x) = x^2$. However, $v'(x) = 2x$, and so in order to make the present method applicable we first apply rule (2). This gives

$$\int x e^{x^2} \, dx = \frac{1}{2} \int 2x e^{x^2} \, dx = \frac{1}{2} \int e^t \, dt = \frac{1}{2} e^t = \frac{1}{2} e^{x^2}.$$

(5) Consider an increasing (or decreasing) function u, and let v be its inverse function. Then the statements $x = u(t)$ and $t = v(x)$ are equivalent, and the derivative of v is given as usual by the formula

$$v'(x) = \frac{1}{u'(v(x))} . \tag{1}$$

We shall show that an antiderivative for a function f is given by the rule

$$\int f(x)\,dx = \int f(u(t))u'(t)\,dt,$$

where it is understood that after the right side has been calculated, t is to be replaced by $v(x)$. To see this, let

$$G'(t) = f(u(t))u'(t). \tag{2}$$

Then, since $u(v(x)) = x$, we find using (1) and (2),

$$\begin{aligned}(G \circ v)'(x) &= G'(v(x))v'(x) \\ &= f(u(v(x)))u'(v(x))v'(x) = f(x).\end{aligned}$$

This shall be referred to as the *second method of substitution*. As an example, consider

$$\int x\sqrt{2 + 3x}\,dx.$$

Let $\sqrt{2 + 3x} = t$, or in other words, $x = \dfrac{t^2 - 2}{3}$. Then

$$\begin{aligned}\int x\sqrt{2 + 3x}\,dx &= \int \frac{t^2 - 2}{3} \cdot t \cdot \frac{2t}{3}\,dt \\ &= \frac{2}{9}\int (t^4 - 2t^2)\,dt \\ &= \frac{2}{9}\left(\frac{t^5}{5} - \frac{2t^3}{3}\right) \\ &= \frac{2}{45}(2 + 3x)^{5/2} - \frac{4}{27}(2 + 3x)^{3/2}.\end{aligned}$$

This method enables us to find an antiderivative for any expression of the form

$$p(x)\sqrt{a + bx}$$

where $p(x)$ is a polynomial and a and b are constants with $b \neq 0$ (see exercise 6).

The above rules of antidifferentiation by parts and substitution were rather loosely stated and proved. Nevertheless, one can give precise analogous theorems for integrals, and this we now proceed to do.

Theorem 3.1 (Integration by Parts): *Suppose that f' and g' are integrable on $[a, b]$. Then so are fg' and $f'g$, and*

$$\int_a^b fg' = f(b)g(b) - f(a)g(a) - \int_a^b f'g.$$

Proof: Since f has a derivative throughout $[a, b]$, it is certainly continuous, hence integrable. Since g' is also integrable, so is the product fg' (corollary 8.3 of chapter IV). Similarly, $f'g$ is integrable. Therefore, from the product rule

$$(fg)' = f'g + fg',$$

we see that $(fg)'$ is integrable. Consequently, using theorem 7.3 of chapter IV, we obtain

$$f(b)g(b) - f(a)g(a) = \int_a^b f'g + \int_a^b fg',$$

as required. ∎

Theorem 3.2 (Integration by Substitution): *Let f be continuous in some interval I, and let u be a function whose derivative is integrable on some interval $[a, b]$. Suppose further that $u(t)$ is in I for all t in $[a, b]$. Then*

$$\int_{u(a)}^{u(b)} f(x)\, dx = \int_a^b f(u(t))u'(t)\, dt. \tag{3}$$

Proof: Since u has a derivative throughout $[a, b]$, it is certainly continuous. Therefore, since f is also continuous, the composition $f \circ u$ is continuous in $[a, b]$, and hence is integrable. Since u' is also integrable on $[a, b]$, the product $(f \circ u) \cdot u'$ is integrable, and so the right side of (3) makes sense. Now, since f is continuous in I, by the fundamental theorem of the calculus (theorem 4.3 of chapter IV) f has an antiderivative F in I. The composition $F \circ u$ has a derivative in $[a, b]$ given by the chain rule as follows:

$$(F \circ u)'(t) = F'(u(t))u'(t) = f(u(t))u'(t).$$

In other words, $F \circ u$ is an antiderivative for $(f \circ u)u'$. Then, applying theorem 7.3 of chapter IV twice, we obtain

$$\int_a^b (f \circ u)u' = (F \circ u)(b) - (F \circ u)(a)$$

$$= F(u(b)) - F(u(a)) = \int_{u(a)}^{u(b)} f,$$

as required. ∎

Example: Consider $\int_0^1 x\sqrt{2 + 3x}\, dx$. According to theorem 3.2, this integral is equal to any integral of the form

$$\int_a^b u(t)\sqrt{2 + 3u(t)}\, u'(t)\, dt, \tag{4}$$

where u is a function with an integrable derivative on $[a, b]$ such that $u(a) = 0$ and $u(b) = 1$, and such that $u(t) \geq -2/3$ for all t in $[a, b]$. In particular, if we take $u(t) = (t^2 - 2)/3$ with $a = \sqrt{2}$, and $b = \sqrt{5}$, then (4) becomes

$$\int_{\sqrt{2}}^{\sqrt{5}} \frac{(t^2 - 2)}{3} \cdot t \cdot \frac{2t}{3}\, dt,$$

and since the expression inside the integral sign is just a polynomial, it is straightforward to evaluate the integral.

EXERCISES

1. Use parts to find $\int x^n \log |x|\, dx$ for $n \neq -1$. In particular, what is $\int \log |x|\, dx$?

2. Use the first method of substitution (with $g(t) = t^n$) to find $\displaystyle\int \frac{\log^n |x|}{x}\, dx$.

   (Remember that the case $n = -1$ is special.)

3. Use parts to establish the formula

$$\int e^{ax} \cos bx = \frac{1}{a^2 + b^2} (a \cos bx + b \sin bx)e^{ax}.$$

   Check your result by differentiating the right side. Then establish a similar formula with cos replaced by sin.

4. Use the first method of substitution for each of the following:

$$\int x(x^2 + 1)^{10}\, dx, \quad \int \frac{x\, dx}{\sqrt{1 - x^2}}, \quad \int \frac{x}{1 + x^2}\, dx, \quad \int x \cos x^2 \log (\sin x^2)\, dx.$$

5. Find $\int \arcsin x\, dx$ and $\int \arctan x\, dx$. (Hint: Take $g(x) = x$ and use parts.)

6. Explain how the second method of substitution can be used to find any antiderivative of the form

$$\int p(x)\sqrt{a + bx}\, dx$$

   where $p(x)$ is a polynomial and $b \neq 0$. Illustrate your method by finding

$$\int (2x^2 + 3x - 1)\sqrt{1 - x}\, dx.$$

7. Show that

$$\int_0^1 x\sqrt{2 + 3x}\, dx = \int_{-\sqrt{2}}^{-\sqrt{5}} \frac{(t^2 - 2)}{3}(-t)\frac{2t}{3}\, dt.$$

8. If n is a positive integer, show that

$$\int x^n \sin x\, dx = -x^n \cos x + n \int x^{n-1} \cos x\, dx$$

$$\int x^n \cos x\, dx = x^n \sin x - n \int x^{n-1} \sin x\, dx.$$

   Then explain how repeated application of these two formulas would give an antiderivative for any expression of the form $x^n \sin x$ or $x^n \cos x$ where n is a positive integer. Illustrate by finding $\int x^4 \cos x \, dx$.

9. (a) Find $\int \tan x \, dx$. (Hint: Take $v(x) = \cos x$ in the first method of substitution.)

   (b) Show how the equality

   $$\tan^n x = \tan^{n-2} x \, (1 + \tan^2 x) - \tan^{n-2} x$$

   leads to the formula

   $$\int \tan^n x = \frac{\tan^{n-1} x}{n-1} - \int \tan^{n-2} x \, dx, \quad n \neq -1.$$

   Then explain how repeated use of this formula, together with part (a) in the case where n is odd, would give an antiderivative for any expression of the form $\tan^n x$ where n is a positive integer.

10. Repeat exercise 9 with tan replaced by cot.

11. Consider the relations

   $$\sin ax \cos bx = \frac{\sin (a + b)x + \sin (a - b)x}{2},$$

   $$\cos ax \cos bx = \frac{\cos (a + b)x + \cos (a - b)x}{2},$$

   $$\sin ax \sin bx = \frac{\cos (a - b)x - \cos (a + b)x}{2},$$

   which were established in exercise 4, § 23, chapter I. Use these relations to find

   $$\int \sin ax \cos bx \, dx, \quad \int \cos ax \cos bx \, dx, \quad \int \sin ax \sin bx \, dx,$$

   where a and b are positive constants. (The case $a = b$ must be treated separately.)

12. Show that if $(m + 1)/n$ is an integer, then the substitution $t = (a + bx^n)^{1/q}$ will reduce $\int x^m (a + bx^n)^{p/q}$ to the case of a rational function. Here m, n, p, and q are integers.

4. ANTIDERIVATIVES OF RATIONAL FUNCTIONS

In this section we shall show that every rational function has an antiderivative which can be written in terms of functions we are already familiar with. We shall begin by stating two theorems without giving their proofs. The first theorem is best proved in the theory of complex numbers. The second theorem can be proved in an introductory course in modern algebra. (See, for example, *A Survey of Modern Algebra* by G. Birkhoff and S. MacLane, 3rd edition, Macmillan, New York, 1965.) This will be the only place in this book where we shall use theorems which we have not proved. Furthermore, they shall not be used outside of this section.

Theorem A: *Every polynomial can be written as a product of polynomials of degrees 1 and 2 (i.e. linear polynomials and quadratic polynomials).* ∎

Theorem A could equally well be stated: "Every polynomial of degree greater than 2 can be factored into two polynomials of lower degree." Thus for example, the theorem tells us that $3x^7 + 4x^4 - 2x^2 + 1$ can be factored into two polynomials of degree less than 7. Any factor having degree greater than 2 can in turn be factored. However, theorem A does not imply that we always have a quick way of finding the factorization. In the examples and exercises which follow, the polynomials will either be easy to factor or will be given already factored.

Recall that a rational function is a quotient $p(x)/q(x)$ of two polynomials. By dividing both $p(x)$ and $q(x)$ by the leading coefficient of $q(x)$, we may assume that the leading coefficient of $q(x)$ is 1. Then by theorem A, $q(x)$ can be expressed as a product of linear terms of the form $x - a$ and quadratic terms of the form $x^2 + bx + c$. Furthermore we may assume that $4c - b^2 > 0$, for otherwise $x^2 + bx + c$ itself could be written as the product of two linear terms (see chapter III, § 4). Now if $4c - b^2 > 0$, then we can write

$$x^2 + bx + c = (x + \beta)^2 + \alpha^2$$

where $\beta = b/2$ and $\alpha = \sqrt{c - b^2/4}$. Thus, if we collect together equal factors, we see finally that $q(x)$ can be written as a product of distinct factors of the form $(x - a)^n$ and distinct factors of the form $((x + \beta)^2 + \alpha^2)^m$ where m and n are positive integers and $\alpha > 0$. We shall refer to this as the *standard factorization* of $q(x)$. The second theorem referred to above can now be stated.

Theorem B: *Consider a rational function $p(x)/q(x)$ where $q(x)$ has leading coefficient 1, and suppose that the degree of $q(x)$ is greater than the degree of $p(x)$. Then $p(x)/q(x)$ can be written as a sum of terms as follows. For each factor of the form $(x - a)^n$ in the standard factorization of $q(x)$, there is a sum of terms of the form*

$$\frac{A_1}{x - a} + \frac{A_2}{(x - a)^2} + \cdots + \frac{A_n}{(x - a)^n}$$

where the A_i's are constants. For each term of the form $((x + \beta)^2 + \alpha^2)^m$ in the standard factorization of $q(x)$ there is a sum of terms of the form

$$\frac{B_1 x + C_1}{(x + \beta)^2 + \alpha^2} + \frac{B_2 x + C_2}{((x + \beta)^2 + \alpha^2)^2} + \cdots + \frac{B_m x + C_m}{((x + \beta)^2 + \alpha^2)^m}$$

where the B_i's and C_i's are constants. ∎

Example 1: Consider

$$\frac{2x^5 - 2x^4 + 5x^3 - x^2 - 12x + 23}{x^3 - x^2 + 4x - 4}. \tag{1}$$

Theorem B does not apply yet, since the degree of the denominator is less than the degree of the numerator. However, by the process of "long division" described in § 22 of chapter I, (1) can be rewritten

$$2x^2 - 3 + \frac{4x^2 + 11}{x^3 - x^2 + 4x - 4}.$$

Now the denominator $x^3 - x^2 + 4x - 4$ can be factored as $(x - 1)(x^2 + 4)$. Consequently, by theorem B we should be able to write

$$\frac{4x^2 + 11}{(x - 1)(x^2 + 4)} = \frac{A}{x - 1} + \frac{Bx + C}{x^2 + 4}. \tag{2}$$

To find the values of A, B, and C, we first get rid of denominators by multiplying both sides of (2) by $(x - 1)(x^2 + 4)$. This gives

$$4x^2 + 11 = A(x^2 + 4) + (Bx + C)(x - 1). \tag{3}$$

Since this must be true for all x, the coefficients of the powers of x on either side must be equal. Thus we find

$$\begin{aligned}
A + B &= 4, \\
- B + C &= 0, \\
4A - C &= 11.
\end{aligned}$$

Solving these three equations for the three unknowns gives $A = 3$, $B = 1$, and $C = 1$. Thus we see finally that (1) can be written as

$$2x^2 - 3 + \frac{3}{x - 1} + \frac{x + 1}{x^2 - 4}.$$

The value of A could also have been found immediately from equation (3) by observing that when $x = 1$, the other term on the right side is 0. This gives $15 = 5A + 0$, or $A = 3$ as before.

Example 2:   Consider

$$\frac{4x^3 + 11x^2 + 21x + 13}{(x + 2)^2(x^2 - 4x + 5)}. \tag{4}$$

Then by theorem B we can write this as

$$\frac{A}{x + 2} + \frac{B}{(x + 2)^2} + \frac{Cx + D}{x^2 - 4x + 5}. \tag{5}$$

Multiplying (4) and (5) by the denominator of (4), we find

$$\begin{aligned}
4x^3 + 11x^2 + 21x + 13 &= A(x + 2)(x^2 - 4x + 5) \\
&\quad + B(x^2 - 4x + 5) \\
&\quad + (Cx + D)(x + 2)^2. \tag{6}
\end{aligned}$$

Equating coefficients, we obtain

$$\begin{aligned}
A + C &= 4, \\
-2A + B + 4C + D &= 11, \\
-3A - 4B + 4C + 4D &= 21, \\
10A + 5B + 4D &= 13.
\end{aligned}$$

We can solve these 4 equations directly for the 4 unknowns. However, it is simpler to obtain the value of B first by putting $x = -2$ in (6). This gives $B = -1$, and then using this value of B in three of the above four equations yields $A = 1$, $C = 3$, and $D = 2$. Thus (4) can be rewritten as

$$\frac{1}{x + 2} - \frac{1}{(x + 2)^2} + \frac{3x + 2}{x^2 - 4x + 5}.$$

Example 3: Consider

$$\frac{x^7 - 5x^3 + 2}{x(x + 4)^2(x^2 + 2x + 4)^3}. \tag{7}$$

By theorem B this can be written

$$\frac{A}{x} + \frac{B}{x + 4} + \frac{C}{(x + 4)^2} + \frac{Dx + E}{x^2 + 2x + 4} + \frac{Fx + G}{(x^2 + 2x + 4)^2}$$
$$+ \frac{Hx + I}{(x^2 + 2x + 4)^3}. \tag{8}$$

Multiplying (7) and (8) by the denominator of (7) and equating the coefficients of the resulting polynomials, we would get 9 equations for the 9 unknowns. The fact that there is a solution is precisely what theorem B guarantees.

From theorem B it follows that in order to find an antiderivative for a rational function, it suffices to find antiderivatives of the form

$$\int \frac{dx}{(x - a)^n}, \quad \int \frac{x + \gamma}{((x - \beta)^2 + \alpha^2)^m} dx$$

where m and n are positive integers. The first of these is given by

$$\int \frac{dx}{(x - a)^n} = \frac{1}{(1 - n)(x - a)^{n-1}} \quad \text{for } n > 1,$$
$$= \log |x - a| \quad \text{for } n = 1.$$

For the second we use the first method of substitution with $t = x + \beta$. This gives

$$\int \frac{x + \gamma}{((x + \beta)^2 + \alpha^2)^m} dx = \int \frac{t}{(t^2 + \alpha^2)^m} dt$$
$$+ (\gamma - \beta) \int \frac{dt}{(t^2 + \alpha^2)^m}. \tag{9}$$

The first of the antiderivatives on the right is given by

$$\int \frac{t}{(t^2 + \alpha^2)^m} dt = \frac{1}{2(1 - m)(t^2 + \alpha^2)^{m-1}} \quad \text{for } m > 1,$$
$$= \tfrac{1}{2} \log (t^2 + \alpha^2) \quad \text{for } m = 1.$$

Thus it remains only to evaluate the second antiderivative on the right side of (9). In the formula for antidifferentiation by parts, take $f(t) = 1/(t^2 + \alpha^2)^m$ and let $g(t) = t$. This gives

$$\int \frac{dt}{(t^2 + \alpha^2)^m} = \frac{t}{(t^2 + \alpha^2)^m} + 2m \int \frac{t^2}{(t^2 + \alpha^2)^{m+1}} dt.$$

If we write $(t^2 + \alpha^2) - \alpha^2$ in place of t^2 in the numerator of the antiderivative on the right, this becomes

$$\int \frac{dt}{(t^2 + \alpha^2)^m} = \frac{t}{(t^2 + \alpha^2)^m} + 2m \int \frac{dt}{(t^2 + \alpha^2)^m}$$
$$- 2m\alpha^2 \int \frac{dt}{(t^2 + \alpha^2)^{m+1}},$$

which can be rewritten

$$\int \frac{dt}{(t^2 + \alpha^2)^{m+1}} = \frac{1}{2m\alpha^2} \frac{t}{(t^2 + \alpha^2)^m} + \frac{2m - 1}{2m\alpha^2} \int \frac{dt}{(t^2 + \alpha^2)^m}. \quad (10)$$

Formula (10) shows how to express an antiderivative of a power of $1/(t^2 + \alpha^2)$ in terms of an antiderivative of the next lower power. It can be repeated until the power is 1. In that case we have

$$\int \frac{dt}{t^2 + \alpha^2} = \frac{1}{\alpha} \arctan \left(\frac{t}{\alpha}\right).$$

Thus we see that $1/(t^2 + \alpha^2)^m$ has an antiderivative in the form of a rational function of t plus a constant times arctan (t/α). Replacing t by $x + \beta$ in a rational function of t yields a rational function of x. We can therefore summarize our results as follows:

Theorem 4.1:   *Every rational function has an antiderivative in the form of a rational function plus constants multiplying terms of the following form:*

$\log |x - a|, \quad \log ((x + \beta)^2 + \alpha^2), \quad \arctan (x + \delta).$ ∎

To illustrate theorem 4.1, we have, using example 1,

$$\int \frac{2x^5 - 2x^4 + 5x^3 - x^2 - 12x + 23}{x^3 - x^2 + 4x - 4} dx$$
$$= \int (2x^2 - 3) dx + 3 \int \frac{dx}{x - 1} + \int \frac{x + 1}{x^2 + 4} dx$$
$$= \tfrac{2}{3}x^3 - 3x + 3 \log |x - 1| + \tfrac{1}{2} \log (x^2 + 4) + \tfrac{1}{2} \arctan \left(\frac{x}{2}\right).$$

From example 2, we find

$$\int \frac{4x^3 + 11x^2 + 21x + 13}{(x + 2)^2(x^2 - 4x + 5)} dx$$
$$= \int \frac{dx}{x + 2} - \int \frac{dx}{(x + 2)^2} + \int \frac{3x + 2}{(x - 2)^2 + 1} dx$$
$$= \log |x + 2| + \frac{1}{x + 2} + \frac{3}{2} \log ((x - 2)^2 + 1) + 8 \arctan (x - 2).$$

The antiderivative of the rational function of example 3 would require two uses of the reduction formula (10).

EXERCISES

Find the following antiderivatives.

1. $\displaystyle\int \frac{x\,dx}{(2x+1)^2}$

2. $\displaystyle\int \frac{dx}{x^2+3x+2}$

3. $\displaystyle\int \frac{dx}{(x^2+4)^3}$

4. $\displaystyle\int \frac{dx}{x^3+1}$

5. $\displaystyle\int \frac{5x^2-3x+1}{x^3+x}\,dx$

6. $\displaystyle\int \frac{x^3-5x+1}{x^3+x^2-2x}\,dx$

7. $\displaystyle\int \frac{5x^2+6x+17}{(x^2+x+1)^2(2-x)}\,dx$

8. $\displaystyle\int \frac{3x+1}{(x^2-4)^2}\,dx$

9. $\displaystyle\int \frac{x^2}{x^4-16}\,dx$

10. $\displaystyle\int \frac{x}{(x+1)(x+2)^2}\,dx$

11. Assuming $a \neq b$, find

$$\int \frac{dx}{(x-a)(x-b)}, \qquad \int \frac{x\,dx}{(x-a)(x-b)}.$$

12. Assuming a, b, and c distinct, find

$$\int \frac{dx}{(x-a)(x-b)(x-c)}.$$

5. TRIGONOMETRIC ANTIDERIVATIVES

In this section we shall show how to find an antiderivative of the form

$$\int \cos^m x \sin^n x\,dx$$

where m and n are any integers. We single out first the cases where m and n are each one of the three integers -1, 0, or 1. This gives rise to nine anti-derivatives; namely

$$\int 1\,dx, \qquad \int \sin x\,dx, \qquad \int \cos x\,dx, \qquad \int \sin x \cos x\,dx,$$

$$\int \sec x\,dx, \qquad \int \csc x\,dx, \qquad \int \tan x\,dx, \qquad \int \cot x\,dx,$$

$$\int \sec x \csc x\,dx.$$

Each of these either is trivial or is an easy application of the methods of the previous section after making one of the substitutions $t = \sin x$ or $t = \cos x$.

For example, using the substitution $t = \sin x$, we can write

$$\int \sec x \, dx = \int \frac{dx}{\cos x} = \int \frac{\cos x \, dx}{\cos^2 x}$$

$$= \int \frac{dt}{1 - t^2} = \frac{1}{2} \int \frac{dt}{1 + t} + \frac{1}{2} \int \frac{dt}{1 - t}$$

$$= \tfrac{1}{2} \log |1 + t| - \tfrac{1}{2} \log |1 - t|$$

$$= \log \sqrt{\left|\frac{1 + t}{1 - t}\right|} = \log \sqrt{\frac{1 + \sin x}{1 - \sin x}}.$$

Using the identity

$$\frac{1 + \sin x}{1 - \sin x} = (\sec x + \tan x)^2,$$

we may equally well write

$$\int \sec x \, dx = \log |\sec x + \tan x|.$$

Now let m and n be any integers, and let us take $f(x) = \cos^{m-1} x \sin^n x$ and $g(x) = \sin x$ in the formula for antidifferentiation by parts. This gives

$$\int \cos^m x \sin^n x \, dx = \cos^{m-1} x \sin^{n+1} x$$

$$- \int (n \cos^m x \sin^n x - (m - 1) \cos^{m-2} x \sin^{n+2} x) \, dx.$$

Writing $\sin^{n+2} x = \sin^n x(1 - \cos^2 x)$, this becomes

$$(m + n) \int \cos^m x \sin^n x \, dx$$

$$= \cos^{m-1} x \sin^{n+1} x + (m - 1) \int \cos^{m-2} x \sin^n x \, dx. \qquad (1)$$

Similarly, taking $f(x) = \cos^m x \sin^{n-1} x$ and $g(x) = -\cos x$, we obtain

$$(m + n) \int \cos^m x \sin^n x \, dx$$

$$= -\cos^{m+1} x \sin^{n-1} x + (n - 1) \int \cos^m x \sin^{n-2} x \, dx. \qquad (2)$$

Now equation (1) can be used *either* to express an antiderivative for $\cos^m x \sin^n x$ in terms of one for $\cos^{m-2} x \sin^n x$ in the case where $m + n \neq 0$, *or* to express an antiderivative for $\cos^{m-2} x \sin^n x$ in terms of one for $\cos^m x \sin^n x$ in the case where $m - 1 \neq 0$. A similar remark can be made for equation (2).

Case 1: Suppose $m \geq 0$ and $n \geq 0$. Then formula (1) can be used repeatedly until the power of cos in the antiderivative is 0 or 1. Several applications of formula (2) (with 0 or 1 playing the role of m) will then reduce the power of sin to 0 or 1 also.

Case 2: Suppose $m < 0$ and $n \geq 0$. We first apply formula (1) until the power of cos in the antiderivative is 0 or -1. Then we use formula (2) (with 0 or -1 playing the role of m) until the power of sin is reduced to 0 or 1.

Case 3: Suppose $m \geq 0$ and $n < 0$. Then we simply interchange the roles of formulas (1) and (2) in case 2.

Case 4: If $m < 0$ and $n < 0$, then formulas (1) and (2) together can be used to reduce the powers of cos and sin to -1 or 0.

Example 1: Consider $\int \cos^2 x \sin^4 x \, dx$. This is case 1. One application of (1) yields

$$\int \cos^2 x \sin^4 x \, dx = \tfrac{1}{6} \cos x \sin^5 x + \tfrac{1}{6} \int \sin^4 x \, dx. \tag{3}$$

Then (2) gives

$$\int \sin^4 x \, dx = -\tfrac{1}{4} \sin^3 x \cos x + \tfrac{3}{4} \int \sin^2 x \, dx. \tag{4}$$

A second application of (2) yields

$$\int \sin^2 x \, dx = \frac{-1}{2} \sin x \cos x + \frac{x}{2}. \tag{5}$$

Combining (3), (4), and (5), we obtain

$$\int \cos^2 x \sin^4 x \, dx$$
$$= \frac{1}{6} \cos x \sin^5 x - \frac{1}{24} \sin^3 x \cos x - \frac{1}{16} \sin x \cos x + \frac{x}{16}.$$

Example 2: Consider $\displaystyle\int \frac{\sin^2 x}{\cos^3 x} \, dx$. This is case 2. Using (1) we obtain

$$\int \cos^{-3} x \sin^2 x \, dx = \tfrac{1}{2} \cos^{-2} x \sin^3 x - \tfrac{1}{2} \int \cos^{-1} x \sin^2 x \, dx.$$

Then applying (2),

$$\int \cos^{-1} x \sin^2 x \, dx = -\sin x + \int \cos^{-1} x \, dx,$$

and so

$$\int \frac{\sin^2 x}{\cos^3 x} \, dx = \frac{1}{2} \frac{\sin x}{\cos^2 x} - \frac{1}{2} \log |\sec x + \tan x|.$$

Consider now the antiderivatives

$$\int x^p \sqrt{(a^2 - x^2)^q} \, dx \tag{6}$$

$$\int x^p \sqrt{(a^2 + x^2)^q} \, dx \tag{7}$$

$$\int x^p \sqrt{(x^2 - a^2)^q} \, dx \tag{8}$$

where p and q are any integers. Using the second method of substitution we can reduce each of these to one of the trigonometric expressions we have just dealt with. In (6) we put $x = a \sin t$, obtaining

$$\int x^p \sqrt{(a^2 - x^2)^q} \, dx = \int a^p \sin^p t \sqrt{(a^2 - a^2 \sin^2 t)^q} \, a \cos t \, dt$$

$$= a^{p+q+1} \int \sin^p t \cos^{q+1} t \, dt.$$

In (7) we put $x = a \tan t$, to obtain

$$\int x^p \sqrt{(a^2 + x^2)^q} \, dx = \int a^p \tan^p t \sqrt{(a^2 + a^2 \tan^2 t)^q} \, a \sec^2 t \, dt$$

$$= a^{p+q+1} \int \tan^p t \sec^{q+2} t \, dt.$$

In (8) we put $x = a \sec t$, so that

$$\int x^p \sqrt{(x^2 - a^2)^q} \, dx = \int a^p \sec^p t \sqrt{(a^2 \sec^2 t - a^2)^q} \, a \tan t \sec t \, dt$$

$$= a^{p+q+1} \int \sec^{p+1} t \tan^{q+1} t \, dt.$$

The three substitutions we have just made are represented respectively by figures 5.1, 5.2, and 5.3, which are useful in converting the trigonometric functions of t back into functions of x.

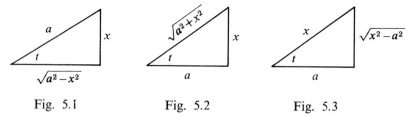

Fig. 5.1   Fig. 5.2   Fig. 5.3

Example 3:   Consider $\int \sqrt{a^2 - x^2} \, dx$. Using figure 5.1 and equation (1), we find

$$\int \sqrt{a^2 - x^2} \, dx = a^2 \int \cos^2 t \, dt = \frac{a^2}{2} (\sin t \cos t + t)$$

$$= \frac{a^2}{2} \left(\frac{x}{a} \frac{\sqrt{a^2 - x^2}}{a} + \arcsin \frac{x}{a} \right)$$

$$= \frac{1}{2} \left(x\sqrt{a^2 - x^2} + a^2 \arcsin \frac{x}{a} \right).$$

Example 4: Consider $\int \dfrac{x^2}{\sqrt{a^2 + x^2}}\, dx$. Using figure 5.2 and example 2

we find

$$\int \frac{x^2}{\sqrt{a^2 + x^2}}\, dx = a^2 \int \tan^2 t \sec t\, dt = a^2 \int \frac{\sin^2 t}{\cos^3 t}\, dt$$

$$= \frac{a^2}{2}\left(\frac{\sin t}{\cos^2 t} - \log |\sec t + \tan t|\right)$$

$$= \frac{a^2}{2}\left(\frac{x/\sqrt{a^2 + x^2}}{a^2/(a^2 + x^2)} - \log \left|\frac{\sqrt{a^2 + x^2}}{a} + \frac{x}{a}\right|\right)$$

$$= \tfrac{1}{2}x\sqrt{a^2 + x^2} - \frac{a^2}{2}\log |\sqrt{a^2 + x^2} + x| + \frac{a^2}{2}\log |a|.$$

Omission of the last term, which is just a constant, would equally well give an antiderivative.

Example 5: Consider $\int \dfrac{x}{(4x^2 + 4x - 1)^{3/2}}\, dx$. We first write

$$s = 2x + 1,$$

and then in turn $s = \sqrt{2}\sec t$, so as to obtain

$$\int \frac{x}{(4x^2 + 4x - 1)^{3/2}}\, dx = \frac{1}{4}\int \frac{(2x + 1) - 1}{\sqrt{((2x + 1)^2 - 2)^3}} \cdot 2\, dx$$

$$= \frac{1}{4}\int \frac{s - 1}{\sqrt{(s^2 - 2)^3}}\, ds$$

$$= \frac{1}{4}\left(\frac{1}{\sqrt{2}}\int \sec^2 t \tan^{-2} t\, dt\right.$$

$$\left. - \tfrac{1}{2}\int \sec t \tan^{-2} t\, dt\right)$$

$$= \tfrac{1}{8}(-\sqrt{2}\cot t + \csc t)$$

$$= \frac{1}{8}\left(-\sqrt{2}\frac{\sqrt{2}}{\sqrt{s^2 - 2}} + \frac{s}{\sqrt{s^2 - 2}}\right)$$

$$= \frac{2x - 1}{8\sqrt{4x^2 + 4x - 1}}\,.$$

EXERCISES

1. Find each of the nine antiderivatives listed at the beginning of this section. In each case check your answer by differentiation.

2. Find each of the following:

   (a) $\displaystyle\int \cos^5 x \sin^3 x\, dx$

   (b) $\displaystyle\int \sec^2 x \csc^2 x\, dx$

(c) $\displaystyle\int \sec^5 x \sin^2 x \, dx$

(d) $\displaystyle\int \cos^4 x \tan^5 x \, dx$

(e) $\displaystyle\int \sin^8 x \, dx$

(f) $\displaystyle\int \cos^4 x \csc^3 x \, dx$

3. Find each of the following:

(a) $\displaystyle\int \frac{dx}{(1 - x^2)^{3/2}}$

(b) $\displaystyle\int \frac{dx}{x\sqrt{2 + x^2}}$

(c) $\displaystyle\int \frac{x^2 \, dx}{\sqrt{x^2 - a^2}}$

(d) $\displaystyle\int \frac{x \, dx}{\sqrt{x^2 - 2x + 5}}$

(e) $\displaystyle\int x(4 - x^2)^{5/2} \, dx$

(f) $\displaystyle\int \frac{x + 1}{\sqrt{2x - x^2}} \, dx$

(g) $\displaystyle\int \frac{dx}{x^2 \sqrt{x^2 - 4}}$

(h) $\displaystyle\int \frac{dx}{(x^2 + 2x)^{5/2}}$

4. If n is a positive integer, show that

$$\int_0^{\pi/2} \sin^{2n} x \, dx = \frac{1}{2}\frac{3}{4}\frac{5}{6}\cdots\frac{2n - 1}{2n}\frac{\pi}{2},$$

$$\int_0^{\pi/2} \sin^{2n+1} x \, dx = \frac{2}{3}\frac{4}{5}\frac{6}{7}\cdots\frac{2n}{2n + 1}.$$

5. If $t = \tan(x/2)$, show that

$$\cos x = \frac{1 - t^2}{1 + t^2}, \qquad \sin x = \frac{2t}{1 + t^2}.$$

Hence, if $f(x)$ and $g(x)$ are each sums of expressions of the type $\cos^m x \sin^n x$, show that the substitution $x = 2 \arctan t$ will reduce the antiderivative $\displaystyle\int \frac{f(x)}{g(x)} \, dx$ to that of a rational function.

6. AREA

The integral was motivated (but *not* defined) by the notion of area. The problem of defining what we mean by area for general sets of points in the plane is a sophisticated one which we shall not go into in this book. (Not all sets of points have area, even after the most general definitions have been made.) However, for the set of points bounded by the graph of a continuous, non-negative valued function f, the first axis, and the lines $x = a$ and $x = b$, it is reasonable to *define* the area A as the integral $\int_a^b f$ (figure 6.1).

Of course, if one were to make a more general definition of area, then it would have to be shown that in the special case referred to above the general definition agrees with the special definition. The same remark will apply to the discussion of volumes of revolution in § 7 and surfaces of revolution in § 8.

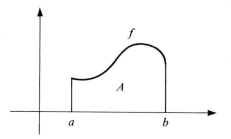

Fig. 6.1

Let g be another continuous, nonnegative valued function such that $g(x) \le f(x)$ for all x in $[a, b]$, and let B be the area under the graph of g (figure 6.2). Then the area bounded by graphs of f and g and the lines $x = a$ and $x = b$ is given by

$$C = A - B = \int_a^b f - \int_a^b g = \int_a^b (f - g). \tag{1}$$

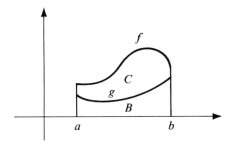

Fig. 6.2

If the graph of g drops below the first axis as in figure 6.3, then by adding a big enough constant M to both f and g, we can arrange that the graphs of $f + M$ and $g + M$ lie above the first axis as in figure 6.2. Now the area C between f and g is the same as that between $f + M$ and $g + M$, and so, using (1) applied to $f + M$ and $g + M$, we find

$$C = \int_a^b ((f + M) - (g + M)) = \int_a^b (f - g)$$

as before.

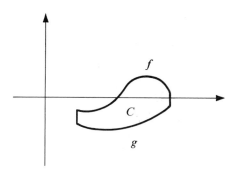

Fig. 6.3

Example 1:   Find the area bounded by the parabola $y^2 = x$ and the line $x = 4$. The area is indicated in the following figure. It may be computed as the area bounded by the line $x = 4$ and the graphs of f and g where $f(x) = \sqrt{x}$ and $g(x) = -\sqrt{x}$. This is given by

$$\int_0^4 (\sqrt{x} - (-\sqrt{x}))\, dx = 2[\tfrac{2}{3}x^{3/2}]_0^4 = \tfrac{32}{3}.$$

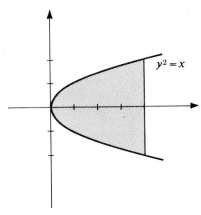

$y^2 = x$

Fig. 6.4

Example 2:   Find the area bounded by the graphs of f and g where $f(x) = x^3 - 2x$ and $g(x) = x^2$. We must first find the places where the graphs intersect. This is given by setting $f(x) - g(x) = 0$. That is,

$$0 = x^3 - x^2 - 2x = x(x + 1)(x - 2),$$

and so the graphs intersect when $x = 0$, $x = -1$, and $x = 2$. The situation is represented in figure 6.5. For $-1 \le x \le 0$ we have $f(x) \ge g(x)$, whereas for $0 \le x \le 2$ we have $g(x) \ge f(x)$. Hence the area is given by

$$\int_{-1}^0 ((x^3 - 2x) - x^2)\, dx + \int_0^2 (x^2 - (x^3 - 2x))\, dx$$

$$= \left[\frac{x^4}{4} - \frac{x^3}{3} - x^2\right]_{-1}^0 + \left[\frac{-x^4}{4} + \frac{x^3}{3} + x^2\right]_0^2 = \frac{37}{12}.$$

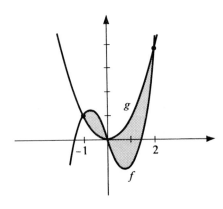

g

-1 2

f

Fig. 6.5

Example 3:   Find the area enclosed by the ellipse $\dfrac{x^2}{a^2} + \dfrac{y^2}{b^2} = 1$.   The area is 4 times the area under the graph of f between 0 and a where f is given by $f(x) = \dfrac{b}{a}\sqrt{a^2 - x^2}$ (figure 6.6).   Therefore, using example 3 of § 5, we see that the area is

$$4\int_0^a \frac{b}{a}\sqrt{a^2 - x^2}\, dx = 4\frac{b}{a}\cdot\frac{1}{2}\left[x\sqrt{a^2 - x^2} + a^2\arcsin\frac{x}{a}\right]_0^a$$

$$= 2\frac{b}{a}a^2\frac{\pi}{2} = \pi ab.$$

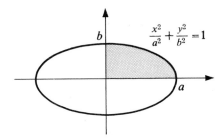

Fig. 6.6

In particular, if $a = b$, then the ellipse is just a circle of radius a, and the area is πa^2.   This agrees with the formula found in chapter I, § 23, where we considered the area of the circle as a limit of sums of areas of small triangles.

EXERCISES

1. Determine the area bounded by the graphs of sin and cos between two consecutive points where they intersect.
2. Find the area bounded by the parabola $y^2 - 4x = 0$ and the line

   $y - 2x + 4 = 0$.

   (Hint: Draw a diagram, and divide the region in question into two parts.)
3. Let $f(x) = -\sqrt{x}$. Find the area bounded by the graphs of f and arctan between $x = 1$ and $x = \sqrt{3}$.
4. Find the area bounded by the graphs of f and g when
   - (a) $f(x) = x^4$ and $g(x) = x^2$
   - (b) $f(x) = 2x^3 - 7x$ and $g(x) = x^2 - 6$
   - (c) $f(x) = x^4 + 3x$ and $g(x) = 3x^3 + x^2$.
5. Find the area bounded by the graphs of $\sin x$ and $\dfrac{2}{\pi}x$.

7. VOLUMES OF REVOLUTION

Let f be continuous in $[a, b]$. Consider the solid obtained by revolving about the first axis the area bounded by the graph of f, the first axis, and the lines $x = a$ and $x = b$ (figure 7.1). We wish to find an expression for the volume

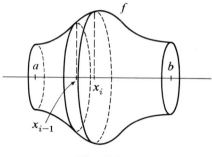

Fig. 7.1

V of this solid. If f is a constant function c, then the solid is called a *right circular cylinder* of radius c and length $b - a$ (figure 7.2). The volume in this case is clearly equal to the area of one end times the length, or in other words, $\pi c^2(b - a)$.

In the case of a general function f, consider any partition

$$a = x_0 < x_1 < x_2 < \cdots < x_{n-1} < x_n = b$$

of the interval $[a, b]$, and let V_i denote the volume of the slice obtained by cutting perpendicular to the first axis through x_{i-1} and x_i (figure 7.1). Then V is the sum of all the V_i's. Now if we let m_i and M_i denote the minimum and

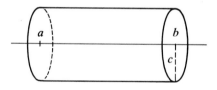

Fig. 7.2

maximum values of f on $[x_{i-1}, x_i]$, then V_i will be greater than or equal to the volume of the solid right circular cylinder of radius m_i and length $x_i - x_{i-1}$, and less than or equal to that of the cylinder of radius M_i and length $x_i - x_{i-1}$. In other words,

$$\pi m_i^2(x_i - x_{i-1}) \leq V_i \leq \pi M_i^2(x_i - x_{i-1}).$$

Adding these inequalities we obtain

$$\sum_{i=1}^{n} \pi m_i^2(x_i - x_{i-1}) \leq V \leq \sum_{i=1}^{n} \pi M_i^2(x_i - x_{i-1}). \tag{1}$$

But πm_i^2 and πM_i^2 are the minimum and maximum values respectively for the function πf^2 on $[x_{i-1}, x_i]$, and so the left and right sides of (1) are just the lower and upper sums for the function πf^2 relative to the given partition. Thus we find that V is a number which lies between every lower and upper sum for πf^2. Since there is only one such number, namely the integral of πf^2 between a and b, this leads to the formula

$$V = \pi \int_a^b f^2(x)\, dx. \tag{2}$$

Example 1: Let f be given by $f(x) = mx$ where $m > 0$, so that the graph of f is a straight line of positive slope passing through the origin. If we take $a = 0$ and denote $r = mb$, then the solid of revolution about the first axis is known as a *right circular cone* of height b and radius of the base r (figure 7.3). From (2), its volume is given by

$$V = \pi \int_0^b (mx)^2\, dx = \pi m^2 \frac{b^3}{3} = \frac{1}{3}\pi r^2 b,$$

or in other words, one third the area of the base times the height.

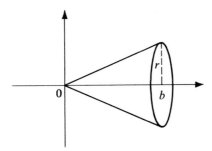

Fig. 7.3

Example 2: The surface obtained by revolving the ellipse

$$\frac{x^2}{a^2} + \frac{y^2}{b^2} = 1$$

about the first axis is called an *ellipsoid of revolution* (figure 7.4). To find the volume it encloses, we have, taking $f(x) = \frac{b}{a}\sqrt{a^2 - x^2}$ in (2),

$$V = \pi \int_{-a}^a \frac{b^2}{a^2}(a^2 - x^2)\, dx = 2\pi \frac{b^2}{a^2}\left(a^3 - \frac{a^3}{3}\right) = \frac{4}{3}\pi a b^2.$$

In particular, when $a = b$, we see that the volume of a sphere of radius a is $\frac{4}{3}\pi a^3$.

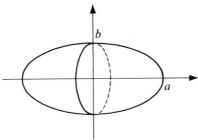

Fig. 7.4

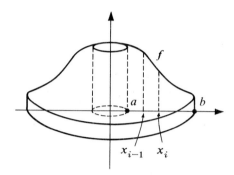

Fig. 7.5

Now suppose that $0 \leq a < b$, and let f be a continuous function such that $f(x) \geq 0$ for all x in $[a, b]$. Instead of revolving the area under the graph of f about the first axis, let us revolve it about the second axis so as to get the ring-shaped solid of figure 7.5. To find its volume V, consider a partition of the interval $[a, b]$, and let V_i be the volume obtained by revolving the strip under the graph of f between x_{i-1} and x_i about the second axis. If m_i is the minimum value of f in $[x_{i-1}, x_i]$, then V_i will be greater than or equal to the volume of the right circular cylindrical shell of inner radius x_{i-1}, outer radius x_i, and height m_i (figure 7.6). The volume of the latter is given simply by the difference in the volumes of two cylinders, one of radius x_i and the other of radius x_{i-1}, and so we obtain

$$m_i \pi x_i^2 - m_i \pi x_{i-1}^2 \leq V_i. \tag{3}$$

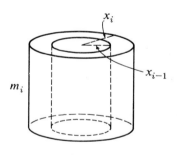

Fig. 7.6

Let x_i' be the midpoint of the interval $[x_{i-1}, x_i]$, or in other words,

$$x_i' = (x_i + x_{i-1})/2,$$

and let x_i'' be a point of $[x_{i-1}, x_i]$ such that $f(x_i'') = m_i$. Then (3) becomes

$$2\pi x_i' f(x_i'')(x_i - x_{i-1}) \leq V_i. \tag{4}$$

Similarly, if x_i''' is a point in $[x_{i-1}, x_i]$ where f has its maximum value M_i, then

$$V_i \leq 2\pi x_i' f(x_i''')(x_i - x_{i-1}). \tag{5}$$

Adding the inequalities (4) and (5), we obtain

$$\sum_{i=1}^{n} 2\pi x_i' f(x_i'')(x_i - x_{i-1})$$

$$\leq V \leq \sum_{i=1}^{n} 2\pi x_i' f(x_i''')(x_i - x_{i-1}). \qquad (6)$$

Now if we let $g(x) = 2\pi x$, then by Duhamel's principle (example 1 of chapter IV, §9) we see that the expressions on the left and right of (6) approach the integral of fg from a to b as $|P|$ approaches zero. Since V is always between these two expressions, this leads to the formula

$$V = 2\pi \int_a^b x f(x)\, dx. \qquad (7)$$

Example 3: Suppose $0 < a \leq r$. Consider the circle of radius a centered at the point $(r, 0)$ (figure 7.7). It is the set of all those points (x, y) whose distance to $(r, 0)$ is a, or in other words, points (x, y) such that

$$(x - r)^2 + y^2 = a^2.$$

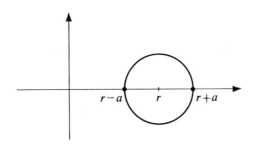

Fig. 7.7

If we rotate this circle about the second axis, we obtain what is known as a *torus*. Its volume V will be twice the volume obtained by revolving the area under the graph of the function f given by $f(x) = \sqrt{a^2 - (x - r)^2}$ about the second axis. Thus by equation (7),

$$V = 4\pi \int_{r-a}^{r+a} x\sqrt{a^2 - (x - r)^2}\, dx.$$

To integrate we make the substitution $x = t + r$ and use example 3 of §5. This gives

$$V = 4\pi \int_{-a}^{a} (t + r)\sqrt{a^2 - t^2}\, dt$$

$$= 4\pi \left[\frac{-1}{3}(a^2 - t^2)^{3/2} + \frac{r}{2}\left(t\sqrt{a^2 - t^2} + a^2 \arcsin \frac{t}{a} \right) \right]_{-a}^{a}$$

$$= (2\pi r)(\pi a^2).$$

Thus the volume is the area of the circle of cross section of the torus times the circumference of a circle of radius r.

EXERCISES

1. Suppose that f is continuous in $[a, b]$, and let A denote the region bounded by the graph of f and the lines $x = a$, $x = b$, and $y = c$. Show that the volume obtained by revolving A about the line $y = c$ is

$$\pi \int_a^b (f(x) - c)^2 \, dx.$$

2. Suppose that $0 \le a < b$, and that f and g are continuous functions such that $g(x) \le f(x)$ for all x in $[a, b]$. Let A denote the region bounded by the graphs of f and g and the lines $x = a$ and $x = b$. Using equation (7) and an argument similar to that given in § 6 for area, show that the volume obtained by revolving A about the second axis is

$$2\pi \int_a^b x(f(x) - g(x)) \, dx.$$

More generally, if c is any point not in (a, b), show that the volume obtained by revolving A about the line $x = c$ is

$$2\pi \int_a^b |x - c|(f(x) - g(x)) \, dx.$$

3. Let A denote the region under the graph of sin between 0 and π. Find the volume generated by revolving A about (a) the first axis and (b) the second axis.

4. If $0 < a < b$ and $m > 0$, then the volume obtained by rotating the area bounded by the lines $y = mx$, $y = 0$, $x = a$, and $x = b$ about the second axis is known as a *baseball stadium*. Find the volume of a baseball stadium. If the builders misinterpret the architect's plans and rotate about the first axis instead of the second, what volume will they obtain?

5. Let A denote the region under the graph of e^x between 0 and 1. Find the volume generated by revolving A about (a) the first axis and (b) the line $x = 1$.

6. Find the volume obtained by rotating the area bounded by the parabola $y^2 = 4x$ and the line $x = a$ $(a > 0)$ about the first axis.

7. Find the volume obtained by revolving the area bounded by the graphs of x^2 and $3x - 2$ about (a) the line $x = -1$ and (b) the line $y = 5$.

8. If a hole of radius a is drilled through the center of a sphere of radius $2a$, what volume remains?

8. SURFACES OF REVOLUTION

In this section we assume that f is a function with a continuous derivative in an interval $[a, b]$. If we revolve the graph of f about the first axis, we obtain what is known as a *surface of revolution*. We wish to find a formula for the area of such a surface. First we consider the case where $f(x) = \dfrac{R}{b} x$, so that the graph of f is a straight line passing through the origin and the point (b, R). Suppose that $0 \le a < b$, and that $f(a) = r$. Then the surface of revolution is just a frustrum of a cone. The situation is represented in figure 8.1, where we have let L denote the slant length of the frustrum.

We partition the interval $[a, b]$, and we let S_i denote the area obtained by revolving about the first axis that part of the graph of f between x_{i-1} and x_i. Also we denote the length of this part of the graph by l_i, so that S_i is somewhat less than the surface area of a cylinder of radius $f(x_i)$ and length l_i, and somewhat greater than the surface area of a cylinder of radius $f(x_{i-1})$ and length l_i. Thus we find

$$2\pi f(x_{i-1})l_i \leq S_i \leq 2\pi f(x_i)l_i. \tag{1}$$

But by similar triangles,

$$l_i = \frac{L}{b-a}(x_i - x_{i-1}),$$

and so (1) becomes

$$2\pi \frac{L}{b-a} f(x_{i-1})(x_i - x_{i-1}) \leq S_i \leq 2\pi \frac{L}{b-a} f(x_i)(x_i - x_{i-1}). \tag{2}$$

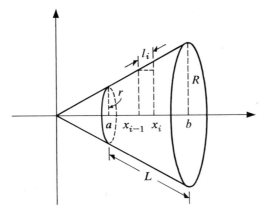

Fig. 8.1

If we add the inequalities (2), the left side becomes a lower sum for the function $2\pi \frac{L}{b-a} f$, the right side becomes an upper sum, and the middle term becomes S. Since this holds for all partitions, we find

$$S = \int_a^b 2\pi \frac{L}{b-a} f(x)\, dx$$

$$= 2\pi \frac{L}{b-a} \int_a^b \frac{R}{b} x\, dx$$

$$= \pi \frac{L}{b-a} \cdot \frac{R}{b} (b^2 - a^2) = \pi L(R + r). \tag{3}$$

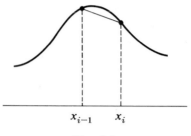

Fig. 8.2

For a general function f, we again partition the interval $[a, b]$ and for each i we join the point on the graph of f above x_{i-1} to that above x_i (figure 8.2). In this way we see that the area S of the surface of revolution can be approximated by the combined surface areas of n frustrums. In accordance with formula (3), the area of the ith frustrum is given by

$$\pi(f(x_{i-1}) + f(x_i))\sqrt{(x_i - x_{i-1})^2 + (f(x_i) - f(x_{i-1}))^2}. \qquad (4)$$

By the intermediate value theorem we can write

$$f(x_{i-1}) + f(x_i) = 2f(x_i') \qquad (5)$$

for some x_i' in $[x_{i-1}, x_i]$, and by the mean value theorem we have

$$\frac{f(x_i) - f(x_{i-1})}{x_i - x_{i-1}} = f'(x_i'') \qquad (6)$$

for some x_i'' in $[x_{i-1}, x_i]$. Using (5) and (6) in (4) and adding over i, we therefore see that S can be approximated by

$$\sum_{i=1}^{n} 2\pi f(x_i')\sqrt{1 + f'^2(x_i'')} \,(x_i - x_{i-1}). \qquad (7)$$

S will then be the limit of such expressions (7) as the mesh of the partition approaches 0. Therefore by Duhamel's principle (chapter IV, § 9, example 1), we find

$$S = 2\pi \int_a^b f(x)\sqrt{1 + f'^2(x)} \, dx. \qquad (8)$$

Example: Let $f(x) = \sqrt{r^2 - x^2}$ for $a \le x \le b$, where $-r < a < b < r$ (figure 8.3). Then the surface of revolution is called a *zone* of the sphere of radius r. The number $b - a$ is called the *height* of the zone. By formula (8) the area of the zone is

$$S = 2\pi \int_a^b \sqrt{r^2 - x^2} \sqrt{1 + \frac{x^2}{r^2 - x^2}} \, dx$$

$$= 2\pi \int_a^b r \, dx = 2\pi r(b - a). \qquad (9)$$

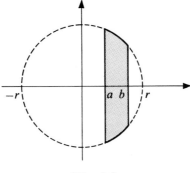

Fig. 8.3

In other words, any two zones of the same height have the same area. In particular, the surface area of the sphere, obtained by taking the limit of (9) as a approaches $-r$ and b approaches r, is $4\pi r^2$.

EXERCISES

1. Consider the ellipse

$$\frac{x^2}{a^2} + \frac{y^2}{b^2} = 1$$

where $a > b$. Show that the area of the ellipsoid of revolution about the first axis is given by

$$S = 2\pi \left(b^2 + \frac{ba^2}{\sqrt{a^2 - b^2}} \arcsin \frac{\sqrt{a^2 - b^2}}{a} \right).$$

2. Show that the area obtained by revolving the parabola $y^2 = 4x$ about the first axis between $x = 0$ and $x = 3$ is $56\pi/3$.

3. Find the area of the surface of revolution of the graph of e^x between $x = -1$ and $x = 3$.

4. Find the area of a thorn. (A thorn is obtained by revolving the graph of x^3 about the first axis between $x = 0$ and $x = 1$.)

5. Find the area of a football. (A football is obtained by revolving the graph of sin about the first axis between $x = 0$ and $x = \pi$.)

9. LENGTH OF A PATH

In the previous three sections we have depended to a certain extent on our intuitive notions of area and volume. This will not be the case in the present section, where our definitions and results, although guided by geometry, will be perfectly rigorous.

Let γ be a function from a finite closed interval $[a, b]$ to the set $R \times R$ of ordered pairs of real numbers. We can think of $R \times R$ geometrically as the

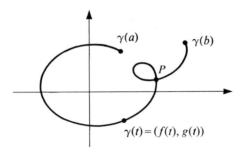

Fig. 9.1

plane, so that as t varies between a and b, $\gamma(t)$ will move about in the plane (figure 9.1). Now, for each t in $[a, b]$, $\gamma(t)$ is an ordered pair of real numbers. Let us denote the first of these numbers by $f(t)$ and the second by $g(t)$, so that $\gamma(t) = (f(t), g(t))$. Thus we see that γ is determined by two functions f and g from $[a, b]$ to R. If f and g are both continuous in $[a, b]$, then we shall call γ a *path*. The points $\gamma(a)$ and $\gamma(b)$ are called the *initial point* and the *terminal point* respectively. If these two points coincide, then we shall say that the path is *closed*.

    Any point (x, y) such that $x = f(t)$ and $y = g(t)$ for some t in $[a, b]$ (possibly for several such t) will be said to be *on* the path. However, it must be emphasized that it is the function γ which we have defined as the path, and not the set of points on it. If the latter set were all that we were given, then we wouldn't know "where to go" if we were at a point such as P in figure 9.1.

    Example 1:   Let $f(t) = t^2$ and $g(t) = t^3$ for $-1 \leq t \leq 1$. By locating a few points corresponding to various values of t, we find that the path is as in figure 9.2. It is not closed. It is easily seen that a point (x, y) is on the path if and only if $y = x^{3/2}$ or $y = -x^{3/2}$ and $0 \leq x \leq 1$.

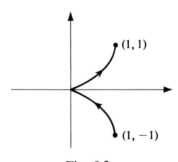

Fig. 9.2

    Example 2:   Let $f(t) = a \cos t$ and $g(t) = b \sin t$ for $0 \leq t \leq 2\pi$, where a and b are positive. Then any point (x, y) on the path must satisfy

$$\frac{x^2}{a^2} + \frac{y^2}{b^2} = 1,$$

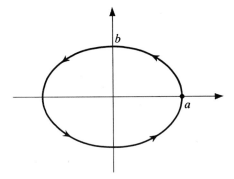

Fig. 9.3

and so we see that as t varies between 0 and 2π, the point $(f(t), g(t))$ moves around an ellipse (figure 9.3). The path in this case is closed.

Example 3: The graph of any continuous function g on a closed interval $[a, b]$ becomes the set of points on a path if we take $f(t) = t$ for $a \leq t \leq b$ (figure 9.4). Such a path has the property that any line parallel to the second axis contains at most one point on the path.

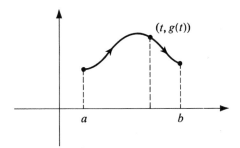

Fig. 9.4

Let γ be a path defined in an interval $[a, b]$, and consider a partition $a = t_0 < t_1 < \cdots < t_n = b$. For each i consider the straight line segment joining the points $\gamma(t_{i-1})$ and $\gamma(t_i)$ (figure 9.5). If P denotes the given partition, then we shall let $L(P)$ denote the total length of all the above line segments. Thus $L(P)$ is defined by

$$L(P) = \sum_{i=1}^{n} \sqrt{(f(t_i) - f(t_{i-1}))^2 + (g(t_i) - g(t_{i-1}))^2}. \qquad (1)$$

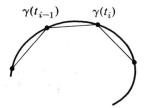

Fig. 9.5

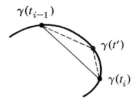

Fig. 9.6

Lemma 9.1:   *If P is a subset of P', then $L(P) \le L(P')$.*

Proof: In the case where P' is obtained from P by the addition of a single point t', say in the interval $[t_{i-1}, t_i]$, then it follows from the triangle inequality (chapter III, § 4) that $L(P) \le L(P')$. (See figure 9.6.) The general case then follows by induction on the number of points one must add to P to obtain P'. ∎

If for all possible partitions P of $[a, b]$ the numbers $L(P)$ are bounded, then their least upper bound is called the *length* of γ. Otherwise we say that γ has *infinite length*.

Example 4:   We shall give an example of a path which has infinite length. First observe that by leaving out the first term under each square root sign in (1), we obtain

$$L(P) \ge \sum_{i=1}^{n} |g(t_i) - g(t_{i-1})|. \tag{2}$$

Now let $g(t) = t \sin(1/t)$ for $0 < t \le 2/\pi$, and define $g(0) = 0$. Then, as we saw in chapter II, § 12, g is continuous in $[0, 2/\pi]$. Define $\gamma(t) = (t, g(t))$ for all t in $[0, 2/\pi]$. Then, relative to the partition P whose points are

$$0 < \frac{2}{2n\pi} < \frac{2}{(2n-1)\pi} < \cdots < \frac{2}{3\pi} < \frac{2}{2\pi} < \frac{2}{\pi},$$

the inequality (2) becomes

$$L(P) \ge \frac{2}{(2n-1)\pi} + \frac{2}{(2n-1)\pi} + \frac{2}{(2n-3)\pi} + \cdots + \frac{2}{3\pi} + \frac{2}{2\pi} + \frac{2}{\pi}$$

$$> \frac{2}{\pi}\left(\frac{1}{2n} + \frac{1}{2n-1} + \frac{1}{2n-2} + \cdots + \frac{1}{4} + \frac{1}{3} + \frac{1}{2}\right)$$

But as we shall see in the following chapter, this last expression can be made as large as we wish by taking n large enough. This proves that the numbers $L(P)$ are unbounded, and so γ has infinite length.

If f and g have continuous derivatives in $[a, b]$ and if $\gamma(t) = (f(t), g(t))$ for all t in $[a, b]$, then γ is called a *smooth* path. The path of example 4 is not smooth since g does not have a derivative at 0.

Theorem 9.2:   *If γ is a smooth path, then γ has finite length L given by the formula*

$$L = \int_a^b \sqrt{f'^2(t) + g'^2(t)}\, dt. \tag{3}$$

Proof: If P is the partition $a = t_0 < t_1 < \cdots < t_n = b$, then by the mean value theorem we can write for each i

$$f(t_i) - f(t_{i-1}) = f'(r_i)(t_i - t_{i-1})$$
$$g(t_i) - g(t_{i-1}) = g'(s_i)(t_i - t_{i-1})$$

for some numbers r_i and s_i in $[t_{i-1}, t_i]$. Then equation (1) becomes

$$L(P) = \sum_{i=1}^n \sqrt{f'^2(r_i) + g'^2(s_i)}\, (t_i - t_{i-1}). \tag{4}$$

Since f' and g' are continuous in $[a, b]$, they are bounded, say $|f'(t)| \le M$ and $|g'(t)| \le N$ for all t in $[a, b]$. Then from (4) we find

$$L(P) \le \sum_{i=1}^n \sqrt{M^2 + N^2}\, (t_i - t_{i-1}) = \sqrt{M^2 + N^2}\, (b - a).$$

Thus the numbers $L(P)$ are bounded, and so γ has finite length L.

We must now prove formula (3). From equation (4) and Duhamel's principle (chapter IV, §9, example 2) we find that given $\epsilon > 0$, there is a $\delta > 0$ such that

$$\left| L(P) - \int_a^b \sqrt{f'^2 + g'^2}\, \right| < \frac{\epsilon}{2} \tag{5}$$

whenever $|P| < \delta$. Since L is the least upper bound of the numbers $L(P)$, there is at least one partition, say P_1, such that

$$0 \le L - L(P_1) < \frac{\epsilon}{2}. \tag{6}$$

Let P be any partition such that $P_1 \subset P$ and such that $|P| < \delta$. Then from (6) and lemma 9.1 we find that P also satisfies (6). Therefore,

$$\left| L - \int_a^b \sqrt{f'^2 + g'^2}\, \right| \le |L - L(P)| + \left| L(P) - \int_a^b \sqrt{f'^2 + g'^2}\, \right|$$
$$< \frac{\epsilon}{2} + \frac{\epsilon}{2} = \epsilon.$$

Since this holds for every positive ϵ, this proves (3). ∎

As an application of theorem 9.2, let $f(t) = a \cos t$ and $g(t) = b \sin t$ for $0 \le t \le 2\pi$, where $0 < b \le a$. From example 2, we see that the length L of this path will give us the circumference of an ellipse (and thus, as a special instance, the distance that the earth travels in a year). By formula (3) we find

$$L = \int_0^{2\pi} \sqrt{a^2 \sin^2 t + b^2 \cos^2 t}\, dt$$

$$= a \int_0^{2\pi} \sqrt{1 - e^2 \cos^2 t}\, dt \qquad\qquad (7)$$

where the number $e = \sqrt{1 - b^2/a^2}$ is called the *eccentricity* of the ellipse. If $b = a$, so that the ellipse is just a circle with radius a, then $e = 0$ and we obtain easily $L = 2\pi a$, which agrees with the formula for the circumference of a circle found in chapter I. However, if $b < a$, so that $e > 0$, then we cannot find an antiderivative for $\sqrt{1 - e^2 \cos^2 t}$ in terms of the functions we are familiar with. Nevertheless, the integral (7) (which is called an *elliptic integral*) can be computed by various means, and in fact this integral is used so much that tables have been published for it.

EXERCISES

1. If a bicycle wheel rolling in the plane along the first axis picks up a piece of chewing gum (abbreviation c.g.) at the origin, the path of the c.g. (not to be confused with center of gravity) is known as a *cycloid* (figure 9.7). If the radius of the wheel is r, show that when the center of the wheel is at a distance rt from the second axis, the c.g. is at the point $(r(t - \sin t), r(1 - \cos t))$. Hence, show that the length of the path of the c.g. between two consecutive places where it touches down is $8r$. (Use the relation $\cos t = 1 - 2 \sin^2 (t/2)$ in calculating the integral.)

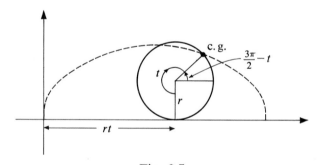

Fig. 9.7

2. If $\gamma(t) = (a + ht, b + kt)$ for $0 \le t \le 1$, and if h and k are not both zero, show that the points on the path are just the points on the straight line segment joining (a, b) to $(a + h, b + k)$. According to formula (6), what is the length of γ? How many points are on the path if $h = k = 0$?
3. Find the length of the path of example 1.
4. If $\gamma(t) = (\cos^3 t, \sin^3 t)$ for $0 \le t \le \pi$, find the length of γ.
5. Find a path such that the points on it are the same as the points on the parabola $y^2 = x$ between $(1, -1)$ and $(4, 2)$. Find the length of this path.
6. Let cosh and sinh be as in § 2, exercise 6, and let $\gamma(t) = (t, \cosh t)$ for $0 \le t \le a$. Show that the length of γ is $\sinh a$.

7. If $\gamma(t) = (e^t \cos t, e^t \sin t)$ for $0 \le t \le 2$, find the length of γ.

8. If one travels a distance x on the unit circle starting at $(1, 0)$, one ends up at $(\cos x, \sin x)$ by definition of cos and sin. Check that this is true by defining $\gamma(t) = (\cos t, \sin t)$ for $0 \le t \le x$ and finding the length of γ.

10. L'HÔPITAL'S RULE

The theorems of this section have nothing to do with integrals, and in fact they could have been included in chapter III. However, since some of the applications of these theorems have to do with logarithms and exponents, we have chosen to place them here.

Suppose that f and g are defined in some open interval (a, b) and that $g(x) \ne 0$ for each x in (a, b). If $\lim\limits_{x \to a+} f = L$ and $\lim\limits_{x \to a+} g = M$, then the quotient rule for limits gives

$$\lim_{x \to a+} \frac{f(x)}{g(x)} = \frac{L}{M}$$

provided $M \ne 0$. However, in many important cases we need to know the limit of the quotient even though $M = 0$. Now if g is continuous, then since $g(x) \ne 0$ in (a, b), by the intermediate value theorem $g(x)$ must either be always positive or always negative in (a, b). We may always assume the former by taking a factor of -1 up into the numerator if necessary. Thus if $M = 0$ but $L \ne 0$, then it is easily seen that the limit of the quotient is ∞ or $-\infty$ depending on whether $L > 0$ or $L < 0$ (see chapter II, § 13, exercise 5).

Hence, the only case where the limit of the quotient is not obvious is the case where L and M are both 0. For example, we have so far no means of finding a limit such as

$$\lim_{x \to 0} \frac{x - \sin x}{x^3} . \tag{1}$$

Another limit of this type is one of the form

$$\lim_{h \to 0} \frac{f(a + h) - f(a)}{h}$$

where f is continuous at a. It is therefore not surprising to find that a solution to the general problem has to do with derivatives. The following theorem was known as early as 1696 by the French mathematician Guillaume de l'Hôpital (1661–1704).

Theorem 10.1 (L'Hôpital's Rule): *Let f and g be differentiable in (a, b), and suppose that $g'(x) \ne 0$ for all x in (a, b). If*

$$\lim_{x \to a+} f(x) = 0 = \lim_{x \to a+} g(x) \tag{2}$$

and if

$$\lim_{x \to a+} \frac{f'(x)}{g'(x)} = L, \tag{3}$$

then also

$$\lim_{x \to a+} \frac{f(x)}{g(x)} = L. \tag{4}$$

The theorem is also true if L is replaced by ∞ or $-\infty$.

Proof: If we define $f(a) = 0 = g(a)$, then from (2) we see that this makes f and g continuous at a. Hence, if x is any point in (a, b), then by Cauchy's mean value theorem (chapter III, theorem 9.2) we can write

$$\frac{f(x)}{g(x)} = \frac{f(x) - f(a)}{g(x) - g(a)} = \frac{f'(c)}{g'(c)} \tag{5}$$

for some c in (a, x). Let ϵ be any positive number. Then by (3) we can find a positive δ such that

$$\left| \frac{f'(x)}{g'(x)} - L \right| < \epsilon$$

whenever x is in $(a, a + \delta)$. But if x is in $(a, a + \delta)$, then so also is c, and so from (5) we find

$$\left| \frac{f(x)}{g(x)} - L \right| < \epsilon.$$

This proves (4).

The argument if L is replaced by ∞ or $-\infty$ is quite similar. For example in the former case, given any number B we can find δ such that $f'(x)/g'(x) > B$ for all x in $(a, a + \delta)$. Hence, again from (5) it follows that for such x,

$$\frac{f(x)}{g(x)} > B$$

as well, and so $\lim\limits_{x \to a+} f(x)/g(x) = \infty$. ∎

Of course a similar theorem holds for left-hand limits. Also the theorem remains valid for limits at ∞ (or $-\infty$). To see this, we resort to the trick introduced in chapter II, § 14 whereby we express a limit at ∞ as a limit at 0, and we apply the theorem as we have stated it above. This gives

$$\lim_{x \to \infty} \frac{f(x)}{g(x)} = \lim_{t \to 0+} \frac{f(1/t)}{g(1/t)} = \lim_{t \to 0+} \frac{f'(1/t)(-1/t^2)}{g'(1/t)(-1/t^2)}$$

$$= \lim_{t \to 0+} \frac{f'(1/t)}{g'(1/t)} = \lim_{x \to \infty} \frac{f'(x)}{g'(x)}. \tag{6}$$

Example 1: To compute the limit (1), we find using l'Hôpital's rule,

$$\lim_{x \to 0} \frac{x - \sin x}{x^3} = \lim_{x \to 0} \frac{1 - \cos x}{3x^2}$$

providing the limit on the right exists. Again both numerator and denominator have limit 0, and so once more we apply l'Hôpital's rule. This gives

$$\lim_{x\to 0} \frac{1 - \cos x}{3x^2} = \lim_{x\to 0} \frac{\sin x}{6x},$$

providing the limit on the right exists. At this point we can either recall from chapter II, § 8 that $\lim_{x\to 0} \dfrac{\sin x}{x} = 1$, or we can apply l'Hôpital's rule still again to obtain

$$\lim_{x\to 0} \frac{\sin x}{6x} = \lim_{x\to 0} \frac{\cos x}{6} = \frac{1}{6}.$$

Example 2: We find $\lim_{x\to \pi/2} (\sec x - \tan x)$. Both terms have infinite limits, and so it is not clear what the limit of the difference should be. However, a slight bit of algebra puts us in a position to apply l'Hôpital's rule. Thus

$$\lim_{x\to \pi/2} (\sec x - \tan x) = \lim_{x\to \pi/2} \frac{1 - \sin x}{\cos x} = \lim_{x\to \pi/2} \frac{-\cos x}{-\sin x} = 0.$$

Remark: There is an economical aspect to l'Hôpital's rule in that the only cases where it applies are the only cases where we need it. For example, if $f(x) = 1$ and $g(x) = x$ for all x, then

$$\lim_{x\to 0+} \frac{f'(x)}{g'(x)} = \lim_{x\to 0+} \frac{0}{1} = 0,$$

whereas

$$\lim_{x\to 0+} \frac{f(x)}{g(x)} = \lim_{x\to 0+} \frac{1}{x} = \infty.$$

The reason the limits are not the same is that $f(x)$ does not have limit 0.

So far, we have restricted our attention to limits of quotients where the limit of both numerator and denominator is finite. If one of the limits is finite but the other is infinite, then the limit of the quotient is easy to determine. The reader can examine the various possibilities. Thus the only case which remains open is the one where the limit of both denominator and numerator is infinite. It turns out that l'Hôpital's rule applies here as well. The proof is a little longer than that of theorem 10.1, although it proceeds along much the same lines. Actually we only need to assume that the limit of the denominator is infinite in the hypothesis.

Theorem 10.2: *Let f and g be differentiable in (a, b), and suppose that $g'(x) \neq 0$ for all x in (a, b). If*

$$\lim_{x\to a+} g(x) = \infty, \tag{7}$$

and if

$$\lim_{x \to a+} \frac{f'(x)}{g'(x)} = L, \tag{8}$$

then also

$$\lim_{x \to a+} \frac{f(x)}{g(x)} = L. \tag{9}$$

The·theorem is also true if L is replaced by ∞ or $-\infty$.

Proof: If x and y are any two numbers such that $a < x < y < b$, then again from Cauchy's mean value theorem we can write

$$\frac{f(x) - f(y)}{g(x) - g(y)} = \frac{f'(c)}{g'(c)} \tag{10}$$

for some c satisfying $x < c < y$. Let ϵ be any positive number. In view of (8), we can find a positive number δ_1 such that

$$L - \frac{\epsilon}{2} < \frac{f'(c)}{g'(c)} < L + \frac{\epsilon}{2} \tag{11}$$

for any c in $(a, a + \delta_1)$. Therefore, if we set $y = a + \delta_1$, then from (10) and (11) we find

$$L - \frac{\epsilon}{2} < \frac{f(x) - f(y)}{g(x) - g(y)} < L + \frac{\epsilon}{2}$$

whenever $a < x < y$. If we divide the numerator and denominator of the middle term by $g(x)$, we obtain

$$L - \frac{\epsilon}{2} < \frac{f(x)/g(x) - f(y)/g(x)}{1 - g(y)/g(x)} < L + \frac{\epsilon}{2}. \tag{12}$$

Now, because of (7), we can find a positive number δ_2 such that

$$1 - \frac{g(y)}{g(x)} > 0$$

for all x in $(a, a + \delta_2)$. For such x we can multiply each term in (12) by $1 - g(y)/g(x)$ without changing the direction of the inequalities, and then after adding $f(y)/g(x)$ to all three terms, we obtain

$$\left(1 - \frac{g(y)}{g(x)}\right)\left(L - \frac{\epsilon}{2}\right) + \frac{f(y)}{g(x)}$$
$$< \frac{f(x)}{g(x)} < \left(1 - \frac{g(y)}{g(x)}\right)\left(L + \frac{\epsilon}{2}\right) + \frac{f(y)}{g(x)}. \tag{13}$$

The limit of the left side of (13) is $L - \frac{\epsilon}{2}$ as x approaches $a+$, and so we can find a positive number δ_3 such that the left side is greater than $L - \epsilon$ for x in $(a, a + \delta_3)$. Likewise we can find a positive δ_4 such that the right side is less than $L + \epsilon$. Therefore, if we let δ be the smallest of the four numbers δ_1, δ_2, δ_3, and δ_4, we obtain

$$L - \epsilon < \frac{f(x)}{g(x)} < L + \epsilon$$

for all x in $(a + \delta)$. This proves (9).

We leave it to the reader to make the changes necessary for the case where L is replaced by ∞. ∎

Again, the theorem can be stated for left-hand limits, and the argument (6) still applies to take care of the case of limits at ∞.

Example 3:   We shall show by induction on n that

$$\lim_{x \to \infty} \frac{x^n}{e^x} = 0.$$

If $n = 0$, this is obvious. Assume that the assertion is true with n replaced by $n - 1$. Then we have, using theorem 10.2.

$$\lim_{x \to \infty} \frac{x^n}{e^x} = \lim_{x \to \infty} \frac{nx^{n-1}}{e^x} = n \lim_{x \to \infty} \frac{x^{n-1}}{e^x} = 0.$$

Thus the assertion is true for all n.

Remark: If we write e^{-x}/x^{-n} in place of x^n/e^x, then the limit at infinity of both numerator and denominator is 0, and so we are in a position to apply theorem 10.1. However, that theorem yields

$$\lim_{x \to \infty} \frac{x^{-n}}{e^{-x}} = \lim_{x \to \infty} \frac{nx^{-(n+1)}}{e^{-x}},$$

which only makes the situation worse.

Consider a limit of the form

$$\lim f(x)g(x)$$

where $\lim f(x) = 0$ and $\lim g(x) = \infty$. Then, either we can write

$$f(x)g(x) = \frac{f(x)}{1/g(x)}$$

so as to make theorem 10.1 applicable, or we can write

$$f(x)g(x) = \frac{g(x)}{1/f(x)}$$

so as to make theorem 10.2 applicable. Now consider a limit of the form

$$\lim f(x)^{g(x)} = \lim \exp\left(g(x) \log f(x)\right). \tag{14}$$

Since exp is a continuous function with limit 0 at $-\infty$ and limit ∞ at ∞, it follows that in order to find (14), it suffices to find

$$\lim g(x) \log f(x). \tag{15}$$

If we know the limits of both $f(x)$ and $g(x)$, then the only cases where the limit (15) will not be obvious are where one of $g(x)$ and $\log f(x)$ has limit 0 and the other has limit ∞. This happens in the following cases.

(a) $\lim g(x) = 0$ and $\lim f(x) = 0$,
(b) $\lim g(x) = 0$ and $\lim f(x) = \infty$,
(c) $\lim g(x) = \infty$ and $\lim f(x) = 1$.

Example 4: We find $\lim\limits_{x \to 0+} x^{\sin x}$. This falls under case (a) above. We have

$$x^{\sin x} = \exp(\sin x \log x),$$

and so we compute

$$
\begin{aligned}
\lim_{x \to 0+} \sin x \log x &= \lim_{x \to 0+} \frac{\log x}{1/\sin x} \\
&= \lim_{x \to 0+} \frac{1/x}{-\cos x/\sin^2 x} \quad \text{(by theorem 10.2)} \\
&= -\lim_{x \to 0+} \frac{\sin x}{x} \tan x \quad \text{(by algebra)} \\
&= (-1)(0) \\
&= 0.
\end{aligned}
$$

Thus

$$\lim_{x \to 0+} x^{\sin x} = \exp(0) = 1.$$

EXERCISES

1. Prove theorem 10.2 for the case where L is replaced by ∞.

2. State and prove theorems 10.1 and 10.2 for left-hand limits.

3. Find $\lim\limits_{x \to a} \dfrac{x^n - a^n}{x - a}$ by canceling something from numerator and denominator. Then find it using l'Hôpital's rule.

4. Show that l'Hôpital's rule leads nowhere when applied to

$$\lim_{x \to \pi/2} \frac{\tan x}{\sec x}.$$

Nevertheless, show that the limit is 1.

5. Find each of the following limits.

(a) $\lim\limits_{x \to 0} \dfrac{\tan x - x}{x - \sin x}$
(b) $\lim\limits_{x \to \infty} \dfrac{e^x}{\log x}$

(c) $\lim\limits_{x\to 0} \dfrac{a^x - e^x}{x}$

(d) $\lim\limits_{x\to 0+} x^x$

(e) $\lim\limits_{x\to 0}\left(\dfrac{1}{x} - \dfrac{1}{\sin x}\right)$

(f) $\lim\limits_{x\to 0} x^n e^{-1/x^2}$ (n any integer)

(g) $\lim\limits_{x\to 0}\left(\dfrac{1}{x} - \dfrac{1}{\arctan x}\right)$

(h) $\lim\limits_{x\to 1} x^{1/(1-x)}$

(i) $\lim\limits_{x\to\pi/2} \sin x^{\tan x}$

(j) $\lim\limits_{x\to\infty} \dfrac{\log x}{\sqrt{x}}$

6. In § 2 it was shown that

$$\lim_{h\to 0} (1 + h)^{1/h} = e.$$

Prove this using l'Hôpital's rule.

11. IMPROPER INTEGRALS

Let f be a function which is continuous throughout an interval of the form (a, ∞). So far our definition of integral attaches no meaning to the symbol

$$\int_a^\infty f(x)\, dx \tag{1}$$

since the integral has been defined only relative to *finite* intervals. Nevertheless, it sometimes happens that the limit

$$\lim_{t\to\infty} \int_a^t f(x)\, dx$$

exists, and when this is the case, we take this limit as our definition of (1). We then call (1) an *improper* integral.

Example 1: Consider $\int_1^\infty \dfrac{dx}{x}$. We have

$$\int_1^t \frac{dx}{x} = [\log x]_1^t = \log t.$$

But $\lim\limits_{t\to\infty} \log t = \infty$, and so the improper integral does not exist.

Example 2: Consider $\int_1^\infty \dfrac{dx}{x^2}$. Here we have

$$\int_1^t \frac{dx}{x^2} = \left[\frac{-1}{x}\right]_1^t = 1 - \frac{1}{t}.$$

Thus

$$\int_1^\infty \frac{dx}{x^2} = \lim_{t\to\infty}\left(1 - \frac{1}{t}\right) = 1.$$

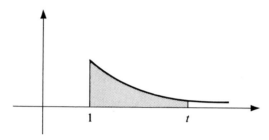

Fig. 11.1

The graphs of both $1/x$ and $1/x^2$ for $x \geq 1$ have the form indicated in figure 11.1. However, example 1 shows that in the case of $1/x$ the shaded area can be made as large as we wish, whereas example 2 shows that in the case of $1/x^2$ the shaded area is always less than 1.

Suppose now that f is a function which is continuous in a finite, half open interval of the form $(a, b]$, but that

$$\lim_{x \to a+} f(x) = \infty \quad (\text{or} -\infty).$$

Again we have attached no meaning to the symbol

$$\int_a^b f(x)\, dx \tag{2}$$

since the integral has been defined only for *bounded* functions. Now if $a < t < b$, then f is continuous in the closed interval $[t, b]$, and so the integral $\int_t^a f(x)\, dx$ is defined. If it is the case that the limit

$$\lim_{t \to a+} \int_t^b f(x)\, dx$$

exists, then we shall take this limit as our definition of (2). We shall again refer to (2) as an improper integral. Similarly, if f is continuous in $[a, b)$, but $\lim_{x \to b-} f(x) = \infty$ (or $-\infty$), we define

$$\int_a^b f(x)\, dx = \lim_{t \to b-} \int_a^t f(x)\, dx$$

providing the limit exists.

Example 3: Consider $\displaystyle\int_0^1 \frac{dx}{x}$. For $0 < t < 1$ we have

$$\int_t^1 \frac{dx}{x} = [\log x]_t^1 = -\log t.$$

But $\lim_{t \to 0+} (-\log t) = \infty$, and so the improper integral does not exist.

Example 4: Consider $\displaystyle\int_0^1 \frac{dx}{\sqrt{x}}$. For $0 < t < 1$ we have

$$\int_t^1 \frac{dx}{\sqrt{x}} = [2\sqrt{x}]_t^1 = 2 - 2\sqrt{t}.$$

Thus

$$\int_0^1 \frac{dx}{\sqrt{x}} = \lim_{t\to 0+} (2 - 2\sqrt{t}) = 2.$$

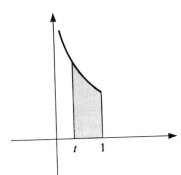

Fig. 11.2

The graphs of both $1/x$ and $1/\sqrt{x}$ for $0 < x \le 1$ have the form indicated in figure 11.2. However, example 3 shows that in the case of $1/x$ the shaded area can be made as large as we wish, whereas example 4 shows that for $1/\sqrt{x}$ the area is always less than 2.

EXERCISES

1. Show that $\displaystyle\int_1^\infty \frac{dx}{x^a}$ does not exist for $a \le 1$, whereas

$$\int_1^\infty \frac{dx}{x^a} = \frac{1}{a-1} \quad \text{for } a > 1.$$

2. Show that $\displaystyle\int_0^1 \frac{dx}{x^a}$ does not exist for $a \ge 1$, whereas

$$\int_0^1 \frac{dx}{x^a} = \frac{1}{1-a} \quad \text{for } a < 1.$$

3. Find the following improper integrals, when they exist.

(a) $\displaystyle\int_0^\infty e^{-x}\,dx$

(b) $\displaystyle\int_0^2 \frac{dx}{2-x}$

(c) $\displaystyle\int_0^\infty \frac{dx}{1+x^2}$

(d) $\displaystyle\int_2^\infty \frac{dx}{x^2-1}$

(e) $\displaystyle\int_0^{\pi/2} \tan x \, dx$

(f) $\displaystyle\int_0^1 \frac{dx}{\sqrt{1-x}}$

(g) $\displaystyle\int_0^1 \log x \, dx$

(h) $\displaystyle\int_2^\infty \frac{x}{1-x^2} \, dx$

4. Suppose that f and g are continuous functions such that $0 \le g(x) \le f(x)$ for all $x \ge a$. If $\int_a^\infty f(x) \, dx$ exists, show that $\int_a^\infty g(x) \, dx$ exists.

5. Suppose that $p(x)$ and $q(x)$ are polynomials of degrees m and n respectively, and that $q(x) \ne 0$ for $x \ge a$. Show that

$$\int_a^\infty \frac{p(x)}{q(x)} \, dx$$

exists if and only if $n > m + 1$. (Hint: Write

$$\frac{p(x)}{q(x)} = \frac{1}{x^{n-m}} f(x)$$

where $f(x)$ has a finite, nonzero limit at ∞. Then use exercises 4 and 1.)

SERIES   VI

1. CONVERGENCE

A *sequence* is a function a from the set of positive integers to the numbers. Thus a sequence may be thought of simply as an infinite list of numbers

$$a_1, \quad a_2, \quad a_3, \quad \ldots, \quad a_n, \ldots \tag{1}$$

where we have written a_n instead of $a(n)$. The *limit* of the sequence is defined as the limit at infinity of the function a in the usual sense, providing the limit exists. In other words, the number L is the limit of the sequence (1) if for each positive number ϵ there is an integer N such that $|a_n - L| < \epsilon$ whenever $n \geq N$. As usual, the number L is denoted by $\lim_{n \to \infty} a_n$.

For example, consider the sequence

$$\frac{1}{3}, \quad \frac{2}{5}, \quad \frac{3}{7}, \quad \ldots \quad \frac{n}{2n+1}, \ldots$$

This sequence has limit $1/2$. In fact, viewed as a function, the sequence is simply the rational function $x/(2x + 1)$ restricted to the positive integers, and we know how to find the limit at infinity of any rational function. An example of a sequence which doesn't have a limit is

$$1, \quad -1, \quad 1, \quad -1, \ldots$$

where the nth term is $(-1)^{n+1}$.

Our usual rules for limits apply in the special case of limits of sequences. For example,

$$\lim_{n \to \infty} (a_n + b_n) = \lim_{n \to \infty} a_n + \lim_{n \to \infty} b_n$$

and

$$\lim_{n \to \infty} (a_n b_n) = \lim_{n \to \infty} a_n \lim_{n \to \infty} b_n$$

providing the limits on the right side exist. In the case where each a_n is the same number c, these rules become

$$\lim_{n \to \infty} (c + b_n) = c + \lim_{n \to \infty} b_n$$

and

$$\lim_{n \to \infty} (cb_n) = c \lim_{n \to \infty} b_n.$$

If for some positive integer k we chop off the first k terms of (1) to obtain the sequence

$$a_{k+1}, \quad a_{k+2}, \ldots$$

where the nth term is a_{k+n}, then it is trivial to verify that the new sequence has limit L if and only if the old sequence has limit L. From this we see that it doesn't really matter what integer we start with in numbering the terms of a sequence.

Given the sequence $a_1, a_2, a_3, \ldots$, we let s_n denote the sum of the first n terms. Thus

$$s_1 = a_1$$
$$s_2 = a_1 + a_2$$
$$s_3 = a_1 + a_2 + a_3$$
$$\vdots$$
$$s_n = a_1 + a_2 + \cdots + a_n.$$

If the sequence $s_1, s_2, \ldots$ has limit L, then we shall write

$$L = a_1 + a_2 + \cdots + a_n + \cdots$$

or, for short,

$$L = \sum_{n=1}^{\infty} a_n. \tag{2}$$

In any case we shall call the expression on the right side of (2) a *series*, and we shall call the numbers $a_1, a_2, \ldots$ the *terms* of the series. The numbers $s_1, s_2, \ldots$ are called the *partial sums* of the series. When the limit L exists we shall say that the series is *convergent* and we shall call L the *sum* of the series. Otherwise we say that the series is *divergent*.

Example: Let r be any number, and consider the series

$$\sum_{n=0}^{\infty} r^n.$$

This is called a *geometric* series. The nth partial sum is

$$s_n = 1 + r + r^2 + \cdots + r^{n-1}.$$

From the identity

$$(1 + r + r^2 + \cdots + r^{n-1})(1 - r) = 1 - r^n,$$

we obtain

$$s_n = \frac{1}{1 - r} - \frac{r^n}{1 - r} \tag{3}$$

providing $r \neq 1$. Now if $|r| < 1$, then $\lim_{n \to \infty} r^n = 0$ (see exercise 8), and so we find

$$\sum_{n=0}^{\infty} r^n = \lim_{n \to \infty} s_n = \frac{1}{1-r}.$$

If $|r| \geq 1$, then the terms of the series are all greater than or equal to 1 in absolute value. The following general theorem then shows us that the series must be divergent in this case.

Theorem 1.1: *If* $\sum_{n=1}^{\infty} a_n$ *is convergent, then*

$$\lim_{n \to \infty} a_n = 0.$$

Proof: By definition of convergence, the sequence of partial sums

$$s_1, \quad s_2, \quad s_3, \quad \cdots$$

has a limit. Therefore, the sequence

$$s_2, \quad s_3, \quad s_4, \quad \cdots$$

has the same limit, and so applying the difference rule for limits, we find

$$\lim_{n \to \infty} (s_n - s_{n-1}) = 0.$$

Since $s_n - s_{n-1} = a_n$, this proves the theorem. ∎

It is natural to ask if the converse of theorem 1.1 is true. That is, if $\lim_{n \to \infty} a_n = 0$, is it true that $\sum_{n=0}^{\infty} a_n$ is convergent? To see that this is not necessarily so, consider the series

$$1 + \frac{1}{2} + \frac{1}{3} + \cdots + \frac{1}{n} + \cdots.$$

We observe the following inequalities:

$$\frac{1}{3} + \frac{1}{4} > \frac{1}{4} + \frac{1}{4} = \frac{2}{4} = \frac{1}{2}$$

$$\frac{1}{5} + \cdots + \frac{1}{8} > \frac{1}{8} + \cdots + \frac{1}{8} = \frac{4}{8} = \frac{1}{2}$$

$$\frac{1}{9} + \cdots + \frac{1}{16} > \frac{1}{16} + \cdots + \frac{1}{16} = \frac{8}{16} = \frac{1}{2}$$

$$\vdots$$

$$\frac{1}{2^n + 1} + \cdots + \frac{1}{2^{n+1}} > \frac{1}{2^{n+1}} + \cdots + \frac{1}{2^{n+1}} = \frac{2^n}{2^{n+1}} = \frac{1}{2}.$$

From this it follows that the partial sum may be made as big as we wish by taking enough terms, and so the series is divergent.

Theorem 1.2: *Suppose that the series* $\sum\limits_{n=1}^{\infty} a_n$ *and* $\sum\limits_{n=1}^{\infty} b_n$ *are convergent with sums L and M respectively. Then the series*

$$\sum_{n=1}^{\infty} (a_n + b_n) \quad and \quad \sum_{n=1}^{\infty} (a_n - b_n)$$

are convergent with sums L + M and L − M respectively. Also, if $\sum\limits_{n=1}^{\infty} a_n$ *is convergent with sum L and c is any number, then* $\sum\limits_{n=1}^{\infty} ca_n$ *is convergent with sum cL.*

Proof: Let s_n and t_n denote the nth partial sums of $\sum\limits_{n=1}^{\infty} a_n$ and $\sum\limits_{n=1}^{\infty} b_n$. Then the nth partial sum of $\sum\limits_{n=1}^{\infty} (a_n + b_n)$ is $s_n + t_n$. Hence, the first assertion follows from the ordinary sum rule for limits. The other assertions are proved similarly. ∎

Suppose that the series

$$\sum_{n=1}^{\infty} a_n \tag{4}$$

is convergent with sum L, and that N is any positive integer. Then the series

$$\sum_{n=N+1}^{\infty} a_n \tag{5}$$

is convergent with sum $L - S_N$, where S_N denotes the Nth partial sum of the series (4). This follows since the partial sums of (5) are obtained from the partial sums of (4) by subtracting the constant S_N. Similarly, one shows that if (5) is convergent with sum M, then (4) is convergent with sum $M + S_N$. Thus we see that the convergence or divergence of a series is unaffected by the deletion of the first N terms of the series. Frequently we know that the terms of a series have a certain property from the $(N + 1)$st term on. Thus, in proving that the series is convergent or divergent, we may as well assume that all the terms of the series have the given property.

EXERCISES

1. In each of the following, the nth term a_n of a sequence is given. Write down the first four terms of the sequence, and determine $\lim\limits_{n \to \infty} a_n$ when it exists.

(a) $\dfrac{3n + 1}{2n^2}$ (b) $\dfrac{n^2 - 1}{2n^2 + 1}$

(c) $\sin n\pi$ (d) $\cos n\pi$

(e) $\left(1 + \dfrac{1}{n}\right)^n$ (f) $\dfrac{n^3 - 1}{2n^2 + 1}$

(g) $\sqrt{n + 2} - \sqrt{n + 1}$ (h) $\dfrac{100^n}{n!}$

(i) $n^{1/n}$

(j) $\dfrac{n^{1000}}{2^n}$

2. Show that for all positive integers n,

$$n! \le \left(\frac{n+1}{2}\right)^n.$$

Hence find $\lim\limits_{n\to\infty} \dfrac{n!}{n^n}$.

3. Let $a_1, a_2, \ldots$ be any sequence. Find a series whose nth partial sum is a_n for all n.

4. In each of the following find the sum of the series, or else explain why the series is divergent.

(a) $1 - \dfrac{1}{3} + \dfrac{1}{9} - \dfrac{1}{27} + \cdots$

(b) $\dfrac{7}{8} + \dfrac{7}{8^2} + \dfrac{7}{8^3} + \cdots$

(c) $\dfrac{1}{3} + \dfrac{2}{5} + \dfrac{3}{7} + \dfrac{4}{9} + \cdots$

(d) $\left(1 - \dfrac{1}{2}\right) + \left(\dfrac{1}{2} - \dfrac{1}{3}\right) + \left(\dfrac{1}{3} - \dfrac{1}{4}\right) + \cdots$

(e) $\dfrac{2}{\sqrt{5^3}} + \dfrac{2}{\sqrt{5^4}} + \dfrac{2}{\sqrt{5^5}} + \cdots$

(f) $\log(1+1) + \log(1 + \tfrac{1}{2}) + \log(1 + \tfrac{1}{3}) + \cdots$

5. State for which x the following series are convergent.

(a) $\dfrac{1}{x} + \dfrac{1}{x^2} + \dfrac{1}{x^3} + \cdots$

(b) $1 + 2x + 4x^2 + 8x^3 + \cdots$

(c) $e^x + e^{2x} + e^{3x} + \cdots$

6. Show that $\lim\limits_{x\to\infty} \dfrac{x^n}{n!} = 0$ for any number x.

7. Prove all the statements in theorem 1.2.

8. If $0 < r < 1$, show that $\lim\limits_{x\to\infty} r^n = 0$ by writing $r = \dfrac{1}{1 + \epsilon}$ for some $\epsilon > 0$. Explain why this follows also from the general theory of exponents developed in chapter V, § 2.

2. SERIES OF POSITIVE TERMS

Recall that a function f is called *nondecreasing* if $f(x) \le f(y)$ whenever x and y are in the domain of f and $x < y$. In particular a sequence $a_1, a_2, a_3, \ldots$ is nondecreasing if

$$a_1 \le a_2 \le a_3 \le \cdots \le a_n \le \cdots.$$

Lemma 2.1: *If f is nondecreasing then* $\lim_{x \to \infty} f(x)$ *exists if and only if the values $f(x)$ have an upper bound, in which case the limit is the least upper bound of these values.*

Proof: Suppose that the values of f have an upper bound, and let L be their least upper bound. Given $\epsilon > 0$, there must then be at least one number X such that $L - \epsilon < f(X) \leq L$. But then, since f is nondecreasing, we must have $L - \epsilon < f(x) \leq L$ for all x in the domain of f such that $x > X$. This proves that $L = \lim_{x \to \infty} f(x)$.

Conversely, assume that $L = \lim_{x \to \infty} f(x)$. Suppose that for some x_0 we have $f(x_0) > L$. Then defining $\epsilon = f(x_0) - L$ and using the fact that f is nondecreasing, we see that $f(x) - L \geq \epsilon$ for all $x > x_0$. But this contradicts the definition of limit. Hence L is an upper bound for the values of f. ∎

We leave to the reader the statement and proof of the corresponding theorem for nonincreasing functions.

Now consider a series $\sum_{n=1}^{\infty} a_n$ where $a_n \geq 0$ for all n. Then the sequence of partial sums is nondecreasing; that is

$$s_1 \leq s_2 \leq s_3 \leq \cdots .$$

Hence, by lemma 2.1, the series is convergent if the numbers s_n are bounded, and is divergent otherwise.

Theorem 2.2 (The Comparison Test): *Suppose that $0 \leq a_n \leq b_n$ for all $n \geq N$, where N is some positive integer. If $\sum_{n=1}^{\infty} b_n$ is convergent, then so is $\sum_{n=1}^{\infty} a_n$.*

Proof: Since the convergence or divergence of a series is unaffected by the deletion of the first N terms of the series, we may as well assume $N = 1$ in the hypothesis. But then we have

$$a_1 + a_2 + \cdots + a_n \leq b_1 + b_2 + \cdots + b_n$$

for all n. Since $\sum_{n=1}^{\infty} b_n$ is convergent, the right side is bounded. Therefore the left side is bounded, and so $\sum_{n=1}^{\infty} a_n$ is convergent. ∎

Example 1: Consider the series

$$\sum_{n=1}^{\infty} \frac{1}{\sqrt{n}} .$$

We shall show that this series is divergent. Assume to the contrary that it is convergent. Then, since

$$\frac{1}{n} \leq \frac{1}{\sqrt{n}}$$

for all $n \geq 1$, it follows from the comparison test that

$$\sum_{n=1}^{\infty} \frac{1}{n}$$

is convergent. But in the last section we saw that this series is divergent. Hence, so is the given one.

Example 2:   Consider a series of the form

$$\sum_{n=1}^{\infty} \frac{a_n}{10^n} \tag{1}$$

where each a_n is an integer satisfying $0 \leq a_n \leq 9$. To show that the series is convergent, by the comparison test it suffices to show that

$$\sum_{n=1}^{\infty} \frac{9}{10^n}$$

is convergent. But using our knowledge of the geometric series, we find

$$\sum_{n=1}^{\infty} \frac{9}{10^n} = \frac{9}{10}\left(1 + \frac{1}{10} + \frac{1}{10^2} + \cdots\right)$$

$$= \frac{9}{10} \cdot \frac{1}{1 - 1/10} = 1.$$

Thus we see that not only is (1) convergent, but also its sum must be less than or equal to 1. In school we are taught to write

$$.a_1 a_2 a_3 \ldots$$

in place of the series (1). In exercise 1 you will show that every number between 0 and 1 is the sum of such a series.

A very important test for convergence is the following.

Theorem 2.3 (The Ratio Test):   *Let* $\sum_{n=0}^{\infty} a_n$ *be a series of positive terms, and suppose that*

$$\lim_{n \to \infty} \frac{a_{n+1}}{a_n} = l.$$

If $l < 1$*, then the series is convergent. If* $l > 1$ *then the series is divergent.*

Proof: Suppose $l < 1$, and let r be any number such that $l < r < 1$. Then there is a positive integer N such that

$$\frac{a_{n+1}}{a_n} < r$$

for all $n \geq N$, and again, since the convergence of a series is unaffected by the removal of the first N terms, we may as well assume $N = 1$. But then we have

$$a_n = a_1 \frac{a_2}{a_1} \frac{a_3}{a_2} \cdots \frac{a_n}{a_{n-1}} < a_1 r^{n-1}.$$

Since $r < 1$, the geometric series $\sum_{n=0}^{\infty} a_1 r^n$ is convergent. Therefore, by the comparison test, so is $\sum_{n=1}^{\infty} a_n$.

If $l > 1$, then there is an integer N such that $\frac{a_{n+1}}{a_n} > 1$, or in other words, $a_{n+1} > a_n$ for all $n \geq N$. Hence, the terms of the series cannot have limit 0, and so by theorem 1.1 the series is divergent. ∎

Example 3: Consider the series

$$\sum_{n=1}^{\infty} \frac{n!}{n^n}.$$

Taking the ratio of consecutive terms, we obtain

$$\frac{(n+1)!/(n+1)^{n+1}}{n!/n^n} = \left(\frac{n}{n+1}\right)^n = \frac{1}{(1+1/n)^n}.$$

Since $\lim_{n \to \infty} \left(1 + \frac{1}{n}\right)^n = e$ and $e > 1$ (see chapter IV, § 2), it follows by the ratio test that the series is convergent.

Remark: The ratio test says nothing about the case where $l = 1$. In such a case the series may be either convergent or divergent. For example, we have seen that $\sum_{n=1}^{\infty} 1/n$ is divergent, whereas in the following section we shall see that $\sum_{n=1}^{\infty} 1/n^2$ is convergent. In both cases $l = 1$.

EXERCISES

1. (a) Suppose that $0 < x \leq 1/10^n$ where n is a nonnegative integer. Show that there is an integer a such that

$$\frac{a}{10^{n+1}} < x \leq \frac{a+1}{10^{n+1}}, \quad \text{where } 0 \leq a \leq 9.$$

(b) Suppose that $0 < x \leq 1$. Using part (a), define by induction a sequence of integers $a_1, a_2, \ldots$ such that

$$0 < x - \left(\frac{a_1}{10} + \frac{a_2}{10^2} + \cdots + \frac{a_n}{10^n}\right) \leq \frac{1}{10^n}$$

and such that $0 \leq a_n \leq 9$ for all n. Conclude that

$$x = \sum_{n=1}^{\infty} \frac{a_n}{10^n}.$$

Explain why there are an infinite number of the a_n's not equal to 0.

(c) Suppose that

$$\sum_{n=1}^{\infty} \frac{a_n}{10^n} = \sum_{n=1}^{\infty} \frac{b_n}{10^n}$$

where a_n and b_n are integers satisfying $0 \le a_n \le 9, 0 \le b_n \le 9$. Suppose that $a_n \ne 0$ for an infinite number of integers n, and similarly for the b_n's. Show that $a_n = b_n$ for all n. (Hint: Let N be the first integer such that $a_N \ne b_N$, say $a_N > b_N$, and deduce

$$\frac{1}{10^N} < \sum_{n=N+1}^{\infty} \frac{9}{10^n} = \frac{1}{10^N}.)$$

2. Repeat exercise 1, but with 10 replaced by any integer $r \ge 2$.

3. Show that the ratio test does not apply to any series of the form

$$\sum_{n=1}^{\infty} \frac{p(n)}{q(n)}$$

where p and q are polynomials.

4. Determine whether the following series are convergent or divergent.

(a) $\displaystyle\sum_{n=0}^{\infty} \frac{1}{n!}$

(b) $\displaystyle\sum_{n=0}^{\infty} \frac{n}{2^n}$

(c) $\displaystyle\sum_{n=0}^{\infty} \frac{2^n}{n!}$

(d) $\displaystyle\sum_{n=1}^{\infty} \frac{n^n}{n!}$

(e) $\displaystyle\sum_{n=1}^{\infty} \frac{2 \cdot 4 \cdot \cdots \cdot (2n)}{4 \cdot 7 \cdot \cdots \cdot (3n + 1)}$

(f) $\displaystyle\sum_{n=1}^{\infty} \frac{1}{n^p}$ where $p < 1$

(g) $\displaystyle\sum_{n=1}^{\infty} \frac{n^n}{3^n n!}$

(h) $\displaystyle\sum_{n=1}^{\infty} \frac{n}{2^n}$

5. If p is any nonzero polynomial, show that

$$\sum_{n=1}^{\infty} p(n)r^n$$

is convergent if $0 \le r < 1$ and is divergent if $r \ge 1$.

6. A mathematics instructor wishes to take advantage of the fact that

$$\lim_{n \to \infty} \frac{2n + 1}{5n + 1} = \frac{2}{5}$$

so as to give his students an exercise in the ratio test. Tell him what series to use. Then tell him how to generalize his method.

7. Suppose that

$$\frac{a_{n+1}}{a_n} > 1 - \frac{1}{n}$$

for all n. Show that the series $\displaystyle\sum_{n=1}^{\infty} a_n$ is divergent.

3. THE INTEGRAL TEST

There is a connection between series and improper integrals which gives us another important test for convergence.

Theorem 3.1 (The Integral Test): *Suppose that f is continuous, nonnegative, and nonincreasing throughout the interval* $[1, \infty)$. *Then the series*

$$\sum_{n=1}^{\infty} f(n)$$

is convergent if and only if the improper integral

$$\int_{1}^{\infty} f(x)\, dx$$

exists.

Proof: The situation is represented in figure 3.1. Since

$$f(m + 1) \leq f(x) \leq f(m)$$

for all x in $[m + 1, m]$, we find

$$f(m + 1) \leq \int_{m}^{m+1} f(x)\, dx \leq f(m)$$

for any integer $m \geq 1$. Adding the first $n - 1$ of these inequalities, we obtain

$$f(2) + \cdots + f(n) \leq \int_{1}^{n} f(x)\, dx \leq f(1) + \cdots + f(n - 1). \quad (1)$$

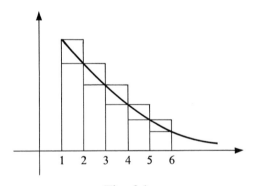

Fig. 3.1

If the improper integral exists, then the middle term in (1) is bounded, and so by the first inequality we see that the partial sums of the series are bounded. Consequently the series is convergent. Conversely, if the series is convergent, then the right side of (1) is bounded. Therefore, since

$$\int_{1}^{t} f(x)\, dx \qquad\qquad\qquad (2)$$

is a nondecreasing function of t, we see from the second inequality in (1) that (2) is bounded for all t. Consequently by lemma 2.1, the improper integral exists. ∎

Example 1: Let p be any positive number, and let $f(x) = 1/x^p$ for all $x \geq 1$. Then f is positive and decreasing. Now the improper integral

$$\int_1^\infty \frac{dx}{x^p}$$

exists if and only if $p > 1$. (See chapter II, § 11, exercise 1.) Consequently, by the integral test, the series

$$\frac{1}{1^p} + \frac{1}{2^p} + \cdots + \frac{1}{n^p} + \cdots$$

is convergent if and only if $p > 1$. In particular when $p = 1$, we see once again that

$$\sum_{n=1}^\infty \frac{1}{n}$$

is divergent.

The following theorem is not much more than a special case of the comparison test.

Theorem 3.2: *Let $\sum_{n=1}^\infty a_n$ and $\sum_{n=1}^\infty b_n$ be series of positive terms, and suppose that $\lim_{n \to \infty} \frac{a_n}{b_n}$ exists. If $\sum_{n=1}^\infty b_n$ is convergent, then so is $\sum_{n=1}^\infty a_n$.*

Proof: Letting c denote the limit in the hypothesis, we know there is an integer N such that $\frac{a_n}{b_n} < c + 1$ for all $n \geq N$. But this is equivalent to

$$a_n < (c + 1)b_n$$

for all $n \geq N$, and so since $\sum_{n=1}^\infty (c + 1)b_n$ is convergent, it follows from the comparison test that $\sum_{n=1}^\infty a_n$ is also convergent. ∎

Example 2: Consider the series

$$\sum_{n=1}^\infty \frac{n}{2n^3 + 1}.$$

In example 1, we saw that the series $\sum_{n=1}^\infty 1/n^2$ is convergent, and so since

$$\lim_{n \to \infty} \frac{n/(2n^3 + 1)}{1/n^2} = \lim_{n \to \infty} \frac{n^3}{2n^3 + 1} = \frac{1}{2},$$

we see by theorem 3.2 that the given series is convergent.

EXERCISES

1. Which of the following series are convergent?

(a) $\sum_{n=1}^{\infty} \frac{1}{n\sqrt{n}}$

(b) $\sum_{n=1}^{\infty} \frac{n}{e^n}$

(c) $\sum_{n=2}^{\infty} \frac{1}{n \log n}$

(d) $\sum_{n=2}^{\infty} \frac{1}{n (\log n)^2}$

(e) $\sum_{n=1}^{\infty} \frac{\sqrt{n}}{n^2 + 1}$

(f) $\sum_{n=1}^{\infty} \frac{n^2 + 1}{n^2 + 2n}$

(g) $\sum_{n=1}^{\infty} \frac{n^4 + 2n}{n^5 + n^2}$

(h) $\sum_{n=2}^{\infty} \frac{n - 3}{n^3 - n}$

(i) $\sum_{n=2}^{\infty} \frac{1}{n \log n \log (\log n)}$

(j) $\sum_{n=1}^{\infty} n e^{-n^2}$

2. Show that the series

$$\sum_{n=2}^{\infty} \frac{1}{n (\log n)^p}$$

is convergent if $p > 1$ and is divergent if $p \leq 1$.

3. Using l'Hôpital's rule, show that

$$\lim_{x \to \infty} \frac{(\log x)^a}{x^b} = 0$$

for $b > 0$ and any a. Hence, show that the series

$$\sum_{n=2}^{\infty} \frac{(\log n)^a}{n^b}$$

is convergent if $b > 1$ and is divergent if $b < 1$. (Use theorem 3.2.)

4. If p and q are polynomials of degrees h and k respectively, show that

$$\sum_{n=1}^{\infty} \frac{p(n)}{q(n)}$$

is convergent if $k - h \geq 2$ and is divergent if $k - h < 2$.

5. Define

$$c_n = 1 + \frac{1}{2} + \frac{1}{3} + \cdots + \frac{1}{n} - \log n.$$

Show that $0 < c_{n+1} < c_n \leq 1$ for all n. (Hint: Let $f(x) = \frac{1}{x}$, and use an argument similar to that used in the proof of the integral test.) Conclude that $\lim_{n \to \infty} c_n$ exists. This limit is called *Euler's constant*, and is approximately equal to .5772. It is named after the famous Swiss mathematician Leonard Euler (1707–1783). It is not known if this number is irrational.

4. ABSOLUTE CONVERGENCE

The tests of the last two sections have been concerned with series of nonnegative terms. In order to apply these tests to series which have both positive and negative terms, we introduce the notion of an *absolutely convergent* series. This is a series $\sum_{n=1}^{\infty} a_n$ such that the series $\sum_{n=1}^{\infty} |a_n|$ is convergent. We mustn't get carried away by our choice of words and assume, without proof, that an absolutely convergent series is convergent.

First, we define

$$a_n^+ = a_n \quad \text{if } a_n \geq 0 \qquad\qquad a_n^- = -a_n \quad \text{if } a_n \leq 0$$
$$= 0 \quad \text{if } a_n \leq 0; \qquad\qquad\qquad = 0 \quad \text{if } a_n \geq 0.$$

Then for all n we have

$$a_n = a_n^+ - a_n^- \tag{1}$$

and

$$|a_n| = a_n^+ + a_n^-. \tag{2}$$

Theorem 4.1: *If $\sum_{n=1}^{\infty} |a_n|$ is convergent, then so is $\sum_{n=1}^{\infty} a_n$. On the other hand, if $\sum_{n=1}^{\infty} a_n$ is convergent, but not absolutely, then each of the series*

$$\sum_{n=1}^{\infty} a_n^+ \tag{3}$$

and

$$\sum_{n=1}^{\infty} a_n^- \tag{4}$$

is divergent.

Proof: If $\sum_{n=1}^{\infty} |a_n|$ is convergent, then since

$$0 \leq a_n^+ \leq |a_n| \quad \text{and} \quad 0 \leq a_n^- \leq |a_n|$$

for all n, it follows by the comparison test that each of the series (3) and (4) is convergent. Hence, from (1) we see that $\sum_{n=1}^{\infty} a_n$ is convergent.

Now suppose that $\sum_{n=1}^{\infty} a_n$ is convergent. If one of (3) and (4) is convergent, then from (1) we see that the other is also convergent. Hence, from (2) it follows that $\sum_{n=1}^{\infty} |a_n|$ is convergent. Consequently, if $\sum_{n=1}^{\infty} a_n$ is convergent, but not absolutely, then we see that each of the series (3) and (4) is divergent. ∎

An example of a series which is convergent but not absolutely, is the series

$$1 - \frac{1}{2} + \frac{1}{3} - \frac{1}{4} + \cdots + \frac{(-1)^{n+1}}{n} + \cdots$$

Here the series of absolute values is

$$1 + \tfrac{1}{2} + \tfrac{1}{3} + \tfrac{1}{4} + \cdots,$$

which we know is divergent. That the given series is convergent follows from the following general theorem.

Theorem 4.2 (The Alternating Series Test): *Suppose that* $\lim\limits_{n \to \infty} a_n = 0$ *and that*

$$a_1 \geq a_2 \geq a_3 \geq \cdots \geq a_n \geq \cdots.$$

Then the series

$$a_1 - a_2 + a_3 - a_4 + \cdots + a_{2n-1} - a_{2n} + \cdots \qquad (5)$$

is convergent.

Proof: The hypothesis implies that $a_n \geq 0$ for all n. Let s_n denote the nth partial sum of (5). Then

$$s_{2n} = (a_1 - a_2) + (a_3 - a_4) + \cdots + (a_{2n-1} - a_{2n}).$$

Since the a_n's are nonincreasing, we see that

$$0 \leq s_2 \leq s_4 \leq \cdots \leq s_{2n} \leq \cdots.$$

Now s_{2n} can also be written in the form

$$s_{2n} = a_1 - (a_2 - a_3) - (a_4 - a_5) - \cdots - (a_{2n-2} - a_{2n-1}) - a_{2n},$$

and so $s_{2n} \leq a_1$ for all n. Thus the sequence $s_2, s_4, \ldots$, being nondecreasing and bounded above, has a limit. Then, since $s_{2n+1} = s_{2n} + a_{2n+1}$, we find

$$\lim_{n \to \infty} s_{2n+1} = \lim_{n \to \infty} s_{2n} + \lim_{n \to \infty} a_{2n+1} = \lim_{n \to \infty} s_{2n}.$$

The common limit of s_{2n} and s_{2n+1} is then the sum of the series. ∎

The following theorem shows that the "triangle inequality" applies to an infinite sum, providing we assume that the series is absolutely convergent.

Theorem 4.3: *If* $\sum\limits_{n=1}^{\infty} a_n$ *is absolutely convergent, then*

$$\left| \sum_{n=1}^{\infty} a_n \right| \leq \sum_{n=1}^{\infty} |a_n|.$$

Proof: Let s_n denote the partial sums of the given series, and let t_n denote the partial sums of the series of absolute values. Then by the triangle inequality for finite sums, we have

$$|s_n| = |a_1 + \cdots + a_n| \leq |a_1| + \cdots + |a_n| = t_n.$$

Therefore, since the limit of a sequence of absolute values is the absolute value of the limit, we have

$$\left| \sum_{n=1}^{\infty} a_n \right| = \left| \lim_{n \to \infty} s_n \right| = \lim_{n \to \infty} |s_n| \leq \lim_{n \to \infty} t_n = \sum_{n=1}^{\infty} |a_n|. \quad \blacksquare$$

EXERCISES

1. In the alternating series test, let L be the sum of the series and let s_n be the nth partial sum. Show that $|L - s_n| \leq a_{n+1}$ for each integer n.

2. Determine which of the following series are convergent, and which are absolutely convergent.

(a) $\displaystyle\sum_{n=1}^{\infty} \frac{(-1)^n}{n^2}$

(b) $\displaystyle\sum_{n=1}^{\infty} \frac{(-1)^n}{\sqrt{n}}$

(c) $\displaystyle\sum_{n=1}^{\infty} (-1)^n \log\left(1 + \frac{1}{n}\right)$

(d) $\displaystyle\sum_{n=1}^{\infty} (-1)^n \frac{n}{2n+1}$

(e) $\displaystyle\sum_{n=1}^{\infty} (-1)^{n+1} \frac{n}{(n+1)^2}$

(f) $\displaystyle\sum_{n=1}^{\infty} \frac{\sin n}{n^2}$

(g) $\displaystyle\sum_{n=1}^{\infty} \frac{\cos(n\pi)}{n}$

(h) $\displaystyle\sum_{n=1}^{\infty} (-1)^{n+1} \left(\frac{n}{n+1}\right)^n$

(i) $\displaystyle\sum_{n=2}^{\infty} (-1)^n \frac{\log n}{n}$

(j) $\displaystyle\sum_{n=1}^{\infty} (-1)^n \frac{\sqrt{n+1}}{n}.$

3. Let p and q be polynomials such that the degree of q is one greater than the degree of p. Show that the series

$$\sum_{n=1}^{\infty} (-1)^n \frac{p(n)}{q(n)}$$

is convergent, but not absolutely. (Hint: Take the derivative of $p(x)/q(x)$ to show that the absolute values of the terms are eventually decreasing.)

4. Show that the series

$$\sum_{n=2}^{\infty} (-1)^n \frac{(\log n)^a}{n^b}$$

is convergent for any positive b and any a.

5.   (a) Show that the series

$$1 - \frac{1}{2^p} + \frac{1}{3} - \frac{1}{4^p} + \frac{1}{5} - \frac{1}{6^p} + \cdots$$

is divergent for $p > 1$.

(b) Show that the above series is divergent for $p < 1$. $\left(\text{Hint: Add it to the series } \sum_{n \to 1}^{\infty} \frac{(-1)^n}{n}.\right)$

5. POWER SERIES

Given a sequence $a_0, a_1, a_2, \ldots$, we consider the series

$$a_0 + a_1 x + a_2 x^2 + \cdots + a_n x^n + \cdots,$$

or in shorthand,

$$\sum_{n=0}^{\infty} a_n x^n. \tag{1}$$

Such a series is called a *power series,* and the numbers a_n are called its *coefficients.* The nth partial sum of the series is

$$a_0 + a_1 x + \cdots + a_n x^n,$$

which is just a polynomial. We are interested in the set S of numbers x for which (1) is convergent. Of course, there is always one value of x for which (1) is convergent, namely $x = 0$. In this case all the terms after a_0 are 0, and so the sum is a_0. It is quite possible, on the other hand, that the power series is convergent for no other x. We shall see this in example 2 which follows.

In any case it turns out that S is an interval. To see this, we first prove a lemma.

Lemma 5.1: *If there is a nonzero number r such that* (1) *is convergent when $x = r$, then* (1) *is absolutely convergent for each x satisfying $|x| < |r|$.*

Proof: Since the series

$$\sum_{n=0}^{\infty} a_n r^n$$

is convergent, its terms have limit 0. Hence, these terms are certainly bounded, say

$$|a_n r^n| \leq B$$

for all n. Then for all n we have

$$|a_n x^n| = |a_n r^n| \left| \frac{x}{r} \right|^n \leq B \left| \frac{x}{r} \right|^n.$$

Now if $|x| < |r|$, then the geometric series

$$\sum_{n=0}^{\infty} B \left| \frac{x}{r} \right|^n$$

is convergent. Thus, by the comparison test we see that

$$\sum_{n=0}^{\infty} |a_n x^n|$$

is convergent. This proves the lemma. ∎

Now consider the set S of all numbers x such that (1) is convergent. Assume first that S is bounded above, and let R be its least upper bound.

Then $R \geq 0$ since $0 \in S$. If $|x| > R$, then $x \notin S$, for otherwise, by lemma 5.1, any number y satisfying $R < y < |x|$ would be in S. This contradicts the fact that R is an upper bound for S. On the other hand, if $|x| < R$, then since R is the *least* upper bound of S, there is a member r of S such that $|x| < r < R$. Thus, by lemma 5.1, we see that (1) is absolutely convergent at x. Summarizing, we have shown that (1) is absolutely convergent for $|x| < R$ and is divergent for $|x| > R$. For $|x| = R$, the series may be either convergent or divergent, as we shall see presently. The number R is called the *radius of convergence* of the power series.

If S is not bounded above, then for any number x there is at least one r in S such that $|x| < r$. Therefore, by lemma 5.1, we see that (1) is absolutely convergent at x. In this case we say that the power series has *infinite* radius of convergence.

The ratio test frequently provides a means for determining the radius of convergence of a power series. This is illustrated by the following examples.

Example 1: Consider the power series

$$1 + \frac{x}{1!} + \frac{x^2}{2!} + \frac{x^3}{3!} + \cdots + \frac{x^n}{n!} + \cdots.$$

Applying the ratio test to the series of absolute values, we obtain for all non-zero x

$$\lim_{n \to \infty} \frac{|x|^{n+1}/(n+1)!}{|x|^n/n!} = \lim_{n \to \infty} \frac{|x|}{n+1} = 0.$$

Hence, the power series is absolutely convergent for all x. In the following section we shall see that the sum of the series is e^x.

Example 2: Consider the power series

$$1 + 1!x + 2!x^2 + \cdots + n!x^n + \cdots.$$

Applying the ratio test here, we find for $x \neq 0$,

$$\lim_{n \to \infty} \frac{(n+1)!|x|^{n+1}}{n!|x|^n} = \lim_{n \to \infty} (n+1)|x| = \infty.$$

Therefore, if $x \neq 0$, the power series is divergent.

Example 3: Consider

$$x - \frac{x^2}{2} + \frac{x^3}{3} - \frac{x^4}{4} + \cdots. \tag{2}$$

Here we have

$$\lim_{n \to \infty} \frac{|x|^{n+1}/(n+1)}{|x|^n/n} = \lim_{n \to \infty} |x| \frac{n}{n+1} = |x|,$$

and so by the ratio test we find that the series converges absolutely for $|x| < 1$, but not for $|x| > 1$. If we put $x = 1$, then (2) becomes

$$1 - \tfrac{1}{2} + \tfrac{1}{3} - \tfrac{1}{4} + \cdots,$$

which converges by the alternating series test. On the other hand, if we put $x = -1$, then the series becomes

$$-1 - \tfrac{1}{2} - \tfrac{1}{3} - \cdots,$$

which we know is divergent. We shall see presently that the sum of (2) is $\log(1 + x)$ for $-1 < x \le 1$.

EXERCISES

Find the radius of convergence of each of the following power series.

1. $\displaystyle\sum_{n=0}^{\infty} n x^n$

2. $\displaystyle\sum_{n=0}^{\infty} \frac{x^n}{n^n}$

3. $\displaystyle\sum_{n=0}^{\infty} \frac{n^n}{n!} x^n$

4. $\displaystyle\sum_{n=2}^{\infty} \frac{x^n}{\log n}$

5. $\displaystyle\sum_{n=0}^{\infty} \frac{x^n}{2^n}$

6. $\displaystyle\sum_{n=0}^{\infty} \frac{10^n}{n!} x^n$

7. $\displaystyle\sum_{n=0}^{\infty} n^3 x^n$

8. $\displaystyle\sum_{n=0}^{\infty} \frac{x^{2n}}{3^n}$

9. $\displaystyle\sum_{n=0}^{\infty} (-1)^n \frac{x^{2n}}{(2n)!}$

10. $\displaystyle\sum_{n=0}^{\infty} \frac{(2n)!}{(n!)^2} x^n$

11. $\displaystyle\sum_{n=2}^{\infty} \frac{\log n}{2^n} x^n$

12. $\displaystyle\sum_{n=0}^{\infty} \frac{(n!)^2}{(2n)!} x^n$

13. $\displaystyle\sum_{n=0}^{\infty} \frac{(n!)^3}{(2n)!} x^n$

14. $\displaystyle\sum_{n=0}^{\infty} \frac{(n!)^{3/2}}{(2n)!} x^n$

15. If R is any positive number, find a power series which has R as radius of convergence.

16. Show that the radius of convergence of $\displaystyle\sum_{n=0}^{\infty} f(n) x^n$ is 1, where f is a nonzero rational function.

17. If the radius of convergence of $\displaystyle\sum_{n=0}^{\infty} a_n x^n$ is R and m is any positive integer, show that the radius of convergence of $\displaystyle\sum_{n=0}^{\infty} a_n x^{nm}$ is $R^{1/m}$.

6. DIFFERENTIATION OF POWER SERIES

Let f be the function defined by

$$f(x) = \sum_{n=0}^{\infty} a_n x^n \tag{1}$$

for all x satisfying $|x| < R$, where R is the radius of convergence of the power series. We shall assume that R is greater than zero (or infinite). It is tempting to use the ordinary sum rule for derivatives to conclude that f has a derivative given by

$$\sum_{n=1}^{\infty} na_n x^{n-1}. \tag{2}$$

This turns out to be true, but we shall need more justification than that given above, since the sum rule for derivatives was proved for only finite sums. First we shall investigate the radius of convergence of the series of derivatives.

Lemma 6.1: *The two power series* (1) *and* (2) *have the same radius of convergence.*

Proof: Let R denote the radius of convergence of (1), and suppose that $|x| < R$. Choose any r such that $|x| < r < R$. Since the series $\sum_{n=0}^{\infty} a_n r^n$ is convergent, its terms are bounded, and so we can write $|a_n| r^n \le B$ for all n. Then, since

$$na_n x^{n-1} = \frac{n}{r} a_n r^n \left(\frac{x}{r} \right)^{n-1},$$

we find

$$|na_n x^{n-1}| \le \frac{B}{r} n \left| \frac{x}{r} \right|^{n-1}. \tag{3}$$

Now, by the ratio test, the series

$$\sum_{n=1}^{\infty} \frac{B}{r} n \left| \frac{x}{r} \right|^{n-1}$$

is convergent, since the limit of the ratio of consecutive terms is

$$\lim_{n \to \infty} \frac{n+1}{n} \left| \frac{x}{r} \right| = \left| \frac{x}{r} \right| < 1.$$

Therefore, from (3) we see by the comparison test that (2) is (absolutely) convergent. This shows that (2) has radius of convergence at least R. In particular, if (1) has infinite radius of convergence, so does (2).

Now if the radius of convergence of (2) were greater than R, then (2) would be absolutely convergent for some x satisfying $|x| > R$. But for $n \ge |x|$ we have

$$|a_n x^n| = |na_n x^{n-1}| \left| \frac{x}{n} \right| < |na_n x^{n-1}|,$$

and so by the comparison test we see that (1) is convergent at x. This contradicts the fact that R is the radius of convergence of (1). Hence the radius of convergence of (2) is R.   ∎

Theorem 6.2:   *Let*

$$f(x) = \sum_{n=0}^{\infty} a_n x^n$$

for $|x| < R$, where R is the radius of convergence of the power series. Then f has a derivative given by

$$f'(x) = \sum_{n=1}^{\infty} na_n x^{n-1}$$

for $|x| < R$.

Proof: In the following, x will be a fixed number satisfying $|x| < R$, and r will be a fixed number such that $|x| < r < R$. We shall then restrict ourselves to values of h satisfying $|x + h| \leq r$. For such h we have

$$f(x + h) - f(x) = \sum_{n=0}^{\infty} a_n(x + h)^n - \sum_{n=0}^{\infty} a_n x^n$$

$$= \sum_{n=1}^{\infty} a_n[(x + h)^n - x^n]. \tag{4}$$

By the mean value theorem, there is a number c_n between x and $x + h$ satisfying

$$(x + h)^n - x^n = nc_n^{n-1}h.$$

From (4) we obtain, therefore,

$$\frac{f(x + h) - f(x)}{h} = \sum_{n=1}^{\infty} na_n c_n^{n-1},$$

and consequently,

$$\frac{f(x + h) - f(x)}{h} - \sum_{n=1}^{\infty} na_n x^{n-1} = \sum_{n=1}^{\infty} na_n(c_n^{n-1} - x^{n-1}). \tag{5}$$

Another application of the mean value theorem yields

$$c_n^{n-1} - x^{n-1} = (n - 1) d_n^{n-2}(c_n - x),$$

for some d_n between x and c_n, and so (5) becomes

$$\frac{f(x + h) - f(x)}{h} - \sum_{n=1}^{\infty} na_n x^{n-1} = \sum_{n=2}^{\infty} n(n - 1)a_n d_n^{n-2}(c_n - x).$$

Therefore, since $|c_n - x| < |h|$ and $|d_n| < r$, we find, using theorem 4.3,

$$\left| \frac{f(x + h) - f(x)}{h} - \sum_{n=1}^{\infty} na_n x^{n-1} \right| \leq \sum_{n=2}^{\infty} n(n - 1)|a_n| \, |d_n|^{n-2}|h|$$

$$\leq |h| \sum_{n=2}^{\infty} n(n - 1)|a_n|r^{n-2}. \tag{6}$$

By two applications of lemma 6.1, the series

$$\sum_{n=2}^{\infty} n(n - 1)|a_n|r^{n-2}$$

is convergent, and, furthermore, its value does not depend on h. Therefore, from (6) we find

$$\lim_{h \to 0} \frac{f(x + h) - f(x)}{h} = \sum_{n=1}^{\infty} n a_n x^{n-1}.$$

By definition of derivative, this is what is required. ∎

Corollary 6.3: *If*

$$f(x) = \sum_{n=0}^{\infty} a_n x^n \tag{7}$$

for $|x| < R$, *then* $f(x)$ *has an antiderivative given by*

$$\int f(x) \, dx = \sum_{n=0}^{\infty} \frac{a_n}{n+1} x^{n+1}. \tag{8}$$

Proof: This follows by replacing the series (7) by the series (8) in lemma 6.1 and theorem 6.2. ∎

Suppose that a function f can be written as a power series

$$f(x) = \sum_{n=0}^{\infty} a_n x^n$$

in some neighborhood of 0. Then by repeated application of theorem 6.2, we see that f has derivatives of all orders in that neighborhood, and that the kth derivative is given by

$$f^{(k)}(x) = \sum_{n=k}^{\infty} n(n - 1) \cdots (n - k + 1) a_n x^{n-k}.$$

In particular, putting $x = 0$, we find

$$f^k(0) = k! a_k.$$

In other words, if $f(x)$ can be written as a power series in a neighborhood of 0, then the kth coefficient of the series must be $f^k(0)/k!$.

Example: We shall find a power series for e^x. The nth derivative of e^x is e^x, and the value of e^x at $x = 0$ is 1. Hence, if e^x can be represented by a power series, then the series must be

$$1 + \frac{x}{1!} + \frac{x^2}{2!} + \cdots + \frac{x^n}{n!} + \cdots.$$

However, this is no guarantee that the sum of the series actually is e^x. Let us tentatively call the sum $f(x)$. Then $f(x)$ is defined for all x, as we saw in example 1 of the preceding section. Also, by theorem 6.2, we have

$$f'(x) = \frac{1}{1!} + 2\frac{x}{2!} + 3\frac{x^2}{3!} + \cdots + n\frac{x^{n-1}}{n!} + \cdots$$

$$= 1 + \frac{x}{1!} + \frac{x^2}{2!} + \cdots + \frac{x^{n-1}}{(n-1)!} + \cdots$$

$$= f(x).$$

It follows that $f(x) = ce^x$ for some constant c (see chapter V, § 2, exercise 8). Since $f(0) = 1$, we see that $c = 1$, and hence $f(x) = e^x$. In particular, putting $x = 1$, we find

$$e = 1 + \frac{1}{1!} + \frac{1}{2!} + \cdots + \frac{1}{n!} + \cdots .$$

EXERCISES

1. Show that if there is a power series for $\sin x$, then it must be

$$x - \frac{x^3}{3!} + \frac{x^5}{5!} - \cdots + (-1)^n \frac{x^{2n+1}}{(2n+1)!} + \cdots .$$

Similarly show that if $\cos x$ has a power series, then it must be

$$1 - \frac{x^2}{2!} + \frac{x^4}{4!} + \cdots + (-1)^n \frac{x^{2n}}{(2n)!} + \cdots .$$

Prove that each of these series has infinite radius of convergence. Then, letting $s(x)$ and $c(x)$ denote the respective sums of these series, show that $s'(x) = c(x)$, $c'(x) = -s(x)$, $s(0) = 0$, and $c(0) = 1$. Conclude from chapter III, § 12 that $s(x) = \sin x$ and $c(x) = \cos x$.

2. Using the series found in the text for e^x, find an antiderivative for e^{-x^2} in the form of a power series.

3. Using the series of exercise 1, find antiderivatives for each of $\cos (x^2)$ and $\dfrac{\sin x}{x}$ in the form of power series.

4. Recalling that

$$\int_0^x \frac{dt}{1-t} = -\log (1 - x),$$

find a power series for $\log (1 - x)$. What is its radius of convergence?

5. Repeat problem 4 with $\log (1 - x)$ replaced by $\arctan x$.

6. Show that the sum of the series $\displaystyle\sum_{n=1}^{\infty} \frac{n}{(n+1)!}$ is 1. $\Big($Hint: Consider the series $\displaystyle\sum_{n=1}^{\infty} \frac{n}{(n+1)!} x^{n-1}$, and write it as the derivative of a series whose sum we know.$\Big)$

7. Using the series for e found in the text, prove that e is irrational. $\Big($Hint: Write

$$\frac{p}{q} = 1 + \frac{1}{1!} + \frac{1}{2!} + \cdots$$

where p and q are integers. Deduce that

$$q! \left(\frac{1}{(q+1)!} + \frac{1}{(q+2)!} + \cdots \right)$$

is an integer. Then compare this last expression with $\displaystyle\sum_{n=1}^{\infty} \frac{1}{(q+1)^n} .\Big)$

8. Suppose that

$$f(x) = \sum_{n=0}^{\infty} a_n(x - c)^n$$

for all x satisfying $|x - c| < R$. Show that for such x, f has a derivative given by

$$f'(x) = \sum_{n=1}^{\infty} na_n(x - c)^{n-1}.$$

7. TAYLOR'S FORMULA

In the example of the previous section we proved that

$$e = 1 + \frac{1}{1!} + \frac{1}{2!} + \cdots + \frac{1}{n!} + \cdots.$$

This appears to give us a method for computing e (that is, for finding the decimal representation of e). For if we want to compute e to within some desired accuracy, say 10^{-4}, then we know that there is some integer N such that

$$1 + \frac{1}{1!} + \frac{1}{2!} + \cdots + \frac{1}{n!}$$

is within 10^{-4} of e for all $n \geq N$. However, the mere knowledge of the existence of such an N is no help in actually finding one, and in fact we have so far no method for finding such an N. The following theorem will not only provide us with such a method, but will also lead to power series representations for many other functions besides e^x. Notice, however, that the theorem itself has nothing to do with infinite sums.

Theorem 7.1 (Taylor's Formula): *Let f be a function whose nth derivative $f^{(n)}$ is continuous on the closed interval between two numbers a and b. (We do not necessarily assume that $a < b$.) Then*

$$f(b) = f(a) + \frac{f'(a)}{1!}(b - a) + \frac{f''(a)}{2!}(b - a)^2 + \cdots$$

$$+ \frac{f^{(n-1)}(a)}{(n-1)!}(b - a)^{n-1} + R_n, \qquad (1)$$

where R_n is given by

$$R_n = \int_a^b f^{(n)}(t)\frac{(b - t)^{n-1}}{(n-1)!}\,dt. \qquad (2)$$

Proof: We prove the theorem by induction on n. For $n = 1$, the theorem says that

$$f(b) = f(a) + \int_a^b f'(t)\,dt,$$

which is certainly true. Now assume the theorem is true for n. Then we let

$$g(t) = -\frac{(b-t)^n}{n!}$$

and we integrate (2) by parts. This gives

$$R_n = \int_a^b f^{(n)}(t) \frac{(b-t)^{n-1}}{(n-1)!} dt$$

$$= \left[-f^{(n)}(t) \frac{(b-t)^n}{n!} \right]_a^b - \int_a^b -f^{(n+1)}(t) \frac{(b-t)^n}{n!} dt$$

$$= \frac{f^{(n)}(a)}{n!} (b-a)^n + R_{n+1}.$$

Substituting this expression for R_n in (1) gives us the desired formula with n replaced by $n + 1$. ∎

The expression R_n defined by (2) is called the *remainder term*. Let us apply theorem 8.4 of chapter IV to the integral (2) by taking

$$g(t) = (b-t)^{n-1}.$$

Notice that $g(t)$ always has the same sign in the interval between a and b, and so we are justified in using that theorem. We obtain

$$R_n = \frac{f^n(c)}{(n-1)!} \int_a^b (b-t)^{n-1} dt$$

$$= \frac{f^n(c)}{n!} (b-a)^n \tag{3}$$

for some c between a and b. The expression (3) is known as *Lagrange's form of the remainder*. It can be arrived at directly by another treatment of Taylor's formula which does not depend on integrals (see exercise 2).

Example: Let us take $f(x) = \sin x$; $a = \dfrac{\pi}{3}$, $b = \dfrac{\pi}{3} + \dfrac{1}{10}$, and $n = 5$ in Taylor's formula. We have

$$f(x) = \sin x, \quad f^{(1)}(x) = \cos x, \quad f^{(2)}(x) = -\sin x,$$
$$f^{(3)}(x) = -\cos x, \quad f^{(4)}(x) = \sin x, \quad f^{(5)}(x) = \cos x.$$

Then, using Lagrange's form of the remainder, we find

$$\sin\left(\frac{\pi}{3} + \frac{1}{10}\right) = \sin(\pi/3) + \frac{\cos(\pi/3)}{1!}\frac{1}{10} - \frac{\sin(\pi/3)}{2!}\frac{1}{10^2}$$

$$- \frac{\cos(\pi/3)}{3!}\frac{1}{10^3} + \frac{\sin(\pi/3)}{4!}\frac{1}{10^4} + \frac{\cos c}{5!}\frac{1}{10^5}$$

$$= \frac{\sqrt{3}}{2} + \frac{1}{20} - \frac{\sqrt{3}}{400} - \frac{1}{12{,}000} + \frac{\sqrt{3}}{480{,}000} + \frac{\cos c}{12{,}000{,}000}$$

where c is somewhere between $\dfrac{\pi}{3}$ and $\dfrac{\pi}{3} + \dfrac{1}{10}$. Now, although we have no way of telling exactly what c is, we know in any case that $|\cos c| \leq 1$. Consequently, if we just leave out the remainder term in the above, then the sum will be within $\dfrac{1}{12,000,000}$ of $\sin\left(\dfrac{\pi}{3} + \dfrac{1}{10}\right)$. If this is not accurate enough, try $n = 6$.

EXERCISES

1. Use the mean value theorem for integrals to show that the remainder term in Taylor's formula can also be written in the form

$$R_n = \frac{f^{(n)}(c)}{(n-1)!}(b-c)^{n-1}(b-a)$$

for some c between a and b.

2. Assume $f^{(n-1)}$ is continuous in the closed interval between a and b, and that $f^{(n)}$ exists in the open interval between a and b. (Notice that we are assuming a little less than what we assumed in theorem 7.1.) Define a function F by the rule

$$F(x) = f(b) - \sum_{k=0}^{n-1} \frac{f^{(k)}(x)}{k!}(b-x)^k$$

for all x in the closed interval, and show that

$$F'(x) = -\frac{f^{(n)}(x)}{n!}(b-x)^n$$

for all x in the open interval. Also define

$$G(x) = \frac{(b-x)^n}{n!}$$

for all x in the closed interval. Apply Cauchy's mean value theorem (theorem 9.2 of chapter III) to F and G to obtain

$$F(a) = f^{(n)}(c)\frac{(b-a)^n}{n!}$$

for some c between a and b. Hence, deduce Taylor's theorem with Lagrange's remainder.

3. Repeat exercise 2 with $G(x) = b - x$, and show that this leads to the form of the remainder given in exercise 1.

4. If f is a polynomial of degree n and a is any number, show that

$$f(x) = f(a) + \frac{f'(a)}{1!}(x-a) + \frac{f''(a)}{2!}(x-a)^2$$

$$+ \cdots + \frac{f^{(n)}(a)}{n!}(x-a)^n \tag{4}$$

for all x. Apply this to the polynomial $f(x) = x^3 - x^2 + 2x + 1$ for $a = 1$, and then check that (4) is true by expanding the powers on the right side.

5. Write Taylor's formula with Lagrange's remainder in each of the following cases:

   (a) $f = \tan$, $\quad a = 0$, $\quad b = \dfrac{\pi}{4}$, $\quad n = 4$

   (b) $f = \log$, $\quad a = 1$, $\quad b = \tfrac{1}{2}$, $\quad n = 100$

   (c) $f = \cos^2$, $\quad a = \dfrac{\pi}{6}$, $\quad b = 0$, $\quad n = 3$

   (d) $f(x) = \dfrac{1}{1 + x^2}$, $\quad a = 0$, $\quad b = 2$, $\quad n = 4$

   (e) $f = \sec$, $\quad a = \dfrac{\pi}{6}$, $\quad b = x$, $\quad n = 4$

   (f) $f = \arcsin$, $\quad a = 0$, $\quad b = \tfrac{1}{2}$, $\quad n = 3$

6. What is wrong with taking $f(x) = \sqrt{x^2 - 1}$, $a = -2$, and $b = 2$ in Taylor's formula?

8. TAYLOR'S SERIES

Let us write x in place of b in Taylor's formula, and assume that $f^{(n)}$ is defined throughout the closed interval between a and x for all n. Then

$$f(x) = f(a) + \frac{f'(a)}{1!}(x - a) + \frac{f''(a)}{2!}(x - a)^2$$

$$+ \cdots + \frac{f^{(n-1)}(a)}{(n - 1)!}(x - a)^{n-1} + R_n(x),$$

where we have written $R_n(x)$ in place of R_n to emphasize that the remainder depends on x as well as on n. Now, if for some particular x we have $\lim\limits_{n \to \infty} R_n(x) = 0$, then by definition of the infinite sum we have

$$f(x) = \sum_{n=0}^{\infty} \frac{f^{(n)}(a)}{n!}(x - a)^n. \tag{1}$$

However, it must be emphasized that $R_n(x)$ does not always have limit 0, and so equation (1) is not always valid. An example is provided in exercise 1 where the series on the right of (1), although convergent for all x, is never equal to $f(x)$ (except in the trivial case where $x = a$).

   The series (1) is called the *Taylor's series for f about a*. It was discovered by the English mathematician Brook Taylor (1685–1731). Usually we take $a = 0$, in which case Taylor's series becomes

$$f(0) + \frac{f'(0)}{1!}x + \frac{f''(0)}{2!}x^2 + \cdots + \frac{f^{(n)}(0)}{n!}x^n + \cdots.$$

This is just a power series.

   The following lemma will be needed in the subsequent examples.

Lemma 8.1: *If x is any number, then*

$$\lim_{n \to \infty} \frac{x^n}{n!} = 0.$$

Proof: By taking absolute values, it suffices to consider the case where x is positive. Let N be any integer such that $x < N/2$. Then for $n > N$ we can write

$$\frac{x^n}{n!} = \frac{x}{1} \cdot \frac{x}{2} \cdot \ldots \cdot \frac{x}{N} \cdot \frac{x}{N+1} \cdot \ldots \cdot \frac{x}{n}$$

$$< \frac{x^N}{N!} \cdot \frac{1}{2} \cdot \frac{1}{2} \cdots \frac{1}{2} = \frac{x^N}{N!} \left(\frac{1}{2}\right)^{n-N}.$$

Since $\lim_{n\to\infty} (\frac{1}{2})^{n-N} = 0$, this proves the lemma. ∎

Example 1: Let $f(x) = e^x$. Then $f^{(n)}(x) = e^x$ for all n, and so $f^{(n)}(0) = 1$ for all n. Therefore Taylor's formula with $a = 0$ yields

$$e^x = 1 + \frac{x}{1!} + \frac{x^2}{2!} + \cdots + \frac{x^{n-1}}{(n-1)!} + R_n(x), \tag{2}$$

where

$$R_n(x) = e^c \frac{x^n}{n!} \tag{3}$$

for some c between 0 and x. Thus

$$|R_n(x)| = e^c \frac{|x|^n}{n!},$$

and so since e^c is no bigger than e^x when x is positive and is no bigger than 1 when x is negative, it follows from lemma 8.1 that $\lim_{n\to\infty} R_n(x) = 0$ for all x. Thus

$$e^x = 1 + \frac{x}{1!} + \frac{x^2}{2!} + \cdots + \frac{x^n}{n!} + \cdots$$

for all x. This is the second time we have found this formula.

Example 2: We shall compute e to four decimal places. Taking $x = 1$ in equation (2), we find

$$e = 1 + \frac{1}{1!} + \frac{1}{2!} + \cdots + \frac{1}{(n-1)!} + R_n,$$

where

$$R_n = \frac{e^c}{n!}$$

for some c between 0 and 1. The trick now is to find n large enough so that $R_n < 10^{-4}$. First recall that $1 < e < 4$, so that since $c \leq 1$, we have $e^c \leq e < 4$. Thus, taking $n = 8$, we find

$$R_8 < \frac{4}{8!} = \frac{4}{40,320} < 10^{-4}.$$

Therefore the sum

$$1 + \frac{1}{1!} + \frac{1}{2!} + \cdots + \frac{1}{7!}$$

is within 10^{-4} of e, and if one does the arithmetic, one finds $e = 2.7183\ldots$.

Example 3: Let $f(x) = \sin x$. Then $f'(x) = \cos x$, $f''(x) = -\sin x$, and so on. Therefore, since $\sin 0 = 0$ and $\cos 0 = 1$, we find, taking $a = 0$ in Taylor's formula,

$$\sin x = x - \frac{x^3}{3!} + \frac{x^5}{5!} - \cdots + (-1)^{n-1}\frac{x^{2n-1}}{(2n-1)!} + R_{2n+1}(x),$$

where

$$R_{2n+1}(x) = (-1)^n \cos c \,\frac{x^{2n+1}}{(2n+1)!}$$

for some c between 0 and x. Thus

$$|R_{2n+1}(x)| \le \frac{|x|^{2n+1}}{(2n+1)!},$$

and so again by lemma 8.1 we see that $R_{2n+1}(x)$ has limit 0 for all x. Consequently,

$$\sin x = x - \frac{x^3}{3!} + \frac{x^5}{5!} - \cdots \tag{4}$$

for all x.

Now recall that $\sin x$ was defined originally using a picture. If we want a definition of sin which depends only on the axioms for the numbers, then we can take (4) as our definition. We can then define cos as the derivative of sin, and all the familiar facts about sin and cos can be proved using these definitions. In fact, if you have done exercise 1 of § 6, then you already know this.

Taylor's formula also gives us a way of computing integrals for which we cannot write down elementary antiderivatives. This is illustrated by the following example.

Example 4: Consider the integral

$$\int_0^b e^{-x^2}\, dx.$$

By example 1 we have

$$e^{-x^2} = 1 - \frac{x^2}{1!} + \frac{x^4}{2!} - \cdots + (-1)^{n-1}\frac{x^{2n-2}}{(n-1)!} + R_n(-x^2),$$

where

$$R_n(-x^2) = (-1)^n e^c \frac{x^{2n}}{n!}$$

for some c satisfying $-x^2 \le c \le 0$. Hence,

$$|R_n(-x^2)| \le \frac{|x|^{2n}}{n!} \le \frac{|b|^{2n}}{n!}$$

for all x in the interval between 0 and b. Consequently,

$$\int_0^b e^{-x^2}\,dx = \left[x - \frac{x^3}{3} + \frac{x^5}{2!5} - \cdots + (-1)^{n-1} \frac{x^{2n-1}}{(n-1)!(2n-1)} \right]_0^b$$

$$+ \int_0^b R_n(-x^2)\,dx$$

$$= b - \frac{b^3}{3} + \frac{b^5}{2!5} - \cdots + (-1)^{n-1} \frac{b^{2n-1}}{(n-1)!(2n-1)} + S_n,$$

where

$$|S_n| \le \left| \int_0^b \frac{|b|^{2n}}{n!}\,dx \right| = \frac{|b|^{2n+1}}{n!}.$$

For example, if $b = 1$, then taking $n = 8$ we find

$$\int_0^1 e^{-x^2}\,dx = 1 - \frac{1}{3} + \frac{1}{2!5} - \cdots + \frac{1}{6!(13)} - \frac{1}{7!(15)}$$

to within an accuracy of $\dfrac{1}{8!}$.

EXERCISES

1. (a) Using l'Hôpital's rule, show that
    $$\lim_{x \to 0} x^{-m} e^{-1/x^2} = 0$$
    for every positive integer m.
    (b) Show by induction on n that the nth derivative of e^{-1/x^2} for $x \ne 0$ is a sum of terms of the form $cx^{-m}e^{-1/x^2}$ where m is a positive integer and c is constant.
    (c) Define
    $$f(x) = e^{-1/x^2} \quad \text{for } x \ne 0$$
    $$= 0 \quad \text{for } x = 0.$$
    Using parts (a) and (b), show by induction on n that
    $$f^{(n)}(0) = 0$$
    for all n. Conclude that Taylor's series for f about 0 is convergent for all x, but has sum $f(x)$ only when $x = 0$. Sketch the graph of f.
2. Compute $\cos\left(\frac{1}{5}\right)$ to five decimal places.
3. Compute $\sin 1$ to three decimal places.
4. Show that $\sqrt[3]{e} = 1.3956$.
5. Compute $\dfrac{1}{e}$ to three decimals, and check your answer by inverting it.

6. For what values of x is the formula

$$\cos x = 1 - \frac{x^2}{2!} + \frac{x^4}{4!} - \frac{x^6}{6!}$$

correct to four decimal places?

7. How large must we take n in order to insure that the formula

$$\int_0^1 \frac{\sin x}{x} dx = 1 - \frac{1}{3!3} + \frac{1}{5!5} - \cdots + \frac{(-1)^{n-1}}{(2n-1)!(2n-1)}$$

is correct to five decimal places.

8. Calculate $\int_0^1 e^{x^2} dx$ to three decimal places.

9. Calculate $\int_0^{1/10} \frac{\cos x - 1}{x} dx$ to four decimal places.

9. LOG AND ARCTAN

In this section we are going to avoid Taylor's formula by using a trick. In equation (3) of § 1 put $r = -t$. This gives

$$\frac{1}{1+t} = 1 - t + t^2 - \cdots + (-1)^{n-1}t^{n-1} + (-1)^n \frac{t^n}{1+t}. \quad (1)$$

Thus we obtain for $x > -1$,

$$\log(1 + x) = \int_0^x \frac{dt}{1+t}$$

$$= x - \frac{x^2}{2} + \frac{x^3}{3} - \cdots + (-1)^{n-1}\frac{x^n}{n} + R_{n+1}(x)$$

where

$$R_{n+1}(x) = (-1)^n \int_0^x \frac{t^n}{1+t} dt.$$

If $0 \le x$, then

$$|R_{n+1}(x)| = \int_0^x \frac{t^n}{1+t} dt \le \int_0^x t^n \, dt = \frac{x^{n+1}}{n+1}. \quad (2)$$

In particular, we find $\lim_{n \to \infty} R_{n+1}(x) = 0$ for $0 \le x \le 1$.

On the other hand, if $-1 < x \le 0$, we have

$$\left| \frac{t^n}{1+t} \right| = \frac{(-t)^n}{1+t} \le \frac{(-t)^n}{1+x}$$

for $x \le t \le 0$, and consequently,

$$|R_{n+1}(x)| \le \int_x^0 \frac{(-t)^n}{1+x} dt = \frac{(-x)^{n+1}}{(n+1)(1+x)}. \quad (3)$$

Therefore, $\lim_{n \to \infty} R_{n+1}(x) = 0$ for $-1 < x \le 0$. Combining the two cases, we see that

$$\log (1 + x) = x - \frac{x^2}{2} + \frac{x^3}{3} - \frac{x^4}{4} + \cdots \tag{4}$$

for all x satisfying $-1 < x \le 1$. In particular, putting $x = 1$, we find

$$\log 2 = 1 - \tfrac{1}{2} + \tfrac{1}{3} - \tfrac{1}{4} + \cdots .$$

The series (4) only gives logarithms of numbers between 0 and 2. However, it is not difficult to find a series which gives logarithms of other positive numbers (see exercise 5).

Now let us replace t by t^2 in (1). This gives

$$\frac{1}{1 + t^2} = 1 - t^2 + t^4 - \cdots + (-1)^{n-1} t^{2n-2} + (-1)^n \frac{t^{2n}}{1 + t^2}.$$

Hence, for any x, we obtain

$$\arctan x = \int_0^x \frac{dt}{1 + t^2} = x - \frac{x^3}{3} + \frac{x^5}{5} - \cdots + (-1)^{n-1} \frac{x^{2n-1}}{2n - 1}$$
$$+ R_{2n+1}(x),$$

where

$$R_{2n+1}(x) = (-1)^n \int_0^x \frac{t^{2n}}{1 + t^2} \, dt.$$

Since

$$|R_{2n+1}(x)| \le \left| \int_0^x t^{2n} \, dt \right| = \frac{|x|^{2n+1}}{2n + 1}, \tag{5}$$

we find $\lim_{n \to \infty} R_{2n+1}(x) = 0$ for $|x| \le 1$. Consequently, for $|x| \le 1$, we have

$$\arctan x = x - \frac{x^3}{3} + \frac{x^5}{5} - \frac{x^7}{7} + \cdots .$$

In particular, setting $x = 1$, we find

$$\frac{\pi}{4} = 1 - \frac{1}{3} + \frac{1}{5} - \frac{1}{7} + \cdots . \tag{6}$$

This gives a method for computing π. However, using the estimate (5) for $R_{2n+1}(x)$, we see that we would have to take 5000 terms of the series (6) before we could be sure of being within 10^{-4} of $\frac{\pi}{4}$. A faster method for computing π which takes advantage of the term $|x|^{2n+1}$ in the numerator of (5) is suggested in exercise 3.

The series (4) for $\log (1 + x)$ could also have been obtained directly from Taylor's formula. The remainder in this case looks different from the one obtained above, but of course they must be the same since they are both the difference between $\log (1 + x)$ and the first n terms of (4). On the other hand, if one tries to apply Taylor's formula to $\arctan x$, one soon becomes tired trying to compute the derivatives $\arctan^{(n)}(x)$.

EXERCISES

1. Show that if we apply Taylor's formula (theorem 7.1) to the function $\log (1 + x)$ with $a = 0$, we obtain

$$\log (1 + x) = x - \frac{x^2}{2} + \frac{x^3}{3} - \cdots + (-1)^{n-1} \frac{x^n}{n} + R_{n+1}(x)$$

where

$$R_{n+1}(x) = (-1)^n \int_0^x \frac{(x - t)^n}{(1 + t)^{n+1}} dt.$$

Conclude that

$$|R_{n+1}(x)| \leq \frac{x^{n+1}}{n + 1} \quad \text{for } 0 \leq x$$

and

$$|R_{n+1}(x)| \leq \frac{(-x)^{n+1}}{(n + 1)(1 + x)^{n+1}} \quad \text{for } -1 < x \leq 0.$$

Is this last estimate for the remainder better or worse than the one found in the text?

2. Apply theorem 7.1 to obtain Taylor's formula for $\arctan x$ with $a = 0$ and $n = 5$.

3. Use the relation

$$\frac{\pi}{4} = 4 \arctan \left(\frac{1}{5}\right) - \arctan \left(\frac{1}{239}\right),$$

which was found in chapter III, § 5, exercise 7, to compute π to four decimal places.

4. Compute the following to three decimal places.

(a) $\log \left(\frac{9}{10}\right)$

(b) $\log \left(\frac{49}{50}\right)$

(c) $\log \left(\frac{51}{50}\right)$

(d) $\log \left(\frac{6}{5}\right)$

5. Show that

$$\log \left(\frac{1 + x}{1 - x}\right) = 2 \left(x + \frac{x^3}{3} + \frac{x^5}{5} + \cdots\right)$$

for $-1 < x < 1$, and that the remainder $R_{2n+1}(x)$ satisfies

$$|R_{2n+1}(x)| \leq 2 \frac{|x|^{2n+1}}{(n + 1)(1 - |x|)}.$$

Explain why this gives a series for the log of any positive number.

6. Use exercise 5 to compute $\log 2$ and $\log 3$ to three decimal places. Then, use parts (a) and (b) of exercise 4 to find $\log n$ for all integers n between 1 and 10.

10. THE BINOMIAL SERIES

Consider the function f defined by

$$f(x) = (1 + x)^m$$

where m is any real number. The nth derivative of f is given by

$$f^{(n)}(x) = m(m - 1) \cdots (m - n + 1)(1 + x)^{m-n}.$$

Thus Taylor's series for f about 0 is

$$1 + mx + \frac{m(m - 1)}{2!} x^2$$

$$+ \cdots + \frac{m(m - 1) \cdots (m - n + 1)}{n!} x^n + \cdots. \qquad (1)$$

If m is a nonnegative integer, then $f^{(m+1)}(x) = 0$ for all x, and so by Taylor's formula we obtain

$$(1 + x)^m = 1 + mx + \frac{m(m - 1)}{2!} x^2 + \cdots + x^m.$$

The binomial theorem proved in chapter I follows from this by writing

$$(a + b)^m = a^m \left(1 + \frac{b}{a}\right)^m.$$

Now assume that m is not a nonnegative integer. In this case, none of the coefficients in the series (1) is 0. We are going to show that (1) has $(1 + x)^m$ as its sum. We shall prove this directly without analyzing the remainder term. First we apply the ratio test to find the radius of convergence of (1). We have

$$\lim_{n \to \infty} \left| \frac{m - n}{n + 1} \right| |x| = |x|,$$

so that (1) is convergent for $|x| < 1$ and is divergent for $|x| > 1$. Thus for $|x| < 1$ we may define

$$g(x) = \sum_{n=0}^{\infty} c_n x^n,$$

where

$$c_n = \frac{m(m - 1) \cdots (m - n + 1)}{n!}.$$

We want to show that $g(x) = (1 + x)^m$ for $|x| < 1$. This is equivalent to showing that the expression

$$g(x)(1 + x)^{-m} \qquad (2)$$

is 1 for $|x| < 1$. We shall show that the derivative of (2) is 0, so that (2) is constant, and the constant is easily seen to be 1 on substitution of $x = 0$. The derivative of (2) is given by

$$g'(x)(1 + x)^{-m} - mg(x)(1 + x)^{-m-1}$$
$$= [g'(x)(1 + x) - mg(x)](1 + x)^{-m-1}.$$

Thus it suffices to show that

$$g'(x)(1 + x) - mg(x) = 0. \tag{3}$$

By theorem 6.2 the derivative of g is given by

$$g'(x) = \sum_{n=1}^{\infty} nc_n x^{n-1},$$

and consequently,

$$g'(x)(1 + x) = \sum_{n=0}^{\infty} [(n + 1)c_{n+1} + nc_n]x^n. \tag{4}$$

Now

$$(n + 1)c_{n+1} + nc_n = (n + 1)\frac{m(m - 1)\cdots(m - n)}{(n + 1)!}$$
$$+ n\frac{m(m - 1)\cdots(m - n + 1)}{n!}$$
$$= \frac{m(m - 1)\cdots(m - n + 1)}{n!}(m - n + n) = mc_n.$$

Substituting this in (4) yields (3).

Example: We shall find a power series for $\dfrac{1}{\sqrt{1 - x}}$. This is accomplished by taking $m = -\frac{1}{2}$ and replacing x by $-x$ in (1). Thus for $|x| < 1$ we have

$$\frac{1}{\sqrt{1 - x}} = 1 + (-\tfrac{1}{2})(-x) + \frac{(-\tfrac{1}{2})(-\tfrac{3}{2})}{2!}(-x)^2 + \cdots$$
$$+ \frac{(-\tfrac{1}{2})(-\tfrac{3}{2})\cdots(-\tfrac{1}{2} - n + 1)}{n!}(-x)^n + \cdots$$
$$= 1 + \tfrac{1}{2}x + \tfrac{3}{8}x^2 + \cdots + \frac{1\cdot 3\cdot 5\cdots(2n - 1)}{2^n n!}x^n + \cdots.$$

EXERCISES

Find a power series for each of the following.

1. $\sqrt{1 + x}$

2. $\dfrac{1}{\sqrt{1 - x^2}}$

3. $\sqrt[3]{2 - x}$

4. $\dfrac{1}{(3 - x)^2}$

5. $(1 + x^2)^{-1/5}$

6. $\sqrt[3]{1 - x^2}$

7. Use exercise 2 to find a power series for $\arcsin x$.

8. Use the relation $(1 - x)(1 + x + x^2 + x^3) = 1 - x^4$ to find a power series for

$$\frac{1}{1 + x + x^2 + x^3}.$$

9. Show that the binomial series (1) diverges for $|x| = 1$ and $m \leq -1$.

11. REARRANGEMENT OF TERMS

Consider a series

$$\sum_{n=1}^{\infty} a_n,$$ (1)

and suppose that we form a new series by introducing parentheses into the given one. Thus, for example, our new series may start out as

$$(a_1 + a_2) + (a_3 + a_4 + a_5) + (a_6) + (a_7 + a_8 + a_9 + a_{10}) + \cdots,$$

so that the first term is $a_1 + a_2$, the second is $a_3 + a_4 + a_5$, and so on. To say formally what we are doing, we consider an increasing sequence of positive integers

$$1 = n_1 < n_3 < \cdots < n_k < \cdots,$$

and we form the series

$$\sum_{k=1}^{\infty} b_k,$$ (2)

where

$$b_k = a_{n_k} + a_{n_k+1} + \cdots + a_{n_{k+1}-1}.$$

In the above example we have $n_1 = 1$, $n_2 = 3$, $n_3 = 6$, $n_4 = 7$, etc. If the original series (1) is convergent with sum L, then the series (2) is also convergent with sum L. This is obvious from the fact that for each integer k, the kth partial sum of (2) is the nth partial sum of (1) for some $n \geq k$. However, if the series (2) is convergent, it does not necessarily follow that (1) is also convergent. For example, consider the series

$$1 - 1 + 1 - 1 + \cdots.$$

The partial sums are alternately 1 and 0, and so the series is not convergent. Nevertheless, the series

$$(1 - 1) + (1 - 1) + \cdots$$

is convergent since all its terms are 0.

We shall now consider the effect of rearranging the terms of the series (1). For example, the first few terms of the new series may look like

$$a_5 + a_9 + a_2 + a_{356} + a_{62} + \cdots.$$

We can make our ideas precise by defining a *rearrangement* of the series (1) to be a series of the form

$$\sum_{n=1}^{\infty} a_{\alpha(n)}$$ (3)

where α is a one to one correspondence from the set of positive integers to itself. In the example above we have $\alpha(1) = 5$, $\alpha(2) = 9$, $\alpha(3) = 2$, and so on. The important thing is that each term of the old series should appear once and only once in the new series. If the original series is convergent, then it is tempting to conclude from the ordinary commutative law that the rearranged series (3) is also convergent and has the same sum. To see how far our intuition can lead us astray here, we shall prove the following theorem.

Theorem 11.1: *If* $\sum_{n=1}^{\infty} a_n$ *is convergent but not absolutely, then for any number L the series can be rearranged so as to have sum L.*

Proof: By theorem 4.1, we know that both of the series

$$\sum_{n=1}^{\infty} a_n^+ \quad \text{and} \quad \sum_{n=1}^{\infty} a_n^-$$

are divergent. This enables us to carry out the following process. In the series $\sum_{n=1}^{\infty} a_n$, take just enough nonnegative terms in the order they appear so as to obtain a sum greater than L. Then add on just enough negative terms in the order they appear so as to make the sum less than L. Then go on adding just enough nonnegative terms so as to make the sum greater than L again. Keeping this up, we obtain a series with partial sums s_n both greater than and less than L for arbitrarily large n. Now, since the original series is convergent, the terms a_n have limit 0. Hence, given $\epsilon > 0$, we can find an integer N such that $|a_n| < \epsilon$ whenever $n \geq N$. It follows that after we have reached the point in the above process where the first N terms of the original series have been used up, the partial sums of the rearranged series will all be within ϵ of L. This shows that the rearranged series is convergent with sum L. ∎

The above proof depended very much on the fact that the series was not absolutely convergent. In fact, if the series is absolutely convergent, then we have the following theorem.

Theorem 11.2: *Suppose that* $\sum_{n=1}^{\infty} a_n$ *is absolutely convergent with sum L. Then any rearrangement is absolutely convergent with sum L.*

Proof: Consider first the case where $a_n \geq 0$ for all n. Let s_n denote the partial sums of the given series, and let t_n denote those of the rearranged series $\sum_{n=1}^{\infty} a_{\alpha(n)}$. Since the terms are nonnegative, it follows that

$$t_n \leq s_N \leq L,$$

where N is the maximum of the integers $\alpha(1)$, $\alpha(2) \ldots$, $\alpha(n)$. Thus the partial sums t_n are bounded above by L, and so the rearranged series is convergent with sum $M \leq L$. But $\sum_{n=1}^{\infty} a_n$ can be regarded as a rearrangement of $\sum_{n=1}^{\infty} a_{\alpha(n)}$, and so, interchanging the roles of the two series in the argument above, we find $L \leq M$. Hence $L = M$, and so the theorem is proved in the case of series of nonnegative terms.

In the general case, since $\sum_{n=1}^{\infty} a_n$ converges absolutely we have

$$L = \sum_{n=1}^{\infty} a_n^+ - \sum_{n=1}^{\infty} a_n^-,$$

were each of the series on the right is a convergent series of nonnegative terms. By what we have already proved, each of these series has the same sum after rearranging the terms. Hence, the difference of these rearranged series, or in other words the sum of $\sum_{n=1}^{\infty} a_{\alpha(n)}$, is L. ∎

Finally, we consider the problem of multiplying infinite sums. The product of two finite sums

$$(a_0 + a_1 + \cdots + a_m)(b_0 + b_1 + \cdots + b_n)$$

is given by summing all products of the form $a_i b_j$ where $0 \leq i \leq m$ and $0 \leq j \leq n$. The order in which these products are summed is irrelevant by the ordinary commutative law. On the other hand, theorem 11.1 indicates that we had better not draw any quick conclusions concerning the product of two infinite sums $\sum_{n=0}^{\infty} a_n$ and $\sum_{n=0}^{\infty} b_n$. First, for each integer $n \geq 0$, let us define c_n as the sum of all products $a_i b_j$ such that the subscripts add up to n. That is, we define

$$c_0 = a_0 b_0$$
$$c_1 = a_0 b_1 + a_1 b_0$$
$$c_2 = a_0 b_2 + a_1 b_1 + a_2 b_0$$
$$\vdots$$
$$c_n = a_0 b_n + a_1 b_{n-1} + \cdots + a_n b_0.$$

The series $\sum_{n=0}^{\infty} c_n$ is then called the *product series* of the two given series. In particular, the product series of two power series $\sum_{n=0}^{\infty} a_n x^n$ and $\sum_{n=0}^{\infty} b_n x^n$ is the power series $\sum_{n=0}^{\infty} c_n x^n$ where c_n is as defined above.

Theorem 11.3: *If $\sum_{n=0}^{\infty} a_n$ and $\sum_{n=0}^{\infty} b_n$ are absolutely convergent with sums A and B respectively, then the product series $\sum_{n=0}^{\infty} c_n$ is absolutely convergent with sum AB.*

Proof: Consider first the series $\sum_{n=0}^{\infty} |a_n|$ and $\sum_{n=0}^{\infty} |b_n|$, which are convergent by hypothesis. Let their sums be P and Q respectively. Then any series whose terms are the numbers $|a_i| \, |b_j|$ taken in some order has its partial sums bounded by PQ. This is because each such partial sum has all of its terms included in the terms of

$$\left(\sum_{n=0}^{N} |a_n|\right) \left(\sum_{n=0}^{N} |b_n|\right)$$

for some large enough N. Thus any such series is convergent, and so any series with the numbers $a_i b_j$ as its terms is absolutely convergent. Therefore, by theorem 11.2 we see that the sum C of such a series is independent of the order of the terms. Since the product series $\sum_{n=0}^{\infty} c_n$ is obtained from such a series by introducing parentheses, we find $\sum_{n=0}^{\infty} c_n = C$. To prove that $C = AB$, we consider another series consisting of the terms $a_i b_j$, namely

$$
\begin{aligned}
&a_0 b_0 \\
&+ a_0 b_1 + a_1 b_1 + a_1 b_0 \\
&+ a_0 b_2 + a_1 b_2 + a_2 b_2 + a_2 b_1 + a_2 b_0 \\
&\qquad\qquad \vdots \\
&+ a_0 b_n + \cdots + a_n b_n + a_n b_{n-1} + \cdots + a_n b_0 \\
&\qquad\qquad \vdots
\end{aligned}
\qquad (4)
$$

The scheme is to put in the nth row all terms of the form $a_i b_j$ such that at least one of i or j is n. The sum of the first n rows is then

$$\left(\sum_{i=0}^{n} a_i\right) \left(\sum_{j=0}^{n} b_j\right)$$

By taking the limit as n tends to infinity, we find that the sum of the series (4) is AB. Since its sum is also C, this proves that $C = AB$, as required. ∎

Example: Suppose that we had never heard of e^x, and let us define

$$f(x) = 1 + \frac{x}{1!} + \frac{x^2}{2!} + \cdots + \frac{x^n}{n!} + \cdots$$

As we saw in § 5, example 1, the series is absolutely convergent for all x. Therefore, if x and y are any numbers, by theorem 11.3 we have

$$
\begin{aligned}
f(x)f(y) &= \sum_{n=0}^{\infty} \left(\frac{y^n}{n!} + \frac{y^{n-1}}{(n-1)!} x + \cdots + \frac{y^{n-i}}{(n-i)!}\frac{x^i}{i!} + \cdots + \frac{x^n}{n!}\right) \\
&= \sum_{n=0}^{\infty} \frac{(x+y)^n}{n!} = f(x+y).
\end{aligned}
$$

This is just the familiar rule of exponents $e^x e^y = e^{x+y}$.

EXERCISES

1. Show that if $\sum_{n=1}^{\infty} a_n$ is convergent but not absolutely, then the terms can be arranged such that $\lim_{n\to\infty} t_n = \infty$, where t_n denotes the nth partial sum of the rearranged series.

2. Suppose that α is a one to one correspondence from the set of positive integers to itself, and that $|\alpha(n) - n| \leq 1000$ for all n. If $\sum\limits_{n=1}^{\infty} a_n$ is convergent, show that $\sum\limits_{n=1}^{\infty} a_{\alpha(n)}$ is convergent with the same sum.

3. Let $a_n = b_n = \dfrac{(-1)^n}{\sqrt{n+1}}$ for all $n \geq 0$. Then $\sum\limits_{n=0}^{\infty} a_n$ and $\sum\limits_{n=0}^{\infty} b_n$ are convergent, but the product series $\sum\limits_{n=0}^{\infty} c_n$ is divergent. (Hint: Show that $|c_{n-1}| \geq \sqrt{n}$ for all $n \geq 1$.) Why does this not contradict theorem 11.3?

4. Assume that you have never heard of sin and cos, and define

$$s(x) = x - \frac{x^3}{3!} + \frac{x^5}{5!} + \cdots + (-1)^n \frac{x^{2n+1}}{(2n+1)!} + \cdots$$

$$c(x) = 1 - \frac{x^2}{2!} + \frac{x^4}{4!} + \cdots + (-1)^n \frac{x^{2n}}{(2n)!} + \cdots.$$

Prove the following formulas using theorem 11.3:

$$s(x + y) = s(x)c(y) + c(x)s(y)$$
$$c(x + y) = c(x)c(y) - s(x)s(y)$$
$$s^2(x) + c^2(x) = 1.$$

5. Show that

$$\frac{1}{(1 - x)} \log \frac{1}{(1 - x)} = x + (1 + \tfrac{1}{2})x^2 + (1 + \tfrac{1}{2} + \tfrac{1}{3})x^3 + \cdots$$

for $|x| < 1$.

6. Use theorem 11.3 to show that

$$\sum_{n=0}^{\infty} x^n \sum_{n=0}^{\infty} (-1)^n x^n = \sum_{n=0}^{\infty} x^{2n}$$

for $|x| < 1$. Check that this is true using your knowledge of geometric series.

7. Recall that

$$\log 2 = 1 - \tfrac{1}{2} + \tfrac{1}{3} - \tfrac{1}{4} + \cdots$$

Show that the rearranged series

$$1 + \tfrac{1}{3} - \tfrac{1}{2} + \tfrac{1}{5} + \tfrac{1}{7} - \tfrac{1}{4} + \tfrac{1}{9} + \tfrac{1}{11} - \tfrac{1}{6} + \cdots$$

has sum $\tfrac{3}{2} \log 2$. (Hint: Consider

$$\tfrac{1}{2} \log 2 = 0 + \tfrac{1}{2} + 0 - \tfrac{1}{4} + 0 + \tfrac{1}{6} + \cdots.)$$

INDEX